WITHDRAWN

The Transform Analysis of Linear Systems

by

ERIK V. BOHN

University of British Columbia

ADDISON-WESLEY PUBLISHING COMPANY, INC.

READING, MASSACHUSETTS · PALO ALTO · LONDON

105764

PREFACE

Due to the increasing pressure of technological advances engineering curricula are currently undergoing extensive revisions, with special emphasis on a thorough presentation of the fundamentals in applied science and mathematics. Particular importance is now placed on general courses in the analysis of linear systems. One of the purposes of this book is to develop the basic material presented in mathematics and network courses and apply it to a wide variety of lumped- and distributed-parameter linear systems. The text stresses the concept of spectral resolution and both the Laplace and Fourier transforms are introduced from this point of view.

The response of distributed-parameter mechanical systems, which are of great importance and interest as electromechanical transducers, is discussed in Chapter 10. Since the historical treatment (based on the separation of variables and the determination of the possible modes of oscillation) as well as the Laplace transform can be used to solve response problems of this kind, both methods are presented, and Chapter 12 is devoted to a comparison of the two techniques. The mode method is treated from a more modern point of view, stressing the basic philosophy of resolution into fundamental terms or modes. The geometric terminology used is applicable to all problems dealing with spectral resolution.

From the practical point of view, transform analysis must deal with the numerical solution of problems. When transform tables are used, the transform must first be represented by a partial-fraction expansion which requires considerable experience and effort since there are numerous possibilities. Since the text stresses the physical significance of the Laplace transform and avoids emphasizing mathematically abstract transform tables, a simpler and more direct approach to the solution of problems is possible. The poles represent the natural frequencies of oscillation of the system, and, associated with each pole, is a characteristic exponential response. A general response of the system is represented by a linear combination of all characteristic exponentials. In mathematical terms, the response $v(t)$ is the sum of the residues of the function $V(s)e^{st}$. The text stresses this point of view by means of a function called the *pole coefficient*, which can be found by inspection once the poles are known. The residue is easily evaluated by use of the pole coefficient and is directly related to the contribution of each pole to the resultant response. This procedure does not require a partial-fraction expansion or the use of transform tables. It emphasizes both the physical and mathematical significance of the quantities. The same method is also used in dealing with systems of high order.

Throughout the text, emphasis is placed on the mathematical foundations from which the solutions are obtained. For filters and transmission lines, all transforms and formulas are derived, using only the elementary operations of differentiation and integration. In addition, an attempt has been made to indicate, wherever possible, systematic means of simplifying the algebraic manipulations required to obtain a useful solution. In Chapter 4, for example, this objective is achieved by extensive use of the symmetric functions of the roots. In later chapters many problems illustrating the properties of error and Bessel functions are discussed. The methods used in determining the transforms of these functions are reviewed in the Appendixes.

Numerical and graphical methods are discussed in Chapters 7 and 8. Many examples are given and a large number of system responses are illustrated graphically. Response parameters of engineering interest such as rise time and time delay are emphasized.

The book is suitable for the advanced undergraduate-introductory graduate level course. It contains sufficient material to be of interest to research workers who need a good knowledge of systems analysis from the Laplace-transform point of view. The text requires an adequate background in calculus and elementary circuit theory, and hence assumes that the reader has a basic understanding of the classical and phasor methods of solving differential equations which are based on exponential-type solutions. The introduction to the Laplace integral transform is then possible by a simple and natural extension of these methods.

I would like to express my sincere appreciation to Professor A. D. Moore for his review of the entire manuscript and for his many constructive suggestions.

Vancouver, B.C.   E. V. B.
March 1963

CONTENTS

Chapter 10.   Distributed-Parameter Mechanical Systems

Chapter 11.   Traveling Waves on Distortionless Transmission Lines

Chapter 12.   Comparison of Mode and Laplace Transform Methods

Chapter 13.   Steady-State Response of Systems

Chapter 14.   The Diffusion Equation

CHAPTER 15. THE GENERAL TRANSMISSION LINE

CHAPTER 16. LINEAR SYSTEMS with RANDOM INPUTS

CHAPTER 1

THE SPECTRAL RESOLUTION OF INPUT AND OUTPUT SIGNALS OF LINEAR SYSTEMS

1–1 Introduction. The analysis of a linear system H involves the determination of the relationship between system parameters and the output response $v_o(t)$ to an input signal $v_i(t)$ (see Fig. 1–1). The systems to be analyzed may be of an electrical, mechanical, or electromechanical nature. We can, for example, consider a feedback control system in which the output signal must follow the input signal very accurately, or a communications system consisting of networks and amplifiers where the output signal has a specified functional relationship to particular kinds of input signals.

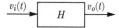

$$v_i(t) \quad \boxed{H} \quad v_o(t)$$

FIG. 1–1. The response of a linear system.

A system may be characterized by the manner in which it operates on specified input signals. It is desirable to express this characteristic of a system in the simplest and most useful form possible. To see how this can be done, we consider an input signal

$$v_i(t) = V_i e^{st}, \tag{1-1}$$

where $s = \sigma + j\omega$, and V_i is a constant. From a physical point of view, the signal actually applied to the system can be taken as the real part of Eq. (1–1). The possible input signals for various σ are shown in Fig. 1–2. The case of $\sigma = 0$ is of particular significance, since it is easily realized experimentally. This is the type of input signal used in determining the conventional frequency response of a system.

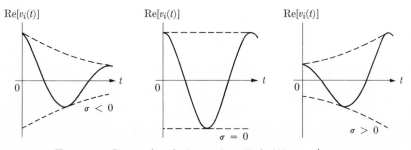

FIG. 1–2. Input signals for various $\mathrm{Re}[v_i(t)] = e^{\sigma t} \cos \omega t$.

The systems to be considered consist of various interconnected physical elements whose properties are characterized by linear integrodifferential equations. For example, the voltage-current relations for the time-invariant resistive, inductive, and capacitive circuit elements are given respectively by

$$v(t) = Ri(t), \tag{1-2a}$$

$$v(t) = L\,\frac{di(t)}{dt}, \tag{1-2b}$$

$$\frac{dv(t)}{dt} = \frac{1}{C}\,i(t). \tag{1-2c}$$

If we set $v(t) = Ve^{st}$, $i(t) = Ie^{st}$, and determine the ratio $v(t)/i(t) = V/I = Z(s)$, which is defined as the *impedance function*,* we find, respectively,

$$Z(s) = R, \tag{1-3a}$$

$$Z(s) = Ls, \tag{1-3b}$$

$$Z(s) = \frac{1}{Cs}. \tag{1-3c}$$

Thus we see that the impedance function is a means of expressing the exponential voltage response of a network element to an exponential current excitation. In formulating the network equations it is usually convenient to express Eq. (1–2c) in the form of an indefinite integral. Thus

$$v(t) = \frac{1}{C}\int i(t)\,dt.$$

For an exponential excitation this leads to the same result as given by Eq. (1–3c).

The integrodifferential equations characterizing a linear system are formed by a multiplicity of operations involving differentiation, integration, and linear combinations of these operations. Since

$$\frac{de^{st}}{dt} = se^{st},$$

$$\int e^{st}\,dt = \frac{1}{s}\,e^{st},$$

we see that the exponential form e^{st} remains unchanged by these operations.

---

* It is often more convenient to use the *admittance function* $Y(s) = I/V$.

Thus we can write

$$H\{v_i(t)\} = v_o(t) = H(s)V_ie^{st}, \tag{1-4}$$

where this equation is to be interpreted in the sense that the system H operates on the exponential input signal to yield an exponential output signal. The output response, as given by Eq. (1–4), is readily found by noting that the differentiation and indefinite integration of the exponential e^{st} results in the factors s and $1/s$, respectively. It is interesting to note that e^{st} is the only function having this property, which accounts for its widespread use in linear systems analysis. If we now take the ratio

$$\frac{v_o(t)}{v_i(t)} = \frac{H(s)V_ie^{st}}{V_ie^{st}} = H(s), \tag{1-5}$$

we obtain a quantity which is a function of s but independent of time. If, in particular, $\sigma = 0$, then $s = j\omega$ and Eq. (1–5) gives the ordinary frequency response of the system. This fact justifies calling $H(s)$ the complex frequency response of the system. A simpler terminology is to call $H(s)$ the *system transfer function*.

To see the usefulness of the transfer function concept consider once more Fig. 1–1. Suppose that the input signal is of the form

$$v_i(t) = \sum_{k=1}^{n} a_k e^{s_k t}, \tag{1-6}$$

and it is desired to determine the output response. If the transfer function is $H(s)$, the output response to the input $a_k e^{s_k t}$ is

$$a_k H(s_k)e^{s_k t}.$$

Since the system is linear, the total response due to $v_i(t)$ can be found by superposition, and is given by

$$v_o(t) = \sum_{k=1}^{n} a_k H(s_k)e^{s_k t}. \tag{1-7}$$

This method of determining the system response can now be summarized. The input signal $v_i(t)$ is first resolved into exponential terms. The transfer function $H(s)$, which is the ratio of the exponential response to an exponential excitation, is then determined [see Eq. (1–5)]. The exponential response to each of the exponential terms in the input signal is then known, and the total response is obtained by superposition.

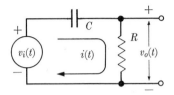

FIG. 1–3. A simple RC network.

To see how the transfer function can be obtained, let us consider the simple RC network shown in Fig. 1–3. For the voltages and current we set

$$v_i(t) = V_i e^{st}, \qquad v_o(t) = H(s) V_i e^{st}, \qquad i(t) = I e^{st}.$$

Since

$$v_i(t) = \frac{1}{C} \int i(t)\, dt + R i(t),$$

we obtain

$$V_i = \left[\frac{1}{Cs} + R \right] I.$$

Thus

$$H(s) = \frac{R i(t)}{v_i(t)} = \frac{\tau s}{1 + \tau s}, \qquad (1\text{–}8)$$

where $\tau = RC$.

In obtaining the transfer function of a linear system in this manner, it is important to note that all responses are taken to be proportional to the assumed exponential excitation. It is only for this case (and no other) that the ratios of the various signals are independent of time.

1–2 The spectral resolution of signals. The problem to be discussed now is the resolution of a signal into exponential terms as given by Eq. (1–6). This is closely related to the problem of representing a periodic signal in terms of a *Fourier series*. We consider, therefore, a signal $v(t)$ having a period T. The Fourier series representation is

$$v(t) = \sum_{n=-\infty}^{+\infty} a_n e^{j\omega_n t}, \qquad (1\text{–}9)$$

where

$$\omega_n = \frac{2\pi n}{T} \qquad \text{and} \qquad a_n = \frac{1}{T} \int_{-T/2}^{+T/2} v(t) e^{-j\omega_n t}\, dt. \qquad (1\text{–}10)$$

Equation (1–9) is the *spectral resolution* of a periodic signal $v(t)$ into *components* a_n with respect to the set of functions

$$e^{j\omega_n t}, \qquad n = 0, \pm 1, \pm 2, \ldots.$$

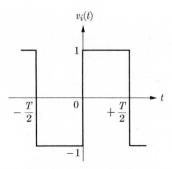

FIG. 1–4. Recurrent rectangular waveform.

The function $a_n e^{j\omega_n t}$ will be referred to as the nth *spectral term*. The summation of all spectral terms yields $v(t)$.

As an example, let us consider the problem of determining the output response of the network shown in Fig. 1–3 to the recurrent input waveform shown in Fig. 1–4. The component a_n is determined from Eq. (1–10):

$$a_n = j \, \frac{\cos \pi n - 1}{\pi n}.$$

Let the output response be represented by

$$v_o(t) = \sum_{n=-\infty}^{+\infty} b_n e^{j\omega_n t}. \tag{1–11}$$

Equations (1–7) and (1–8) yield

$$b_n = a_n H(j\omega_n) = \frac{2\tau}{T} \frac{1 - \cos \pi n}{1 + j\omega_n \tau}. \tag{1–12}$$

Substituting this result into Eq. (1–11) yields the Fourier series representation of the output response. This representation is useful only if it converges rapidly or if it can be summed into a closed form. A more convenient means of solving problems of this type will be discussed in Chapter 13. However, it is interesting to note here that the series can be summed. Consider the waveform shown in Fig. 1–5, where

$$v_o(t) = \begin{cases} v(t), & 0 < t < \dfrac{T}{2}, \\[2mm] -e^{-\alpha} v(t), & -\dfrac{T}{2} < t < 0, \end{cases} \tag{1–13}$$

$$v(t) = \frac{2e^{-t/\tau}}{1 + e^{-\alpha}},$$

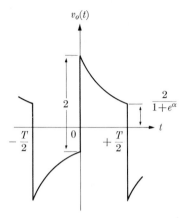

Fig. 1-5. Output voltage response of a simple RC network to a recurrent rectangular waveform, where $\alpha = T/2\tau$.

and $\alpha = T/2\tau$. By means of Eq. (1–10) it can be shown that the components of the waveform described by Eq. (1–13) are given by b_n. For the type of functions considered here it follows from the uniqueness of the Fourier series representation that the waveforms given by Eqs. (1–11) and (1–13) must be identical if they have identical components.

In general, the signal $v(t)$ may not be periodic, and this case can be considered by letting $T \to +\infty$. The following is a heuristic derivation of the *Fourier* and *Laplace integral transforms* which yield the desired resolution of a nonperiodic signal into exponential terms. Let

$$s = j\,\frac{2\pi n}{T}. \tag{1–14}$$

Then, since $\Delta n = 1$,

$$\Delta s = j\,\frac{2\pi}{T}. \tag{1–15}$$

Now let

$$F(s) = \lim_{T \to +\infty} T a_n = \int_{-\infty}^{+\infty} v(t)e^{-st}\,dt. \tag{1–16}$$

It follows from Eqs. (1–15) and (1–16) that

$$a_n \cong \frac{F(s)}{T} = \frac{F(s)\,\Delta s}{2\pi j} \cong \frac{F(s)\,ds}{2\pi j}, \tag{1–17}$$

provided that T is sufficiently large. Substituting Eq. (1–17) into Eq. (1–9) yields

$$v(t) = \lim_{\Delta s \to 0} \sum_{n=-\infty}^{+\infty} \frac{F(s)e^{st}}{2\pi j}\,\Delta s = \frac{1}{2\pi j}\int_{-j\infty}^{+j\infty} F(s)e^{st}\,ds. \tag{1–18}$$

Depending on the nature of the signal, Eqs. (1–16) and (1–18) can be expressed in various forms. The Fourier integral transform is obtained by substituting $s = j\omega$. The result is

$$F(j\omega) = V(\omega) = \int_{-\infty}^{+\infty} v(t)e^{-j\omega t}\, dt \qquad (1\text{–}19)$$

and

$$v(t) = \frac{1}{2\pi} \int_{-\infty}^{+\infty} V(\omega)e^{j\omega t}\, d\omega. \qquad (1\text{–}20)$$

Equation (1–20) is the spectral resolution of the nonperiodic signal $v(t)$ into exponential spectral terms. The spectral term at the angular frequency ω is

$$\frac{V(\omega)\, d\omega}{2\pi} e^{j\omega t},$$

and the component of $e^{j\omega t}$ at this frequency is $V(\omega)\, d\omega/2\pi$. The summation (by integration) of all spectral terms yields $v(t)$. In mathematical terminology, Eq. (1–19) is defined as the Fourier transform of $v(t)$ and is written symbolically as

$$V(\omega) = \mathfrak{F}[v(t)],$$

and Eq. (1–20) is the inverse transform and is written symbolically as

$$v(t) = \mathfrak{F}^{-1}[V(\omega)],$$

where $v(t)$ is restricted to the class of functions for which both these operations exist.

The Fourier transforms of many of the functions used in the determination of system transients do not exist. These functions are considered to satisfy the condition

$$v(t) = 0 \qquad \text{for} \qquad t < 0,$$

which allows a different type of transform to be used. In this case, Eqs. (1–16), (1–17), and (1–18) have the forms

$$F(s) = V(s) = \int_{0}^{\infty} v(t)e^{-st}\, dt, \qquad (1\text{–}21)$$

$$a_n \cong \frac{V(s)\, ds}{2\pi j} \qquad (1\text{–}22)$$

and

$$v(t) = \frac{1}{2\pi j} \int_{c-j\infty}^{c+j\infty} V(s)e^{st}\, ds. \qquad (1\text{–}23)$$

Actually, s should be restricted to a path of integration along the $j\omega$-axis [see Eq. (1–14)]. In Chapter 2, we will show that the path of integration can be moved without altering the value of the integral, and we will explain the choice of the constant c. Equation (1–23) is the spectral resolution of the nonperiodic signal $v(t)$ into exponential spectral terms. The spectral term at the complex frequency $s = c + j\omega$ is $[V(s)\ ds/2\pi j]e^{st}$, and the component of e^{st} at this frequency is $V(s)\ ds/2\pi j$. The summation of all spectral terms (by integration) yields $v(t)$. In mathematical terminology, Eq. (1–21) is defined to be the Laplace transform and is written symbolically as

$$V(s) = \mathcal{L}[v(t)],$$

and Eq. (1–23) is the inverse transform and is written symbolically as

$$v(t) = \mathcal{L}^{-1}[V(s)],$$

where $v(t)$ is restricted to the class of functions for which both these operations exist.

Equation (1–7) can now be given a more rigorous representation. The Laplace transform resolves both $v_i(t)$ and $v_o(t)$ into spectral terms of the form e^{st}. The system response due to the input spectral term is

$$dv_o(t) = \left(\frac{V_o(s)\ ds}{2\pi j}\right) e^{st} = H(s)\left(\frac{V_i(s)\ ds}{2\pi j}\right) e^{st}. \tag{1–24}$$

The summation of all these spectral terms by means of integration yields the total response,

$$v_o(t) = \frac{1}{2\pi j}\int_{c-j\infty}^{c+j\infty} V_o(s)e^{st}\ ds = \frac{1}{2\pi j}\int_{c-j\infty}^{c+j\infty} H(s)V_i(s)e^{st}\ ds. \tag{1–25}$$

From (1–24) it is easy to obtain

$$V_o(s) = H(s)V_i(s), \tag{1–26}$$

which yields

$$\frac{\mathcal{L}[v_o(t)]}{\mathcal{L}[v_i(t)]} = \frac{V_o(s)}{V_i(s)} = H(s). \tag{1–27}$$

Equation (1–27) can be taken as the rigorous definition of the system transfer function, provided that all initial conditions in the system are zero.* It is evidently identical to the definition (1–5).

In the analysis of problems it is important to use the simplest notation possible. This is given by Eqs. (1–26) and (1–27). The importance of the

---

* Initial conditions will be discussed in Chapter 5.

spectral significance of transforms should not be underestimated. However, the factor $(ds/2\pi j)e^{st}$, which distinguishes the spectral approach (1–24) from the mathematical approach (1–27), is redundant in all equations and cancels out.

The representation of the response of a linear system in the forms (1–7) or (1–25) leads to a simple formal solution. At first sight it might appear that the summations and integrations to be performed would limit the practical usefulness of this approach. However, there are several fundamental theorems from complex-variable theory which give a simple means of evaluating these forms. These theorems will be discussed in the following chapter.

PROBLEMS

1–1. For each of the following problems, the input is considered to be $V_i e^{st}$ and the output is to have the form $H(s)V_i e^{st}$. (a) Determine the transfer function for the network shown in Fig. 1–6. (b) The equation of motion of a ballistic galvanometer has the form

$$J\frac{d^2\theta}{dt^2} + D\frac{d\theta}{dt} + K\theta = BANi(t),$$

where $i(t)$ is the input current and θ is the angular deflection. Determine the transfer function. (c) The linearized equation of motion for a small servomotor has the form

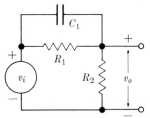

$$J\frac{d^2\theta}{dt^2} + D\frac{d\theta}{dt} = Kv(t),$$

FIGURE 1–6

where $v(t)$ is the input voltage and θ the shaft angle. Find the transfer function.

1–2. Consider a periodic signal of the form

$$v_i(t) = \frac{e^{-bt}}{1 - e^{-bT}}, \qquad 0 < t < T,$$

where T is the period. (a) Show that

$$a_n = \frac{1}{T}\frac{1}{b + j\omega_n},$$

where $\omega_n = 2\pi n/T$. (b) Show that the output response of the RC network shown in Fig. 1–3 can be represented in the form $v_o(t) = \sum_{n=-\infty}^{+\infty} c_n e^{j\omega_n t}$, where

$$c_n = \frac{1}{T}\frac{j\tau\omega_n}{(1 + j\tau\omega_n)}\frac{1}{(b + j\omega_n)}$$

and $\tau = RC$.

(c) The response can be written in the closed form (see Section 13–2, Example 1):

$$v_o(t) = \frac{ae^{-at}}{(a-b)(1-e^{-aT})} + \frac{be^{-bt}}{(b-a)(1-e^{-bT})}, \qquad 0 < t < T,$$

where $a = 1/RC$. Prove that this is the output response by resolving it into exponential spectral terms and comparing its components with the result of part (b).

1–3. Consider Problem 1–2 and let $T \to +\infty$. Show that $v_i(t)$ takes the form

$$v_i(t) = \begin{cases} e^{-bt}, & t > 0, \\ 0, & t < 0. \end{cases}$$

By substituting $s = j\omega_n$ show that $a_n T = 1/(b+s)$. Consider the resolution of $v_i(t)$ into exponential spectral terms of the form e^{st} [see Eq. (1–16)]. Note the distinction between the exponential e^{st}, which is valid for all t, and $v_i(t)$, which has an exponential form only for $t > 0$.

CHAPTER 2

INTRODUCTION TO COMPLEX-VARIABLE THEORY

2–1 Introduction. In Chapter 1, we defined the inverse Laplace transform by Eq. (1–23). This integral is a *complex line integral*, and we shall now be concerned with means of evaluating it. The functions of a complex variable that we consider are of the form

$$F(s) = u(\sigma, \omega) + jv(\sigma, \omega),$$

where $s = \sigma + j\omega$. If a value is assigned to the complex number s, then σ, ω, and consequently the functions $u(\sigma, \omega)$, $v(\sigma, \omega)$, and $F(s)$, are determined.

2–2 The Cauchy-Riemann differential equations. A single-valued function $F(s)$ of the complex variable s is called *analytic* within a region R if the derivative

$$\frac{dF}{ds} = \lim_{\Delta s \to 0} \frac{\Delta F}{\Delta s}$$

exists within R and is independent of the choice of Δs. The necessary and sufficient conditions that will lead to this result are called the *Cauchy-Riemann differential equations* and are given by

$$\frac{\partial u}{\partial \sigma} = \frac{\partial v}{\partial \omega},$$

$$\frac{\partial u}{\partial \omega} = -\frac{\partial v}{\partial \sigma}. \tag{2-1}$$

To demonstrate that these conditions are necessary, let us choose $\Delta s = \Delta\sigma$. Then

$$\frac{dF}{ds} = \frac{\partial u}{\partial \sigma} + j\frac{\partial v}{\partial \sigma}. \tag{2-2}$$

If we now choose $\Delta s = j\,\Delta\omega$, we obtain

$$\frac{dF}{ds} = -j\frac{\partial u}{\partial \omega} + \frac{\partial v}{\partial \omega}. \tag{2-3}$$

Equating expressions (2–2) and (2–3) leads immediately to the conditions (2–1).

2–3 Contour integrals and Cauchy's integral theorem. Consider a simple closed curve C to be subdivided by a set of points s_k $(k = 1, 2, \ldots, n)$ into segments which are all smaller in length than a positive δ. The limit

$$\lim_{\delta \to 0} \sum_{k=1}^{n} F(s_k)(s_k - s_{k-1}) = \oint_C F(s)\, ds,$$

if it exists, is called a *contour integral*. The integration is taken along C in a positive mathematical sense.

If $|F(s)| \leq M$ (M a positive number) for all points on C, the following inequality can be established:

$$\left| \oint_C F(s)\, ds \right| \leq M \lim_{\delta \to 0} \sum_{k=1}^{n} |s_k - s_{k-1}| \leq Ml,$$

where l is the path length of C.

Cauchy's integral theorem states that if $F(s)$ is a single-valued analytic function inside and on C, then

$$\oint_C F(s)\, ds = 0. \tag{2–4}$$

We shall now prove this theorem. Consider the double integral

$$I_1 = - \iint_R \left[\frac{\partial u}{\partial \omega} + \frac{\partial v}{\partial \sigma} \right] d\sigma\, d\omega \tag{2–5}$$

over the region R bounded by the closed curve C (see Fig. 2–1). From the Cauchy-Riemann conditions (2–1) it follows that this integral is

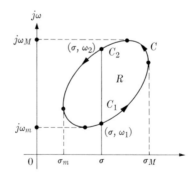

FIG. 2–1. Integration path in the complex s-plane.

identically zero. Partial integration of the first term for a constant value of σ yields

$$-\iint_R \frac{\partial u(\sigma, \omega)}{\partial \omega}\, d\omega\, d\sigma = \int_{\sigma_m}^{\sigma_M} [-u(\sigma, \omega_2) + u(\sigma, \omega_1)]\, d\sigma = \oint_C u(\sigma, \omega)\, d\sigma.$$

The latter integral is a contour integral taken along the path C in a positive mathematical sense. This result is obtained by noting that $d\sigma > 0$ for the lower portion C_1 of this path and $d\sigma < 0$ for the upper portion C_2.

Similarly, for the second term in Eq. (2–5) we obtain

$$-\iint_R \frac{\partial v(\sigma, \omega)}{\partial \sigma}\, d\sigma\, d\omega = \int_{\omega_m}^{\omega_M} [-v(\sigma_2, \omega) + v(\sigma_1, \omega)]\, d\omega$$

$$= -\oint_C v(\sigma, \omega)\, d\omega. \tag{2–6}$$

Thus I_1 can be written in the form

$$I_1 = 0 = \oint_C [u(\sigma, \omega)\, d\sigma - v(\sigma, \omega)\, d\omega]. \tag{2–7}$$

Since $ds = d\sigma + j\, d\omega$, it follows that Eq. (2–7) is the real part of (2–4). Similarly, if we start with the integral

$$I_2 = \iint_R \left[\frac{\partial u}{\partial \sigma} - \frac{\partial v}{\partial \omega}\right] d\sigma\, d\omega,$$

which is identically zero [because of Eq. (2–1)], we can prove that the imaginary part of the integral in Eq. (2–4) vanishes. This result proves Eq. (2–4).

2–4 An extension of Cauchy's integral theorem. Points in the complex s-plane where a single-valued function $F(s)$ is not analytic are called *singular points*. The functions $F(s)$ that we consider contain terms of the form

$$\frac{An}{(s - a)^n},$$

where n is a positive integer. Evidently $F(s)$ is not analytic at $s = a$. This singular point is called a *pole* of order n. If $n = 1$, the singular point is called a simple pole. Cauchy's integral theorem is no longer applicable if the closed curve C encloses a pole. We will now discuss an extension of Cauchy's theorem which deals with this possibility. Consider the situation

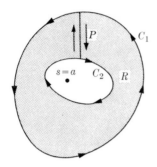

Fig. 2–2. A pole enclosed by the path of integration.

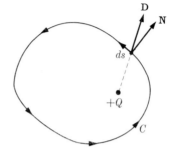

Fig. 2–3. A line source enclosed by a cylindrical surface C.

shown in Fig. 2–2, where $F(s)$ has a pole at $s = a$ which is enclosed by the path C_1. We will now prove that

$$\oint_{C_1} F(s)\, ds = \oint_{C_2} F(s)\, ds, \tag{2-8}$$

i.e., the integral does not depend on the particular closed curve chosen provided only that the curve encloses the pole.

We present the following proof. Connect C_1 and C_2 by means of a path P. Then $F(s)$ is analytic within the region R bounded by the contour consisting of the paths C_1, C_2, and P. Cauchy's integral theorem (2–4) can be applied to this contour, yielding

$$\oint_{C_1} F(s)\, ds + \oint_{C_2} F(s)\, ds = 0, \tag{2-9}$$

where the integral along P cancels out due to the opposed differential elements ds on P. Moving the second integral of Eq. (2–9) to the right-hand side of the equation gives it a negative sign which can be changed to a positive sign by reversing the direction of integration. This leads immediately to Eq. (2–8).

For one becoming acquainted with complex-variable theory for the first time, it appears unusual that the integral in Eq. (2–8) should be independent of the path chosen and that it vanishes when $F(s)$ has no poles within the contour. However, there is an analogy with the electrostatic field theory of long transmission lines which helps to clarify this point. Gauss's theorem for this case is (see Fig. 2–3)

$$\oint_{C} \mathbf{D} \cdot \mathbf{N}\, ds = Q, \tag{2-10}$$

Where Q is the charge per unit length of a line source, $\mathbf{D}$ is the electric flux density, $\mathbf{N}$ is a unit outward normal, and ds is the differential element of the closed curve C enclosing the line source. In this case the line source represents the singularity, or pole, for the field, and the integral in Eq. (2–10) depends only on the charge per unit length, and not on the path C chosen, provided only that it encloses the source. If there is no charge within C, $Q = 0$, and Eq. (2–10) can then be compared with Eq. (2–4). Analogies of this kind serve many useful purposes in network theory.

2–5 Cauchy's integral formulas. We shall now be concerned with the derivation of several important formulas dealing with contour integrals. Consider the integral

$$I = \frac{1}{2\pi j} \oint_C \frac{ds}{(s-a)^n}, \tag{2–11}$$

where n is an integer and the path of integration is along a closed path C enclosing the point $s = a$ (Fig. 2–4). According to Eq. (2–8), one may choose any suitable path enclosing $s = a$; hence we select a small circle of radius ρ. This path will be designated by C_0. Using the substitution

$$s - a = \rho e^{j\phi},$$

we find that the differential element along the path is

$$ds = j\rho e^{j\phi}\, d\phi,$$

and Eq. (2–11) is then given by

$$I = \frac{\rho^{1-n}}{2\pi j} \int_0^{2\pi} e^{j\phi(1-n)}\, d\phi.$$

This expression is easily evaluated, and we obtain

$$I = 0 \quad \text{if} \quad n \neq 1,$$

and

$$I = \frac{1}{2\pi j} \oint_C \frac{ds}{s-a} = 1 \quad \text{if} \quad n = 1. \tag{2–12}$$

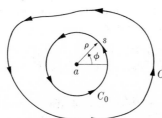

FIG. 2–4. Paths of integration for Cauchy's integral formulas.

Let us now consider the integral

$$I = \frac{1}{2\pi j} \oint_C \frac{F(s)}{s - a} \, ds,$$

where $F(s)$ is analytic on and within C. The path of integration can again be chosen to be the circular path C_0, and the integral I can then be written as

$$\frac{1}{2\pi j} \oint_C \frac{F(s)}{s - a} \, ds = \frac{1}{2\pi j} \oint_{C_0} \frac{F(a) + F(s) - F(a)}{s - a} \, ds$$

$$= F(a) + \frac{1}{2\pi j} \oint_{C_0} \frac{F(s) - F(a)}{s - a} \, ds, \qquad (2\text{-}13)$$

where Eq. (2–12) has been used in the second step. Suppose ϵ is an arbitrarily small positive quantity. It is then possible to choose a ρ sufficiently small so that

$$|F(s) - F(a)| \leq \epsilon,$$

since $F(s)$ is analytic and thus uniformly continuous within C_0. The absolute value of the second term on the right-hand side of Eq. (2–13) is then

$$\left| \frac{1}{2\pi j} \oint_{C_0} \frac{F(s) - F(a)}{s - a} \, ds \right| \leq \frac{\epsilon}{2\pi\rho} \, 2\pi\rho = \epsilon.$$

This proves *Cauchy's integral formula*,

$$F(a) = \frac{1}{2\pi j} \oint_C \frac{F(s)}{s - a} \, ds. \qquad (2\text{-}14)$$

If we differentiate Eq. (2–14) under the integral sign with respect to a, we have

$$\frac{dF(a)}{da} = \frac{dF(s)}{ds} \bigg]_{s=a} = \frac{1}{2\pi j} \oint_C \frac{F(s)}{(s - a)^2} \, ds. \qquad (2\text{-}15)$$

By differentiating Eq. (2–14) n times in this manner we obtain the general form of Cauchy's integral formula,

$$\frac{1}{n!} F^{(n)}(a) = \frac{1}{n!} \frac{d^n F(s)}{ds^n} \bigg]_{s=a} = \frac{1}{2\pi j} \oint_C \frac{F(s)}{(s - a)^{n+1}} \, ds. \qquad (2\text{-}16)$$

The formulas (2–14) and (2–16) are of great importance and should be carefully noted. The function $F(s)$ in the integrand will be called the *pole coefficient.* The proof for the validity of the differentiation under the integral sign is similar to the proof used to obtain Eq. (2–14) and will not be discussed further.

It is possible to establish the validity of the Taylor series

$$F(s) = \sum_{k=0}^{\infty} c_k (s - a)^k$$

within the contour C. The integrand of the integral in Eq. (2–16) is then

$$\frac{F(s)}{(s - a)^{n+1}} = \frac{c_0}{(s - a)^{n+1}} + \cdots + \frac{c_n}{s - a} + \cdots.$$

The coefficient of $(s - a)^{-1}$ in an expansion of this type is called the *residue.* Since $c_n = (1/n!)F^{(n)}(a)$ it is seen that the value of the integral (2–16) is the residue of the integrand.

2–6 The inverse Laplace transform of single-valued functions. The integral that will be our primary concern is the inverse Laplace transform given by the line integral (1–23) which is not a contour integral. We now derive a theorem which will enable us to transform this line integral into a contour integral and also to determine a suitable choice of the constant c. Consider a semicircle C_R of radius R about the origin which is in the right half of the s-plane (see Fig. 2–5) and let I be the line integral of $F(s)e^{st}$ along C_R. The theorem states that

$$\lim_{R \to \infty} I = \lim_{R \to \infty} \int_{C_R} F(s)e^{st}\, ds = 0, \qquad t < 0 \qquad (2\text{–}17)$$

if

$$\lim_{R \to \infty} F(s) = 0 \qquad (2\text{–}18)$$

for all values of s on C_R.

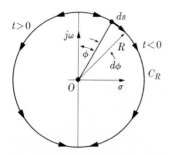

FIG. 2–5. The paths of integration for $t > 0$ and $t < 0$.

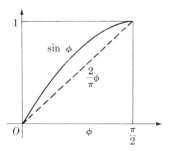

FIG. 2-6. The inequality $\sin \phi \geq 2\phi/\pi$.

The proof is established as follows. Let

$$s = Re^{j(\pi/2-\phi)}.$$

The arc length along the path is then $|ds| = R\,d\phi$, and

Thus

$$e^{st} = e^{Rt\sin\phi}e^{jRt\cos\phi}.$$

$$|e^{st}| = e^{-R|t|\sin\phi}.$$

Now let m be the maximum value of $F(s)$ on the semicircle. Then, by taking the absolute value of I, we obtain

$$|I| \leq mR\int_0^\pi e^{-R|t|\sin\phi}\,d\phi = 2mR\int_0^{\pi/2} e^{-R|t|\sin\phi}\,d\phi. \qquad (2\text{-}19)$$

From Fig. 2-6 it is easily seen that $\sin\phi \geq (2/\pi)\phi$ for $0 \leq \phi \leq \pi/2$. Using this result in the exponential in Eq. (2-19) yields

$$|I| \leq 2mR\int_0^{\pi/2} e^{-2R|t|\phi/\pi}\,d\phi = \frac{\pi m}{|t|}[1 - e^{-R|t|}].$$

From Eq. (2-18) it follows that $m \to 0$ as $R \to \infty$. Thus $I \to 0$. If $t > 0$, we can prove, in a similar way, that

$$\lim_{R\to\infty} \int_{C_R} F(s)e^{st}\,ds = 0, \qquad (2\text{-}20)$$

where the semicircle C_R is now taken in the left half of the s-plane.

The results (2-17) and (2-20) are easily explained from a heuristic point of view. In both integrals, the exponential must vanish for large s, and thus we must have $\text{Re}[st] < 0$ ($\text{Re}[f]$ means the real part of the function f). If $t < 0$, $\text{Re}[s]$ must be greater than zero and the semicircle is chosen in the right half of the s-plane. If $t > 0$, $\text{Re}[s]$ must be less than zero, and

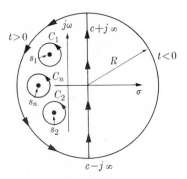

FIG. 2–7. Paths of integration in the s-plane.

the left half of the s-plane is then chosen. By substituting $s' = s + b$ we can show that (2–17) and (2–20) remain unaffected by a displacement b of the center of the circle from the origin of the s-plane.

We are now in a position to deal with the inverse Laplace transform (1–23):

$$v(t) = \frac{1}{2\pi j} \int_{c-j\infty}^{c+j\infty} V(s)e^{st}\, ds. \qquad (2\text{–}21)$$

If $t < 0$, we can add (2–17) to this integral and obtain (see Fig. 2–7)

$$v(t) = \frac{1}{2\pi j} \int_{c-j\infty}^{c+j\infty} V(s)e^{st}\, dst + \lim_{R\to\infty} \frac{1}{2\pi j} \int_{C_R} V(s)e^{st}\, ds = \frac{1}{2\pi j} \oint V(s)e^{st}\, ds.$$

This is a contour integral. The constant c is now chosen so that all singularities of $V(s)$ are to the left of the line $s = c + j\omega$. Using Cauchy's theorem (2–4), we obtain

$$v(t) = 0 \qquad \text{for} \qquad t < 0. \qquad (2\text{–}22)$$

The reason for this choice of c is that in the derivation of the Laplace transform we have already restricted ourselves to signals satisfying the condition (2–22).

Let us now consider that $V(s)$ is a single-valued function of s and that its singularities are poles at $s_1, s_2, \ldots, s_n$ (see Fig. 2–7). If $t > 0$, we can add (2–20) to (2–21) and obtain

$$v(t) = \frac{1}{2\pi j} \int_{c-j\infty}^{c+j\infty} V(s)e^{st}\, ds + \lim_{R\to\infty} \frac{1}{2\pi j} \int_{C_R} V(s)e^{st}\, ds$$

$$= \sum_{k=1}^{n} \frac{1}{2\pi j} \oint_{s=s_k} V(s)e^{st}\, ds. \qquad (2\text{–}23)$$

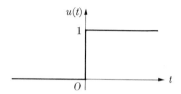

FIG. 2–8. The unit step function.

The final result follows from (2–8), since the value of the integral is independent of the path chosen, provided only that it encloses all poles of the integrand. The integral of $F(s)$ along the path C_k enclosing the pole s_k is represented by the symbol

$$\oint_{s=s_k} F(s)\, ds.$$

EXAMPLE 1. Consider the unit-step function (Fig. 2–8)

$$u(t) = \begin{cases} 1, & t > 0, \\ 0, & t < 0. \end{cases}$$

The Laplace transform can be found from Eq. (1–21) and we obtain

$$\mathcal{L}[u(t)] = U(s) = \int_0^\infty u(t)e^{-st}\, dt = \frac{1}{s}.$$

It should be noted that in order for the integral to converge, Re[s] > 0. However, the function of s so obtained can then be continued analytically into the complete s-plane.

The physical interpretation of the Laplace transform is that of a spectral resolution of the signal $u(t)$ into exponential terms of the form e^{st}. The component of e^{st} is [see Eq. (1–22)]

$$\frac{U(s)\, ds}{2\pi j},$$

and the superposition of all spectral terms by integration yields [see Eq. (1–23)]

$$u(t) = \int_{c-j\infty}^{c+j\infty} \left[\frac{U(s)\, ds}{2\pi j} \right] e^{st}. \tag{2–24}$$

We now verify Eq. (2–24) by contour integration. The function $U(s) = 1/s$ has a simple pole at the origin. The constant c is chosen such that this

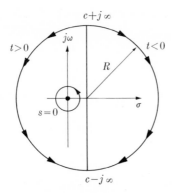

FIG. 2–9. The paths of integration for a pole at the origin.

pole is to the left of the line $s = c + j\omega$ (Fig. 2–9). For $t < 0$, the path can be closed by an infinitely large semicircle in the right half of the s-plane and, using Cauchy's theorem, we obtain $u(t) = 0$. For $t > 0$, the path can be closed by an infinitely large semicircle in the left-half of the s-plane and we obtain

$$u(t) = \frac{1}{2\pi j} \oint_{s=0} \frac{e^{st}}{s}\, ds.$$

This expression can be evaluated by means of Eq. (2–14), where $a = 0$ and $F(s) = e^{st}$. The result, $u(t) = F(0) = 1$, proves the integral representation (2–24). ▲

EXAMPLE 2. Consider the function

$$v(t) = \begin{cases} \sin \omega t, & t > 0, \\ 0, & t < 0. \end{cases}$$

Evaluating the Laplace transform, we obtain

$$V(s) = \frac{1}{2j} \int_0^\infty [e^{j\omega t} - e^{-j\omega t}]e^{-st}\, dt = \frac{\omega}{s^2 + \omega^2}.$$

The inverse Laplace transform for $t > 0$ can be obtained from Eq. (2–23), which yields

$$v(t) = \frac{1}{2\pi j} \oint_{s_1 = -j\omega} \frac{\omega}{(s + j\omega)(s - j\omega)} e^{st}\, ds$$

$$+ \frac{1}{2\pi j} \oint_{s_2 = j\omega} \frac{\omega}{(s + j\omega)(s - j\omega)} e^{st}\, ds.$$

The pole coefficients (see Section 2–5) can be found by inspection; they are

$$F_1(s) = \frac{\omega e^{st}}{s - j\omega} \qquad \text{at} \qquad s_1 = -j\omega,$$

and

$$F_2(s) = \frac{\omega e^{st}}{s + j\omega} \qquad \text{at} \qquad s_1 = j\omega.$$

Using Eq. (2–14) to evaluate the integrals, we obtain the result

$$v(t) = F_1(s_1) + F_2(s_2) = \sin \omega t.$$

[The condition $v(t) = 0$ for $t < 0$ is fulfilled because of the choice of the constant c.] ▲

This method of solving for the inverse Laplace transform by means of Eqs. (2–14) and (2–23) should be carefully noted. It will be used exclusively in the subsequent chapters. In fact, the response $v(t)$ can be immediately obtained from the Laplace transform. It is necessary only to determine the poles $s = s_1, s_2, \ldots, s_n$ of $V(s)$ and, at each pole, note the pole coefficient in the integrand of Eq. (2–23), i.e., write the integrand in the form

$$V(s)e^{st} = \frac{F_k(s)}{(s - s_k)^{n_k}},$$

where n_k is the order of the pole s_k and $F_k(s)$ is the pole coefficient. If the poles are simple, Eq. (2–14) can be used to evaluate Eq. (2–23), and we obtain

$$v(t) = \sum_{k=1}^{n} F_k(s_k). \tag{2–25}$$

This important result is called the Heaviside expansion. It states that the response of a system for $t > 0$ is the sum of the residues of $V(s)e^{st}$. If the poles are of higher order, the general formula (2–16) must be used to evaluate the residues.

2–7 The inverse Laplace transform of multivalued functions. Consider a function of the form $V(s) = \sqrt{s}\, G(s)$, where $G(s)$ is a single-valued function of s that has poles at $s = s_k \neq 0$ $(k = 1, 2, \ldots, n)$. In this case, $V(s)$ is a double-valued function of s, and one must take care in evaluating the inverse transform by contour integration. Let us represent s in the polar form

$$s = re^{j\phi}, \qquad |\phi| \leq \pi,$$

and let the paths C_+ and C_- be defined by the equations $\phi = \pi$ and

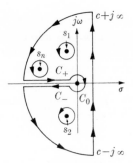

FIG. 2–10. The path of integration for a multivalued function of s with a branch point at $s = 0$.

$\phi = -\pi$, respectively (see Fig. 2–10). We have

$$\sqrt{s} = \begin{cases} j\sqrt{r}, & \phi = \pi, \\ -j\sqrt{r}, & \phi = -\pi. \end{cases}$$

Since the value of $\sqrt{s}$ differs for corresponding points on C_+ and C_-, it is a multivalued functions of s. To obtain a single-valued function of s we must consider C_+ and C_- to be two distinct paths. This can be accomplished if the s-plane is cut along the negative real axis. In mathematical terminology, this cut is designated as a *branch cut*. The upper edge of this cut is taken as C_+ and its lower edge as C_-. The point at $s = 0$ where C_+ and C_- join is designated as a *branch point*. In this cut s-plane, $V(s)$ is a single-valued function of s, and Cauchy's integral theorem can be applied. Thus we can write

$$\sum_{k=1}^{n} \oint_{s=s_k} V(s)e^{st}\, ds = \int_{c-j\infty}^{c+j\infty} V(s)e^{st}\, ds + \lim_{R\to\infty} \int_{C_R} V(s)e^{st}\, ds$$
$$+ \int_{C_+ + C_0 + C_-} V(s)e^{st}\, ds,$$

where C_R designates the path along the semicircle and $C_+ + C_0 + C_-$ designates a path taken along the branch cut and around the branch point in the direction shown in Fig. 2–10. Let $V(s)$ satisfy the condition (2–18) and let $t > 0$. Thus with the aid of Eq. (2–20) we obtain

$$\frac{1}{2\pi j} \int_{c-j\infty}^{c+j\infty} V(s)e^{st}\, ds = \sum_{k=1}^{n} \frac{1}{2\pi j} \oint_{s=s_k} V(s)e^{st}\, ds$$
$$+ \frac{1}{2\pi j} \int_{C_- + C_0 + C_+} V(s)e^{st}\, ds, \qquad (2\text{–}26)$$

where the line integral along the branch cut is now taken in a positive mathematical sense. Equation (2–26) allows us to state that the original path of integration given by $s = c + j\omega$ can be transformed into the path $C_- + C_0 + C_+$ and a set of contours each of which encloses one pole of the integrand. For a multivalued function of s, the integral along the branch cut does not vanish since $V(s)$ has different values for corresponding points on C_+ and C_-. A more complete discussion and illustrative examples are given in Chapter 14.

2–8 Some comments on line integrals. In the inverse Laplace transform the constant c is chosen such that all singularities of the integrand are to the left of the path given by $s = c + j\omega$. However, in general, the integrand of line integrals taken along a path C dividing the s-plane may have poles on either side of C. In some of these integrals we have $t = 0$, and Eq. (2–18) must be replaced by the condition

$$\lim_{R \to \infty} s^n F(s) = 0, \tag{2–27}$$

where $n > 1$. It follows that $|I| \leq m\pi R^{1-n}$, and thus Eqs. (2–17) and (2–20) remain valid. The path C can then be completed along a semicircle C_R in either the left half or right half of the s-plane. The resulting contours enclose all poles to the left or right of C, respectively.

The line integral for the steady-state response of a linear system has the form (13–5), where the integrand has poles on both sides of the line $s = c + j\omega$. In this case we have $0 < t < T$, where T is the period. If $H(s)V_T(s)$ [see Eq. (13–4a)] satisfies (2–18), the path of integration may be completed in the left half of the s-plane. However, it is interesting to note that the path of integration can also be completed in the right half of the s-plane. If $\text{Re}[s] \gg 0$, the integrand takes the form

$$V_o(s)e^{st} \cong -H(s)V_T(s)e^{s(t-T)}.$$

Since $t - T < 0$, it follows that (2–17) is valid, and this fact allows completing the path in the right half of the s-plane.

In the examples discussed in the subsequent chapters it will simply be stated that the path of integration can be completed in the manner designated. It is left as an exercise for the reader to show that in each case the conditions (2–18) or (2–27) are fulfilled.

PROBLEMS

2-1. Let $F = s^3 = u + jv$. (a) By substituting $s = \sigma + j\omega$ determine $u = u(\sigma, \omega)$ and $v = v(\sigma, \omega)$. (b) Prove that the Cauchy-Riemann equations are satisfied.

2-2. Determine the residues of the function $e^{st}/(s + a)(s + b)^2$ at its poles by (a) use of a Taylor series for the respective pole coefficients; (b) use of the Cauchy integral formula.

2-3. Determine the Laplace transform of the functions

$$v(t) = \begin{cases} e^{-at}, & t > 0, \\ 0, & t < 0, \end{cases} \qquad v(t) = \begin{cases} e^{-at} \sin bt, & t > 0, \\ 0, & t < 0. \end{cases}$$

2-4. Consider the Laplace-transforms

$$\frac{1}{s + a} \qquad \text{and} \qquad \frac{1}{s^2 + 2as + b^2}.$$

(a) Determine the poles. (b) Determine the pole coefficients. (c) Determine the inverse Laplace transforms.

2-5. By differentiating $1/s = \int_0^\infty e^{-st} \, ds$ with respect to s prove that $\mathcal{L}[t^n/n!] = 1/s^{n+1}$.

2-6. Determine the inverse Laplace transform of the function $1/s^{n+1}$ by contour integration.

CHAPTER 3

THE RESPONSE OF LUMPED-PARAMETER
PASSIVE NETWORKS

3-1 Introduction. Lumped-parameter networks are composed of elements whose response property can be accurately described by a scalar quantity. For time-invariant electric networks, these quantities are the resistance R, inductance L, and capacitance C. The voltage-current relations for resistive, inductive, and capacitive circuit elements are given by Eqs. (1-2). For convenience these equations are listed below:

$$v(t) = Ri(t), \qquad v(t) = L \frac{di(t)}{dt}, \qquad \frac{dv(t)}{dt} = \frac{1}{C} i(t). \tag{3-1}$$

The transfer functions of these elements can be found by taking $v(t) = Ve^{st}$, $i(t) = Ie^{st}$, and computing the ratio $V/I = Z(s)$, which is defined as the impedance. We obtain

$$Z(s) = R, \qquad Z(s) = Ls, \qquad Z(s) = 1/Cs, \tag{3-2}$$

respectively. The same result can be found by taking the Laplace transform of equations (3-1). By definition,

$$\mathcal{L}[v(t)] = V(s) = \int_0^\infty v(t)e^{-st}\, dt. \tag{3-3}$$

Applying this to $\mathcal{L}[dv/dt]$ and then integrating by parts yield

$$\int_0^\infty \frac{dv}{dt} e^{-st}\, dt = ve^{-st} \Big]_0^\infty + s\int_0^\infty v(t)e^{-st}\, dt. \tag{3-4}$$

If we consider all initial conditions to be identically zero, the first term on the right-hand side of Eq. (3-4) vanishes. Thus

$$\mathcal{L}\left[\frac{dv}{dt}\right] = sV(s). \tag{3-5}$$

Applying the Laplace transform to Eq. (3-1) and using Eqs. (3-3) and (3-5), we obtain

$$V(s) = RI(s), \qquad V(s) = LsI(s), \qquad sV(s) = \frac{1}{C} I(s).$$

These equations yield the same results as (3–2) if we take $Z(s) = V(s)/I(s)$. Since these results are so easily remembered, Kirchhoff's laws for the voltage-current relations in a network can be immediately written in terms of the transforms $V(s)$, $I(s)$, and the impedance $Z(s)$ [or in terms of the admittance if the ratio $I(s)/V(s)$ is more appropriate for the problem]. It should be noted that $V(s)$ does not represent a voltage. By means of $V(s)$ we obtain a resolution of $v(t)$ into exponential spectral terms of the form $[V(s)\, ds/2\pi j]e^{st}$. Thus $V(s)$ can be considered as a representation of the components of the time-domain signal $v(t)$ in the complex-frequency plane. The product $V(s)\, ds$ has the same dimensions as $v(t)$.

3–2 The Laplace transform method. We now present several examples illustrating the use of the Laplace transform method.

EXAMPLE 1. Consider the network shown in Fig. 3–1, where

$$R_1 = 5\,\Omega, \qquad L_1 = 2\,\text{h},$$
$$R_2 = 3\,\Omega, \qquad L_2 = 4\,\text{h},$$
$$R_3 = 8\,\Omega, \qquad M = 2\,\text{h}.$$

The problem is to determine the current responses $i_1(t)$, $i_2(t)$, and $i_3(t)$ to an input voltage $v_i(t)$ suddenly applied at $t = 0$. The Kirchhoff loop equations expressed in terms of Laplace transforms are

$$5I_1(s) - 5I_2(s) + 0 = V_i(s),$$
$$-5I_1(s) + (8 + 2s)I_2(s) + 2sI_3(s) = 0, \qquad (3\text{–}6)$$
$$0 + 2sI_2(s) + (8 + 4s)I_3(s) = 0.$$

The determinant of the system of linear equations (3–6) is

$$\Delta = \begin{vmatrix} 5 & -5 & 0 \\ -5 & 8 + 2s & 2s \\ 0 & 2s & 8 + 4s \end{vmatrix} = 20(s + 1)(s + 6). \qquad (3\text{–}7)$$

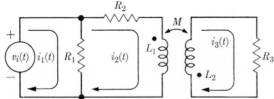

FIG. 3–1. A transformer-coupled network.

Equations (3–6) can be solved by *Cramer's rule* [see Eq. (3–19)], and we obtain

$$I_1(s) = \frac{1}{\Delta} \begin{vmatrix} V_i(s) & -5 & 0 \\ 0 & 8+2s & 2s \\ 0 & 2s & 8+4s \end{vmatrix} = \frac{V_i(s)}{5} \frac{s^2 + 12s + 16}{(s+1)(s+6)}, \qquad (3\text{–}8)$$

$$I_2(s) = \frac{1}{\Delta} \begin{vmatrix} 5 & V_i(s) & 0 \\ -5 & 0 & 2s \\ 0 & 0 & 8+4s \end{vmatrix} = V_i(s) \frac{2+s}{(s+1)(s+6)}, \qquad (3\text{–}9)$$

$$I_3(s) = \frac{1}{\Delta} \begin{vmatrix} 5 & -5 & V_i(s) \\ -5 & 8+2s & 0 \\ 0 & 2s & 0 \end{vmatrix} = -\frac{V_i(s)}{2} \frac{s}{(s+1)(s+6)}. \qquad (3\text{–}10)$$

These equations determine the current transforms in terms of $V_i(s) = \mathcal{L}[v_i(t)]$. The current responses can be obtained by taking the inverse transform of these quantities. Suppose, for example, that the applied voltage is a unit step. Then $V_i(s) = 1/s$. The poles of $I_1(s)$ and $I_2(s)$ occur at $s = 0, -1, -6$. Consider first $I_1(s)e^{st}$. The pole coefficients are

$$F_0(s) = \frac{1}{5} \frac{s^2 + 12s + 16}{(s+1)(s+6)} e^{st} \qquad \text{at} \qquad s_0 = 0,$$

$$F_1(s) = \frac{1}{5s} \frac{s^2 + 12s + 16}{(s+6)} e^{st} \qquad \text{at} \qquad s_1 = -1,$$

$$F_2(s) = \frac{1}{5s} \frac{s^2 + 12s + 16}{(s+1)} e^{st} \qquad \text{at} \qquad s_2 = -6.$$

Using the Heaviside expansion (2–25), we obtain

$$i_1(t) = F_0(0) + F_1(-1) + F_2(-6) = \tfrac{1}{15}(8 - 3e^{-t} - 2e^{-6t}). \quad (3\text{–}11)$$

Similarly, for $I_2(s)e^{st}$, the pole coefficients are

$$F_0(s) = \frac{2+s}{(s+1)(s+6)} e^{st} \qquad \text{at} \qquad s_0 = 0,$$

$$F_1(s) = \frac{2+s}{s(s+6)} e^{st} \qquad \text{at} \qquad s_1 = -1,$$

$$F_2(s) = \frac{2+s}{s(s+1)} e^{st} \qquad \text{at} \qquad s_2 = -6.$$

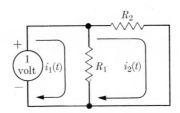

FIG. 3-2. A network for deriving the steady-state conditions.

Thus

$$i_2(t) = F_0(0) + F_1(-1) + F_2(-6) = \tfrac{1}{15}(5 - 3e^{-t} - 2e^{-6t}). \quad (3\text{-}12)$$

The poles for $I_3(s)$ occur at $s = -1, -6$, since the pole at $s = 0$ is cancelled by the s in the numerator. The pole coefficients for $I_3(s)e^{st}$ are

$$F_1(s) = \frac{-1}{2(s+6)} \, e^{st} \qquad \text{at} \qquad s_1 = -1,$$

$$F_2(s) = \frac{-1}{2(s+1)} \, e^{st} \qquad \text{at} \qquad s_2 = -6.$$

Thus

$$i_3(t) = F_1(-1) + F_2(-6) = \tfrac{1}{10}(e^{-6t} - e^{-t}). \qquad (3\text{-}13)$$

If the network conditions at $t = 0$ and $t = \infty$ are simple enough, it is usually advisable to check the results at these extremes. At $t = \infty$ the currents are steady, and the simplified network shown in Fig. 3-2 can be used to determine the steady values. With the aid of this network, we obtain

$$R_1[i_1(\infty) - i_2(\infty)] = 1, \qquad \text{and} \qquad R_2 i_2(\infty) = 1,$$

which yields

$$i_2(\infty) = \tfrac{1}{3} \qquad \text{and} \qquad i_1(\infty) = \tfrac{8}{15}.$$

At $t = 0$ the inductance of the coils prevents any instantaneous change of current. Thus

$$i_2(0) = i_3(0) = 0$$

and

$$R_1 i_1(0) = 5i_1(0) = 1. \qquad (3\text{-}14)$$

These relations agree with those obtained from Eqs. (3-11), (3-12), and (3-13). ▲

EXAMPLE 2. Suppose that the network is the same as that of the previous example and that we are now required to determine the current response to the input voltage

$$v_i(t) = \begin{cases} \cos 2t, & t > 0, \\ 0, & t < 0. \end{cases}$$

The Laplace transform is easily found, either from the tables in the Appendix or from the definition, and is given by

$$V_i(s) = \frac{s}{s^2 + 4}.$$

Substituting this into Eqs. (3–8), (3–9), and (3–10) yields the transforms of the currents. The poles of $I_1(s)$, $I_2(s)$, and $I_3(s)$ are now at $s = -1$, -6, $\pm j2$. Let us consider first $I_1(s)e^{st}$. The pole coefficients are

$$F_1(s) = \frac{1}{5} \frac{s^2 + 12s + 16}{s + 6} \frac{se^{st}}{s^2 + 4} \qquad \text{at} \qquad s_1 = -1,$$

$$F_2(s) = \frac{1}{5} \frac{s^2 + 12s + 16}{s + 1} \frac{se^{st}}{s^2 + 4} \qquad \text{at} \qquad s_2 = -6,$$

$$F_3(s) = \frac{1}{5} \frac{s^2 + 12s + 16}{(s + 1)(s + 6)} \frac{se^{st}}{(s + j2)} \qquad \text{at} \qquad s_3 = j2.$$

Since $s_4 = -j2 = s_3^*$, the residue $F_4(s_4)$ need not be separately evaluated; it may be found directly from $F_3^*(j2)$ after this coefficient has been simplified. Using the Heaviside expansion, we obtain

$$i_1(t) = F_1(-1) + F_2(-6) + F_3(j2) + F_3^*(j2)$$

$$= \tfrac{1}{25}[-e^{-t} - 3e^{-6t} + 9\cos 2t + 3\sin 2t]. \tag{3–15}$$

The pole coefficients for $I_2(s)e^{st}$ are

$$F_1(s) = \frac{s + 2}{s + 6} \frac{se^{st}}{s^2 + 4} \qquad \text{at} \qquad s_1 = -1,$$

$$F_2(s) = \frac{s + 2}{s + 1} \frac{se^{st}}{s^2 + 4} \qquad \text{at} \qquad s_2 = -6,$$

$$F_3(s) = \frac{s + 2}{(s + 1)(s + 6)} \frac{se^{st}}{(s + j2)} \qquad \text{at} \qquad s_3 = j2.$$

Since $s_4 = s_3^*$, we have $F_4(s_4) = F_3^*(s_3)$. Thus

$$i_2(t) = F_1(-1) + F_2(-6) + F_3(j2) + F_3^*(j2)$$

$$= \tfrac{1}{25}[-e^{-t} - 3e^{-6t} + 4\cos 2t + 3\sin 2t]. \tag{3–16}$$

The pole coefficients for $I_3(s)e^{st}$ are

$$F_1(s) = -\frac{s}{2}\frac{1}{s+6}\frac{se^{st}}{s^2+4} \qquad \text{at} \qquad s_1 = -1,$$

$$F_2(s) = -\frac{s}{2}\frac{1}{s+1}\frac{se^{st}}{s^2+4} \qquad \text{at} \qquad s_2 = -6,$$

$$F_3(s) = -\frac{s}{2}\frac{1}{(s+1)(s+6)}\frac{se^{st}}{(s+j2)} \qquad \text{at} \qquad s_3 = j2,$$

and

$$F_4(-j2) = F_3^*(j2).$$

Thus

$$i_3(t) = F_1(-1) + F_2(-6) + F_3(j2) + F_3^*(j2)$$
$$= \tfrac{1}{100}[-2e^{-t} + 9e^{-6t} - 7\cos 2t + \sin 2t]. \qquad (3\text{--}17)$$

As a check on these equations we note that Eqs. (3–15), (3–16), and (3–17) agree with (3–14) at $t = 0$. ▲

3–3 Generalization of the method. For a network of n loops with n driving voltages, Eqs. (3–6) can be generalized to the form

$$Z_{11}(s)I_1(s) + \cdots + Z_{1n}(s)I_n(s) = V_1(s),$$
$$\vdots$$
$$Z_{n1}(s)I_1(s) + \cdots + Z_{nn}(s)I_n(s) = V_n(s), \qquad (3\text{--}18)$$

where the $Z_{kl}(s)$ are the impedance elements of the network. The solution of the system of linear equations (3–18) can be found by Cramer's rule and is given by

$$I_k(s) = \frac{1}{\Delta}\begin{vmatrix} Z_{11}(s) & \cdots & V_1(s) & \cdots & Z_{1n}(s) \\ \vdots & & \vdots & & \vdots \\ Z_{n1}(s) & \cdots & V_n(s) & \cdots & Z_{nn}(s) \end{vmatrix}, \qquad k = 1, 2, \ldots, n, \qquad (3\text{--}19)$$

where

$$\Delta = \begin{vmatrix} Z_{11}(s) & \cdots & Z_{1n}(s) \\ \vdots & & \vdots \\ Z_{n1}(s) & \cdots & Z_{nn}(s) \end{vmatrix}$$

is the determinant of the system (3–18) and the numerator is obtained from Δ by simply replacing the kth column by $V_1(s)$, $V_2(s)$, ..., $V_n(s)$. These transforms are considered known, and the problem is to determine the inverse transform of $I_k(s)$ and obtain the current response $i_k(t)$.

Let the poles of $I_k(s)$ be designated by s_p $(p = 1, 2, \ldots, m)$. In the neighborhood of s_p the integrand in the inverse Laplace transform can be written as

$$I_k(s)e^{st} = \frac{F_p(s)}{s - s_p},$$

provided that the poles are simple [$F_p(s)$ is the pole coefficient]. The Heaviside expansion yields the current response,

$$i_k(t) = \sum_{k=1}^{m} F_p(s_p).$$

If the poles are of higher order, the more general formula (2–16) must be used to evaluate the effect of the pole coefficients on the response.

3–4 The sinusoidal steady-state response. In Eqs. (3–15), (3–16), and (3–17) the exponential terms decay as $t \to +\infty$. The remaining terms are defined as the *sinusoidal steady-state* response of the network. It is of interest to compare the transform and phasor methods of determining the sinusoidal steady-state response of a system. Let us consider Fig. 3–3. A sinusoidal driving voltage $v(t)$ is applied to a network and we are required to determine the sinusoidal steady-state current response. The transfer function (which, in this case, is an admittance),

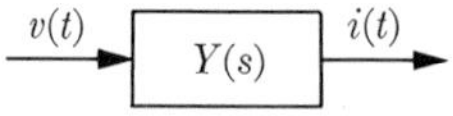

FIG. 3–3. The current response of a network to a driving voltage.

$$Y(s) = \frac{I(s)}{V(s)},$$

can be obtained by means of Kirchhoff's laws. In phasor analysis the driving voltage is taken to have the form

$$v(t) = \mathrm{Re}[V_m e^{j\omega t}],$$

where V_m is called the phasor voltage. As a phase reference we can take V_m to be real. By definition of the transfer function, the current response to the voltage $V_m e^{j\omega t}$ is

$$I_m e^{j\omega t} = Y(j\omega)V_m e^{j\omega t}, \tag{3–20}$$

where I_m is the phasor current. The physical response is taken to be the real part of (3–20):

$$i(t) = \mathrm{Re}[Y(j\omega)V_m e^{j\omega t}]. \tag{3–21}$$

We now compare this approach with the Laplace transform method. The input voltage is

$$v(t) = \begin{cases} V_m \cos \omega t, & t > 0, \\ 0, & t < 0, \end{cases}$$

and the voltage transform is

$$V(s) = \frac{s}{s^2 + \omega^2} V_m.$$

We then have for the current transform,

$$I(s) = Y(s) V(s) = Y(s) \frac{s}{s^2 + \omega^2} V_m.$$

The steady-state response can now be defined as those terms in the Heaviside expansion that are associated with the poles of $V(s)$. These poles are at $s = \pm j\omega$, and the pole coefficient at $s = j\omega$ is

$$F_1(s) = Y(s) \frac{s}{s + j\omega} V_m e^{st}.$$

Thus

$$i(t) = F_1(j\omega) + F_1^*(j\omega) = \mathrm{Re}[Y(j\omega) V_m e^{j\omega t}],$$

which is identical with (3–21).

It has already been stated that in systems analysis it is important to use the simplest notation possible. Phasor analysis has the simpler notation, but it should be remembered that it deals only with the sinusoidal steady-state response. If more information is required about the system response, the Laplace transform method must be used.

3–5 The impulse response of systems. The *unit-impulse function* $\delta(t)$ is defined by

$$\delta(t) = 0 \qquad \text{for} \qquad t \neq 0,$$

and

$$\lim_{\epsilon \to 0} \int_0^\epsilon \delta(t) \, dt = 1. \tag{3–22}$$

Note that $\delta(t)$ is a function whose amplitude is large for a very short time, after which it becomes small (Fig. 3–4). The Laplace transform of a unit impulse is

$$\int_0^\infty \delta(t) e^{-st} \, dt = \int_0^\epsilon \delta(t) e^{-st} \, dt = 1, \tag{3–23}$$

where the final result follows from Eq. (3–22).

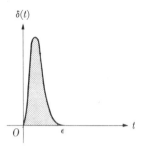

FIG. 3–4. The unit-impulse function.

To illustrate the usefulness of this function, let us consider a system excited by a unit impulse. The system response to a unit impulse will be designated by $h(t)$. Thus

$$\mathcal{L}[h(t)] = H(s) \cdot 1,$$

that is, the transform of the impulse response is the system transfer function. It is this simple relationship which makes the impulse response very useful.

EXAMPLE 3. Consider a ballistic galvanometer whose equation of motion is given by

$$J \frac{d^2\theta}{dt^2} + D \frac{d\theta}{dt} + K\theta = BANi(t), \qquad (3\text{--}24)$$

where $\theta(t)$ is the angular deflection and $i(t)$ is the driving current in the coil. The constants in Eq. (3–24) represent the following quantities:

J = the moment of inertia,
D = the damping coefficient,
K = the spring constant,
B = the magnetic flux density in the air gap,
A = the area of the coil,
N = the number of turns of the coil.

In the usual application of the ballistic galvanometer, the current $i(t)$ is due to the very rapid discharge of a capacitor through the coil. Thus we can write

$$i(t) = Q\, \delta(t), \qquad (3\text{--}25)$$

where $Q = \lim_{\epsilon \to 0} \int_0^\epsilon i(t)\, dt$ is the initial charge on the capacitor. Taking the Laplace transform of (3–24) and substituting $\omega_n^2 = K/J$, $2\zeta\omega_n = D/J$, and $G = BANQ/J$, we obtain

$$\Theta(s) = \frac{G}{s^2 + 2\zeta\omega_n s + \omega_n^2} = \frac{G}{(s - s_1)(s - s_2)}. \qquad (3\text{–}26)$$

The poles of Eq. (3–26) are given by

$$s_1 = -\omega_n(\zeta + j\sqrt{1 - \zeta^2}) \qquad \text{and} \qquad s_2 = -\omega_n(\zeta - j\sqrt{1 - \zeta^2}),$$

where ω_n represents the natural angular frequency of oscillation and ζ is the relative damping coefficient of the galvanometer. There are three alternatives for the value of ζ:

$$0 \leq \zeta < 1, \qquad \text{underdamped,}$$
$$\zeta = 1, \qquad \text{critically damped,}$$
$$\zeta > 1, \qquad \text{overdamped.}$$

We consider the underdamped case. The pole coefficients for $\Theta(s)e^{st}$ are

$$F_1(s) = \frac{G}{s - s_2} e^{st} \qquad \text{at} \qquad s = s_1,$$

$$F_2(s) = \frac{G}{s - s_1} e^{st} \qquad \text{at} \qquad s = s_2.$$

Thus

$$\theta(t) = F_1(s_1) + F_2(s_2) = \frac{Ge^{-\omega_n\zeta t}}{\omega_n\sqrt{1 - \zeta^2}} \sin \omega_n\sqrt{1 - \zeta^2}\, t. \ \blacktriangle$$

3–6 The convolution and superposition integrals. In the examples of Sections 3–2 and 3–5 we determined the step and impulse response of systems. We now derive formulas which permit us to find the response to any kind of input, once the step or impulse response is known.

Let $g(t)$ and $h(t)$ be the system responses to a unit step and unit impulse, respectively. If $G(s) = \mathcal{L}[g(t)]$ and $H(s) = \mathcal{L}[h(t)]$, it follows that

$$G(s) = H(s) \frac{1}{s}$$

and hence

$$H(s) = sG(s). \qquad (3\text{–}27)$$

The inverse transform of (3–27) is easily obtained:

$$h(t) = \frac{dg(t)}{dt},$$

that is, the impulse response is the derivative of the step response.

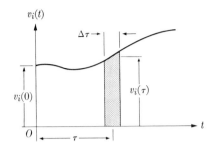

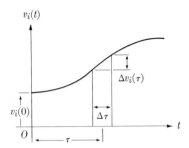

FIG. 3-5. The approximation of a function by a sequence of impulses.

FIG. 3-6. The approximation of a function by a sequence of steps.

Suppose now that the input signal is arbitrary except for the restriction $v(t) = 0$ for $t < 0$ (Fig. 3–5). We consider the signal to consist of a sequence of impulses where the impulse at time τ has an area

$$v_i(\tau) \, \Delta\tau \tag{3–28}$$

and $0 \leq \tau \leq t$. The system response at time t to a unit impulse at time τ is $h(t - \tau)$. The response to (3–28) is then

$$dv_o(t) = [v_i(\tau) \, \Delta\tau]h(t - \tau).$$

The total response is found by the superposition of all elemental responses and is given by

$$v_o(t) = \int_0^t v_i(\tau)h(t - \tau) \, d\tau. \tag{3–29}$$

An integral of this type is called a *convolution integral*.

Suppose now that the input signal consists of a sequence of steps in the interval $0 \leq \tau \leq t$, with amplitudes given by (see Fig. 3–6)

$$v_i(0) \quad\text{at}\quad t = 0,$$

and

$$\Delta v_i(\tau) \quad\text{at}\quad \text{time } \tau.$$

The system response at time t to the step $\Delta v_i(\tau)$ occurring at time τ is

$$dv_o(t) = \Delta v_i(\tau)g(t - \tau), \tag{3–30}$$

and the response to the step $v_i(0)$ is

$$v_i(0)g(t). \tag{3–31}$$

The total response is obtained by the superposition of the component responses given by Eqs. (3–30) and (3–31):

$$v_o(t) = v_i(0)g(t) + \int_0^t \frac{dv_i(\tau)}{d\tau} g(t - \tau)\, d\tau. \qquad (3\text{–}32)$$

Equation (3–32) is known as the *superposition theorem*.

A more general derivation of the convolution integral (3–29) may be given by transform methods and results in the *convolution theorem*.

If

$$\mathcal{L}[f(t)] = F(s)$$

and if

$$\mathcal{L}[g(t)] = G(s),$$

then

$$\mathcal{L}^{-1}[F(s)G(s)] = \int_0^t f(\tau)g(t - \tau)\, d\tau = \int_0^t g(\tau)f(t - \tau)\, d\tau. \qquad (3\text{–}33)$$

We now prove this result. Using the definition for the respective transforms and interchanging the order of integration lead to the following steps:

$$\mathcal{L}^{-1}[F(s)G(s)] = \frac{1}{2\pi j} \int_{c-j\infty}^{c+j\infty} F(s)G(s)e^{st}\, ds$$

$$= \frac{1}{2\pi j} \int_{c-j\infty}^{c+j\infty} F(s)e^{st} \left[\int_0^\infty g(\tau)e^{-s\tau}\, d\tau \right] ds$$

$$= \int_0^\infty g(\tau) \left[\frac{1}{2\pi j} \int_{c-j\infty}^{c+j\infty} F(s)e^{s(t-\tau)}\, ds \right] d\tau$$

$$= \int_0^\infty g(\tau)f(t - \tau)\, d\tau$$

$$= \int_0^t g(\tau)f(t - \tau)\, d\tau.$$

The last step follows from the fact that $f(t) = 0$ if $t < 0$. Evidently, one can interchange the position of g and f without affecting the result.

EXAMPLE 4. To illustrate the use of the superposition integral, let us consider Example 2, i.e., let us assume that the input voltage is $v_i(t) = \cos 2t$ and that the current response $i_1(t)$ is to be determined. The first step is to find the response to a unit step. This has already been done [see Eq. (3–11)]:

$$i_1(t) = g(t) = \tfrac{1}{15}(8 - 3e^{-t} - 2e^{-6t}).$$

Substituting $g(t)$ and $dv_i(\tau)/d\tau = -2 \sin 2\tau$ into Eq. (3–32) yields

$$i_1(t) = \tfrac{1}{15}(8 - 3e^{-t} - 2e^{-6t}) - \tfrac{2}{15} \int_0^t \sin 2\tau[8 - 3e^{-t+\tau} - 2e^{-6t+6\tau}]\, d\tau.$$

To evaluate Eq. (3–34), we use the integral

$$\int_0^t e^{\alpha\tau} \sin \beta\tau \, d\tau = \frac{1}{\alpha^2 + \beta^2} [e^{\alpha t}(\alpha \sin \beta t - \beta \cos \beta t) + \beta],$$

which can be found in any table of integrals. We obtain

$$\begin{aligned}
i_1(t) &= \tfrac{1}{15}(8 - 3e^{-t} - 2e^{-6t}) + \tfrac{8}{15}(\cos 2t - 1) \\
&\quad + \tfrac{6}{75}e^{-t}[e^t(\sin 2t - 2\cos 2t) + 2] \\
&\quad + \tfrac{1}{150}e^{-6t}[e^{6t}(6\sin 2t - 2\cos 2t) + 2] \\
&= \tfrac{1}{25}[-e^{-t} - 3e^{-6t} + 9\cos 2t + 3\sin 2t].
\end{aligned}$$

This is the same result as (3–15). On comparing the two methods, one sees that the transform method is considerably simpler for this particular problem. However, the superposition and convolution integrals are very useful if the system input is of a general form. ▲

PROBLEMS

3–1. Determine the output voltage response to a unit-step input voltage for the network shown in Fig. 3–7.

3–2. Determine the output voltage response for the network shown in Fig. 3–8, given that

$$v_i(t) = \begin{cases} e^{-t/T}, & t > 0, \\ 0, & t < 0, \end{cases}$$

where $T = RC$.

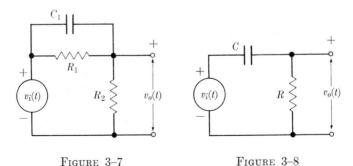

FIGURE 3–7   FIGURE 3–8

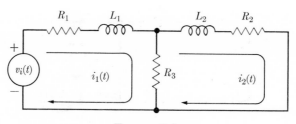

FIGURE 3–9

3–3. Determine the current responses $i_1(t)$ and $i_2(t)$ for the network shown in Fig. 3–9, given that

$$R_1 = R_2 = 2R_3 = 1\,\Omega, \qquad L_1 = L_2 = 1\,\mathrm{h},$$

and that (a) the input is a unit step; (b) the input is

$$v_i(t) = \begin{cases} \sin t, & t > 0, \\ 0 & t < 0. \end{cases}$$

3–4. Determine the response of a ballistic galvanometer to a unit-step input current [see Eq. (3–24)].

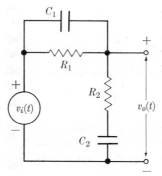

FIGURE 3–10

3–5. Determine the output voltage response for the network shown in Fig. 3–10, given that

$$\frac{C_1}{C_2} = \frac{1}{2}, \qquad \frac{R_2}{R_1} = \frac{5}{4}, \qquad 5R_1C_1 = 1,$$

and that (a) the input is a unit-step voltage; (b) the input is

$$v_i(t) = \begin{cases} \cos 5t, & t > 0, \\ 0, & t < 0. \end{cases}$$

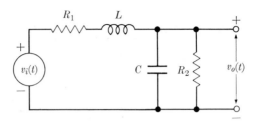

FIGURE 3–11

3–6. (a) Show that the transfer function V_o/V_i for the network illustrated in Fig. 3–11 can be written as

$$\frac{\omega^2}{s^2 + 2\zeta\omega s + \omega^2 a},$$

where

$$\omega^2 LC = 1, \qquad a = 1 + \frac{R_1}{R_2}, \qquad \frac{2\zeta}{\omega} = \frac{L}{R_2} + R_1 C.$$

(b) Determine the output voltage response to a unit-step input voltage.

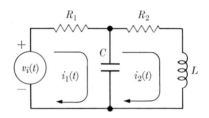

FIGURE 3–12

3–7. Consider the network shown in Fig. 3–12. Let $R_1 = R_2 = \omega_n L$, where $\omega_n^2 LC = 1$. (a) Compute the current responses $i_1(t)$ and $i_2(t)$ to a unit-step voltage. (b) Determine the current responses, given that

$$v_i(t) = \begin{cases} \sin \omega_n t, & t > 0, \\ 0, & t < 0. \end{cases}$$

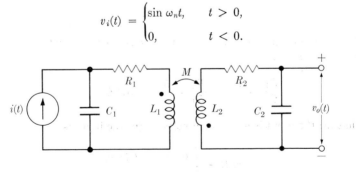

FIGURE 3–13

3–8. A double-tuned transformer-coupled network is shown in Fig. 3–13. (a) Given that

$$\omega_n^2 = \frac{1}{L_1 C_1} = \frac{1}{L_2 C_2}, \qquad 2\zeta\omega_n = \frac{R_1}{L_1} = \frac{R_2}{L_2}, \qquad k = \frac{M}{\sqrt{L_1 L_2}},$$

show that the poles of the transfer function V_o/I of this network are the roots of the equation $(1 \mp k)s^2 + 2\zeta\omega_n s + \omega_n^2 = 0$. (b) If $\omega_n^2 = 82(1 - k) = 65(1 + k)$, determine the output voltage response $v_o(t)$ to a unit-step input current. (c) Determine the output voltage response, given that the input current is

$$i(t) = \begin{cases} \sin\sqrt{72}\, t, & t > 0, \\ 0, & t < 0. \end{cases}$$

CHAPTER 4

THE RESPONSE OF LUMPED-PARAMETER
ACTIVE NETWORKS

4–1 Introduction. The design and synthesis of networks containing active elements (energy sources) is of great importance in the field of communications engineering. The majority of the methods used deal with the system-transfer functions of these networks. Since the ultimate objective is to obtain a suitable reponse in the time domain, it is often advisable to determine the system reponse to impulse and step inputs. It is then possible to relate system parameters to quantities, such as *delay time, rise time,* and *overshoot.*

The frequency range in which linear networks are used is such that it is essential to normalize or scale the variables in some convenient manner. Futhermore, transfer functions having multiple-order poles often result from the cascading of networks in multistage amplifiers. The general formula (2–16) must then be utilized to evaluate the effect of these poles. Unless otherwise stated all initial conditions will be considered to be identically zero.

4–2 The scaling theorem. A transform $V(s)$ can often be simplified by means of the substitution

$$s = ap, \tag{4–1}$$

which leads to a new transform,

$$V(s) = G(p). \tag{4–2}$$

The scaling theorem states that

$$v(t) = ag(\tau), \tag{4–3}$$

where

$$\tau = at \tag{4–4}$$

and

$$g(\tau) = \frac{1}{2\pi j} \int_{c-j\infty}^{c+j\infty} G(p)e^{p\tau}\, dp. \tag{4–5}$$

From Eq. (4–5) it can be seen that the variables s and t have been replaced by p and τ, respectively.

This theorem can be proved by the substitution of Eqs. (4–1) and (4–2) into (4–5), which yields

$$ag(\tau) = \frac{1}{2\pi j} \int_{c-j\infty}^{c+j\infty} V(s)e^{s\tau/a}\, ds = v\left(\frac{\tau}{a}\right). \tag{4–6}$$

Equations (4–3) and (4–4) follow immediately from this result.

It is often convenient to keep the same symbol for the transform. To avoid possible confusion about the argument used, the notation $V(s) = V(ap) = V[p]$ and $v(t) = av[\tau]$ will be adopted.

4–3 The s-translation theorem. The *s-translation theorem* states that

$$\mathcal{L}[e^{-at}v(t)] = V(s + a), \tag{4–7}$$

where $\mathcal{L}[v(t)] = V(s)$. This theorem can be proved by considering the transform

$$V(s + a) = \int_0^\infty v(t)e^{-(s+a)t}\, dt$$

$$= \int_0^\infty [v(t)e^{-at}]e^{-st}\, dt,$$

from which Eq. (4–7) follows. Thus, a translation a in the s-plane, represents an exponential factor e^{-at} in the time domain.

4–4 Operational amplifiers. An important class of active networks is obtained by the use of *operational amplifiers*. Consider Fig. 4–1, which indicates the symbolic representation of an operational amplifier. The transfer function for a vacuum-tube operational amplifier is the ratio of the transforms of the output voltage and the grid voltage:

$$\frac{V_o(s)}{V_g(s)} = -G(s), \tag{4–8}$$

when the negative sign is used simply for convenience in dealing with feedback connections. If impedances Z_1 and Z_2 are connected as shown, the transfer function

$$\frac{V_o(s)}{V_i(s)} = H(s)$$

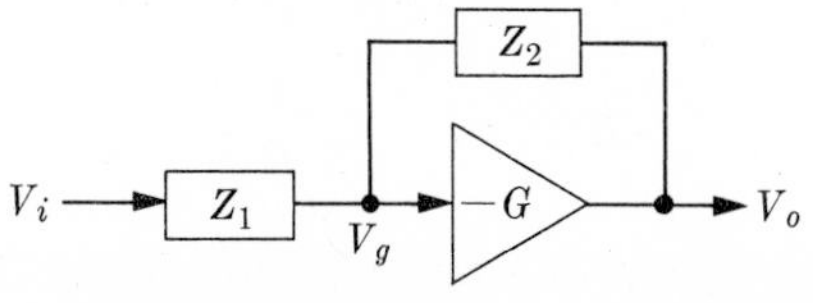

FIG. 4–1. Symbolic representation of an operational amplifier.

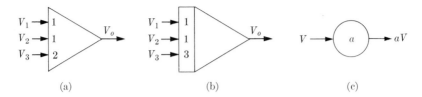

FIG. 4–2. Symbols for (a) summing amplifier, (b) integrator, and (c) voltage scaling.

is of interest. We can obtain this function by assuming that there is no grid current and equating the total flow of current to the grid junction to zero:

$$\frac{V_i - V_g}{Z_1} + \frac{V_o - V_g}{Z_2} = 0.$$

Using Eq. (4–8) to eliminate V_g, we have

$$H(s) = -\frac{Z_2}{Z_1} \frac{1}{1 + [1/G(s)][1 + Z_2/Z_1]}. \qquad (4\text{–}9)$$

An operational amplifier has a very high gain over the frequency range of the signals which are being considered. The second term in the denominator of Eq. (4–9) is therefore small, and we have

$$H(s) \cong -Z_2/Z_1.$$

If the amplifier gain is high, the grid voltage is small compared with the input and output voltages and can be neglected. We can then consider the grid to be at a virtual ground. This approach simplifies the analysis, and hence we shall adopt it in the following discussion.

If the impedances Z_1 and Z_2 are resistors, the network is known as a *summing amplifier*. There may be more than one input, and a symbolic representation of a summing amplifier with three inputs is shown in Fig. 4–2(a). The numbers indicate the relative ratio of the output to input resistors, i.e., for the summing amplifier shown,

$$-V_o = V_1 + V_2 + 2V_3.$$

If $Z_1 = R_1$ and $Z_2 = 1/C_1 s$, the transfer function is

$$H(s) = -\frac{1}{R_1 C_1 s},$$

which represents the operation of integration in the time domain. The symbolic representation of an *integrator* is shown in Fig. 4–2(b). The

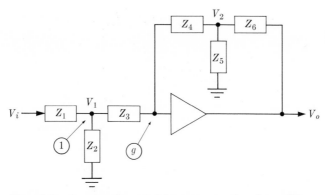

FIG. 4–3. A network containing an operational amplifier.

numbers indicate the relative weighting coefficients for the different inputs, i.e.,

$$-V_o = \frac{1}{s}\,[V_1 + V_2 + 3V_3].$$

The scaling of a voltage is indicated by the symbolism shown in Fig. 4–2(c).

By means of more elaborate networks one can obtain a wide variety of possible transfer functions. Figure 4–3 shows the use of a single operational amplifier for this purpose. The total current into the grid junction g must be zero. Thus

$$\frac{V_1}{Z_3} + \frac{V_2}{Z_4} = 0. \tag{4–10}$$

The current balance at junction 1 yields

$$\frac{V_i - V_1}{Z_1} - \frac{V_1}{Z_2} - \frac{V_1}{Z_3} = 0,$$

which can be rearranged:

$$V_1 = \frac{1/Z_1}{1/Z_1 + 1/Z_2 + 1/Z_3}\,V_i. \tag{4–11}$$

Similarly, we obtain

$$V_2 = \frac{1/Z_6}{1/Z_4 + 1/Z_5 + 1/Z_6}\,V_o. \tag{4–12}$$

The transfer function can now be determined from Eqs. (4–10), (4–11), and (4–12):

$$H(s) = -\left(\frac{Z_4 Z_6}{Z_1 Z_3}\right)\frac{1/Z_4 + 1/Z_5 + 1/Z_6}{1/Z_1 + 1/Z_2 + 1/Z_3}. \tag{4–13}$$

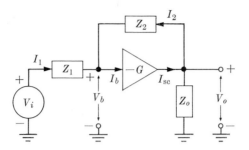

FIG. 4–4. A transistor operational amplifier.

The preceding discussion has dealt with vacuum-tube operational amplifiers. However, if transistors are used, the transfer function takes the same form. Consider the network shown in Fig. 4–4. The transistor operational amplifier is a current-operated device. Thus

$$I_{sc} = -GI_b, \tag{4–14}$$

where I_b is the transform of the base input current and G is the short-circuit current gain. The current balance at the base junction yields

$$I_1 + I_2 = \frac{V_i - V_b}{Z_1} + \frac{V_o - V_b}{Z_2} = I_b,$$

which can be rearranged:

$$\frac{V_i}{Z_1} + \frac{V_o}{Z_2} = I_b\left(1 + \frac{Z_b}{Z_1} + \frac{Z_b}{Z_2}\right), \tag{4–15}$$

where Z_b is the input impedance of the base. To express I_b in terms of V_i let

$$I_2 = \beta I_{sc} = -G\beta I_b.$$

It follows that

$$\frac{V_i - V_b}{Z_1} = I_1 = I_b(1 + G\beta),$$

from which we find

$$I_b = \frac{V_i}{Z_1} \frac{1}{1 + G\beta + Z_b/Z_1}.$$

Substituting this equation into Eq. (4–15) yields

$$H(s) = \frac{V_o}{V_i} = \frac{Z_2}{Z_1} \frac{-G\beta + Z_b/Z_2}{1 + G\beta + Z_b/Z_1}. \tag{4–16}$$

To determine $G\beta$ we substitute

$$V_o = (I_{sc} - I_2)Z_o$$

into

$$I_2 = \frac{V_o - V_b}{Z_2},$$

from which one can determine the ratio $I_2/I_{sc} = \beta$. This ratio yields

$$G\beta = \frac{G + Z_b/Z_o}{1 + Z_2/Z_o}. \tag{4–17}$$

From Eqs. (4–16) and (4–17) we see that Z_b should be small and that G and Z_o should be large. We then find that $H \simeq -Z_2/Z_1$, as before. However, it should be noted that these two kinds of operational amplifiers operate in a different manner. For the vacuum-tube amplifier the input impedance should be very high in order to keep the grid current small. The load impedance has very little effect, provided that it is large compared with the amplifier output impedance. For the transistor amplifier the input impedance should be very small. A small change in base voltage will then give rise to a large base current which in turn leads to a large output current. The load impedance should be very large, since it diverts output current and reduces the feedback current.

EXAMPLE 1. Let us consider Eq. (4–13) and take

$$Z_1 = Z_3 = 2Z_5 = R,$$

$$Z_2 = \tfrac{1}{2}Z_4 = \tfrac{1}{2}Z_6 = 1/Cs.$$

We then have

$$H(s) = -\frac{4}{(RCs)^2}.$$

Suppose that the response of this network to the input,

$$v_i(t) = \begin{cases} \sin \omega t, & t > 0, \\ 0, & t < 0, \end{cases}$$

is to be determined. The output-voltage transform is

$$V_o(s) = -\frac{4}{(RCs)^2} \frac{\omega}{s^2 + \omega^2},$$

and substituting $s = \omega p$ and $T = RC$ yields

$$V_o(s) = V_o[p] = -\frac{1}{\omega} \left(\frac{2}{\omega T} \right)^2 \frac{1}{p^2(p^2 + 1)}.$$

The poles of $V_o[p]$ are at $p = 0$ and $p = \pm j$. The pole coefficients are

$$F_0(p) = -\frac{1}{\omega}\left(\frac{2}{\omega T}\right)^2 \frac{e^{p\tau}}{p^2+1} \quad \text{at} \quad p = 0,$$

$$F_1(p) = -\frac{1}{\omega}\left(\frac{2}{\omega T}\right)^2 \frac{e^{p\tau}}{p^2(p+j)} \quad \text{at} \quad p = j.$$

In applying Heaviside's expansion, one should note that the pole at $p = 0$ is of second order, and hence the general formula (2–16) must be used. We obtain

$$v_o[\tau] = \frac{dF_0(p)}{dp}\bigg|_{p=0} + 2\,\mathrm{Re}[F_1(j)]$$

$$= -\frac{1}{\omega}\left(\frac{2}{\omega T}\right)^2 [\tau - \sin\tau].$$

The response $v_o(t)$ can then be obtained from the scaling theorem (4–3). Thus

$$v_o(t) = \omega v_o[\tau] = -\left(\frac{2}{\omega T}\right)^2 [\tau - \sin\tau],$$

where $\tau = \omega t$. ▲

EXAMPLE 2. Consider the problem of generating the signal $v(t - T)$ from $v(t)$. This operation is of considerable importance in communication theory and represents an ideal delay of T seconds. In Chapter 11 [see Eq. (11–17)] it is shown that the transfer function for an ideal delay is e^{-sT} and that this function can be realized by means of a distributed-parameter transmission line. For the transfer function $H(s) = e^{-sT}$ we have

$$|H(j\omega)| = 1, \tag{4–18a}$$

$$\beta = -\omega T, \tag{4–18b}$$

where β is the phase angle of $H(j\omega)$. A network satisfying condition (4–18a) is known as an *all-pass network*. For the ideal delay, the phase angle is a linear function of ω and the magnitude of the slope is the time delay T. One can obtain an approximation to e^{-sT} by realizing the transfer function

$$H(s) = -\frac{s^2 - 2\zeta\omega_0 s + \omega_0^2}{s^2 + 2\zeta\omega_0 s + \omega_0^2} \tag{4–19}$$

by means of operational amplifiers, using the network shown in Fig. 4–5[1]*. Note that $H(s)$ is an all-pass function. However, β is a linear function of ω only for small ω. Suppose that the response of this network to a unit-step

---

* Numbers in brackets are keyed to the references at the end of the chapter.

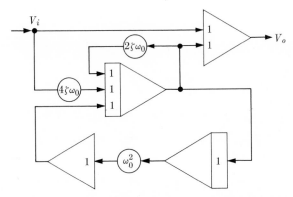

FIG. 4–5. A network which approximates the ideal delay e^{-sT}.

input is to be determined. We have

$$V_o(s) = -\frac{1}{s} \frac{s^2 - 2\zeta\omega_0 s + \omega_0^2}{s^2 + 2\zeta\omega_0 s + \omega_0^2}.$$

The poles of this function are at $s = 0$, $s_1 = \omega_0(-\zeta + j\sqrt{1 - \zeta^2})$ and $s_2 = s_1^*$. The pole coefficients are

$$F_0(s) = -\frac{s^2 - 2\zeta\omega_0 s + \omega_0^2}{s^2 + 2\zeta\omega_0 s + \omega_0^2} e^{st} \qquad \text{at} \qquad s = 0,$$

$$F_1(s) = -\frac{1}{s} \frac{s^2 - 2\zeta\omega_0 s + \omega_0^2}{s - s_2} e^{st} \qquad \text{at} \qquad s = s_1.$$

The Heaviside expansion yields

$$v_o(t) = F_0(0) + 2\,\mathrm{Re}[F_1(s_1)].$$

In evaluating the pole coefficient $F_1(s_1)$ one should note that $s_1 - s_2 = 2j\omega_0\sqrt{1 - \zeta^2}$, $s_1 + s_2 = -2\zeta\omega_0$, and $s_1 s_2 = \omega_0^2$. After multiplying numerator and denominator with s_2, one readily finds that

$$\frac{s_1^2 - 2\zeta\omega_0 s_1 + \omega_0^2}{s_1} \frac{s_2}{s_2} = s_1 - 2\zeta\omega_0 + s_2 = -4\zeta\omega_0.$$

The final result is

$$v_o(t) = -1 + \frac{4\zeta}{\sqrt{1 - \zeta^2}} e^{-\zeta\omega_0 t} \sin \omega_0\sqrt{1 - \zeta^2}\, t. \quad \blacktriangle$$

If the function $v_o(t)$ is plotted, one sees that the approximation to a delayed unit step is not particularly good. More elaborate networks are

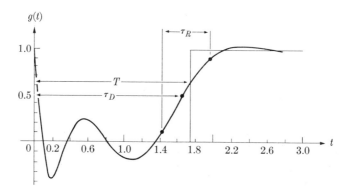

FIG. 4–6. An approximation to a delayed unit-step function.

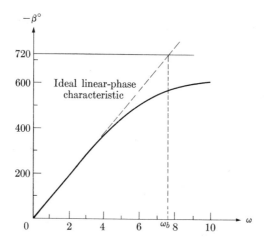

FIG. 4–7. Phase characteristic of Eq. (4–20).

required to achieve better approximations. Figure 4–6 shows the response to a unit-step input for a network having the transfer function

$$H(s) = \frac{s^2 - 2\zeta_1\omega_1 s + \omega_1^2}{s^2 + 2\zeta_1\omega_1 s + \omega_1^2} \frac{s^2 - 2\zeta_2\omega_2 s + \omega_2^2}{s^2 + 2\zeta_2\omega_2 s + \omega_2^2}, \qquad (4\text{–}20)$$

where $\zeta_1\omega_1 = 3$, $\zeta_2\omega_2 = 2$, $\omega_1 = 3.17$, and $\omega_2 = 4$. These values yield a linear-phase characteristic for small ω (see Fig. 4–7). Thus the delay operation is approximately realized for the low-frequency spectral terms in the input signal. Since $\lim_{s\to\infty} H(s) = 1$, the response for the high-frequency spectral terms results in $g(0^+) = 1^*$ (see Fig. 4–6). The low-

* This result follows from the initial value theorem, Eq. (5–5).

frequency spectral terms yield the approximation to the delayed unit step as shown. The time delay T is computed from

$$T = -\beta'(0), \tag{4–21}$$

where $\beta'(\omega)$ is the derivative of β with respect to ω.*

Other quantities of interest are the rise time τ_R, which is the time taken for $g(t)$ to go from 10% to 90% of its final value, and the overshoot, which is the percentage rise above its final value. From an experimental standpoint, time delay is usually measured as the time τ_D taken for $g(t)$ to reach 50% of its final value. However, it should be noted that an oscillatory waveform cannot be completely specified by these quantities. In the above example, the initial transients which appear due to the approximation used cannot be accounted for by these simple specifications.

It is of interest to inquire about the general validity of Eq. (4–21). Let $H(j\omega) = |H(j\omega)|e^{j\beta}$ and consider the class of networks that can be normalized such that $H(0) = 1$. The magnitude characteristic satisfies the condition

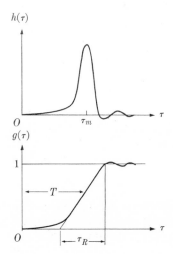

$$\frac{d|H(j\omega)|}{d\omega}\bigg]_{\omega=0} = 0.$$

Thus

$$\frac{dH(j\omega)}{d\omega}\bigg]_{\omega=0} = j\beta'(0).$$

If $H(s) = \mathcal{L}[h(t)]$ is differentiated with respect to s and if $s = 0$ is then substituted, we obtain

$$-\frac{dH(s)}{ds}\bigg]_{s=0} = \int_0^\infty th(t)\,dt, \tag{4–22}$$

and substitution of $s = j\omega$ in Eq. (4–22) yields

$$-\beta'(0) = T = \int_0^\infty th(t)\,dt. \tag{4–23}$$

Fig. 4–8. Definition of time delay T as the first moment of the impulse response and rise time τ_R as the reciprocal of $h(\tau_m)$.

The quantity T defined by this result is the *first moment* of $h(t)$. If the trailing transients of $h(t)$ are of small amplitude and decay sufficiently rapidly, T can be used to represent the time delay of a network (Fig. 4–8).

---

* In the case of sinusoidal signals the time delay is defined by the function $-\beta(\omega)/\omega$, and the envelope or group delay is the function $-\beta'(\omega)$.

An estimate of the rise time can be obtained by using the maximum slope of the step response as shown in the figure. This slope is given by the maximum value of the impulse response. It should be noted that the impulse response of a system having an ideal delay T is $\delta(t - T)$.

4–5 Cascaded vacuum-tube amplifier stages. This section considers the response of cascaded vacuum-tube amplifier stages. Figure 4–9 shows the equivalent circuit for a single RC-coupled stage in which the vacuum tube is represented by a current source shunted by a resistance R_p. The coupling network shown is adequate for determining the low-frequency response properties for amplifiers of this type. At higher frequencies the effect of stray capacitances must be taken into account.

The current response $i(t)$ to the grid voltage, $v_0(t)$, can be determined from the relation

$$I(s) = g_m V_0(s),$$

where g_m is the transconductance of the tube. The transfer function is easily obtained from the two equations,

$$H_1(s) = \frac{V}{V_0} = -g_m Z \quad \text{and} \quad V_1 = \frac{R}{R + 1/Cs} V, \quad (4\text{–}24)$$

where Z is the impedance of the load. We obtain

$$H(s) = \frac{V_1}{V_0} = (-g_m R_1) \frac{s}{s + a}, \quad (4\text{–}25)$$

where

$$R_1 = \frac{R R_p}{R + R_p} \quad \text{and} \quad \frac{1}{a} = C(R_p + R).$$

EXAMPLE 3.   Consider now the problem of determining the output response of n identical cascaded stages to a unit-step input voltage. From Eq. (4–25) we obtain

$$\frac{1}{(-g_m R_1)^n} V_n(s) = G(s) = \frac{1}{s}\left(\frac{s}{s + a}\right)^n, \quad (4\text{–}26)$$

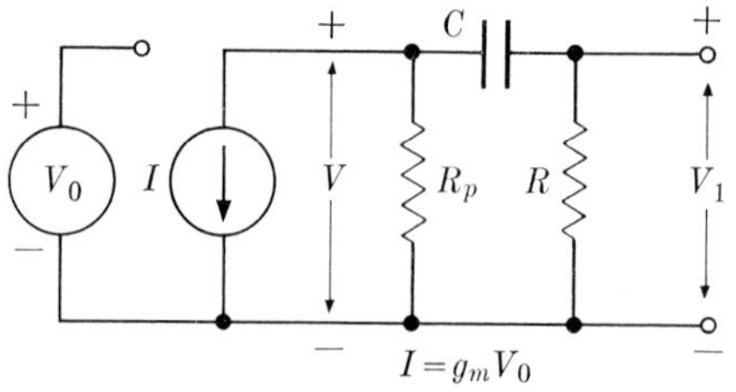

FIG. 4–9. Equivalent circuit of a one-stage RC-coupled amplifier.

where $G(s)$ is the transform of the normalized response. There is an nth-order pole at $s = -a$. The pole coefficient is $F(s) = s^{n-1}e^{st}$, and the normalized response is

$$g(t) = \frac{1}{(n-1)!} \left\{ \frac{d^{n-1}}{ds^{n-1}} (s^{n-1}e^{st}) \right\}_{s=-a} . \tag{4-27}$$

To simplify this result we substitute $st = u$ into Eq. (4-27) and $u = -at$ in the result obtained by the first substition. This yields

$$g(t) = \frac{1}{(n-1)!} \frac{d^{n-1}}{dt^{n-1}} (t^{n-1}e^{-at}). \tag{4-28}$$

The initial sag in the output response to a unit-step input, which is of interest for an RC-coupled amplifier, can be obtained from Eq. (4-28) by expanding this function in a Taylor series. However, the result is more readily derived by expanding Eq. (4-26) in a power series in $1/s$ which yields

$$G(s) = \frac{1}{s} - \frac{an}{s^2} + \frac{n(n+1)}{2!} \frac{a^2}{s^3} - \cdots .$$

The inverse transform of this expression is

$$g(t) = 1 - ant + \frac{n(n+1)}{(2!)^2} (at)^2 - \cdots .$$

For the output to reproduce the unit step accurately during a time interval T it is necessary that $anT \ll 1$. ▲

If the signals to be amplified are in a range extending from about 30 cps to 5 Mc, video amplifiers containing pentodes can be used. In the high-frequency range, the coupling network of a pentode stage often takes the form shown in Fig. 4-10. A network of this type is known as a *shunt-peaked circuit*. Its impedance is

$$Z = \frac{R + Ls}{LCs^2 + RCs + 1},$$

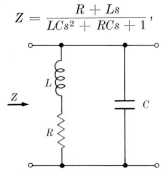

FIG. 4-10. A shunt-peaked circuit.

and the transfer function for a single stage is given by $H_1(s) = -g_m Z$. Substituting $\omega_n^2 = 1/LC$ and $2\zeta\omega_n = R/L$, we obtain

$$H_1(s) = -\frac{g_m}{C}\frac{s + 2\zeta\omega_n}{s^2 + 2\zeta\omega_n s + \omega_n^2}. \tag{4-29}$$

It should be noted that the parameter ζ is related to the Q of the load:

$$Q = \frac{\omega_n L}{R} = \frac{1}{2\zeta}.$$

EXAMPLE 4. If the input is a unit step, we have

$$V_1(s) = -\frac{g_m}{Cs}\frac{s + 2\zeta\omega_n}{s^2 + 2\zeta\omega_n s + \omega_n^2}.$$

This expression can be simplified by means of the substitution

$$s = \omega_n p, \tag{4-30}$$

which yields

$$\frac{1}{(-g_m R)}V_1(s) = G(p) = \frac{1}{2\zeta\omega_n}\frac{p + 2\zeta}{p(p^2 + 2\zeta p + 1)},$$

where $G(p)$ is the normalized transfer function. The function has poles at

$$p = 0, \qquad p_1 = -\zeta + j\beta, \qquad p_2 = p_1^*, \tag{4-31}$$

where $\beta = \sqrt{1 - \zeta^2}$. The pole coefficients are

$$F_0(p) = \frac{1}{2\zeta\omega_n}\frac{p + 2\zeta}{p^2 + 2\zeta p + 1}e^{p\tau} \qquad \text{at} \qquad p = 0,$$

$$F_1(p) = \frac{1}{2\zeta\omega_n}\frac{p + 2\zeta}{p(p - p_2)}e^{p\tau} \qquad \text{at} \qquad p = p_1,$$

and the Heaviside expansion yields

$$g(\tau) = F_0(0) + 2\,\mathrm{Re}[F_1(p_1)].$$

In evaluating $F_1(p)$, one should note that

$$p_1 p_2 = 1 \qquad \text{and} \qquad p_1 + 2\zeta = -p_2. \tag{4-32}$$

Thus

$$\frac{p_1 + 2\zeta}{p_1(p_1 - p_2)} = -\frac{p_2^2}{2j\beta} = -\frac{e^{j2\phi}}{2j\beta},$$

where $\cos \phi = \zeta$. The final result is

$$\omega_n g(\tau) = 1 - \frac{e^{-\zeta\tau}}{2\zeta\beta} \sin (\beta\tau + 2\phi), \qquad (4\text{--}33)$$

where $\tau = \omega_n t$. With the aid of the scaling theorem (4–3), one can see that the normalized response is

$$\frac{1}{(-g_m R)} v_1(t) = \omega_n g(\tau). \quad \blacktriangle$$

EXAMPLE 5. Consider now two identical stages with shunt peaking. The transfer function is

$$H_2(s) = H_1(s)H_1(s) = \left(\frac{g_m R \omega_n}{2\zeta}\right)^2 \frac{(s + 2\zeta\omega_n)^2}{(s^2 + 2\zeta\omega_n s + \omega_n^2)^2}.$$

The response to a unit step can be found from the transform

$$\frac{1}{(g_m R)^2} V_2(s) = G(p) = \frac{1}{4\zeta^2\omega_n} \frac{1}{p} \frac{(p + 2\zeta)^2}{(p^2 + 2\zeta p + 1)^2},$$

where the substitution (4–30) has been used. The poles are given by (4–31), and the pole coefficients are

$$F_0(p) = \frac{1}{4\zeta^2\omega_n} \frac{(p + 2\zeta)^2}{(p^2 + 2\zeta p + 1)^2} e^{p\tau} \qquad \text{at} \qquad p = 0,$$

$$F_1(p) = \frac{1}{4\zeta^2\omega_n} \frac{1}{p} \frac{(p + 2\zeta)^2}{(p - p_2)^2} e^{p\tau} \qquad \text{at} \qquad p = p.$$

The response is given by the Heaviside expansion,

$$g(\tau) = F_0(0) + 2 \operatorname{Re}\left[\frac{dF_1(p)}{dp}\right]_{p=p_1}.$$

To evaluate the second term, one can take the logarithmic derivative of $F_1(p)$:

$$\frac{dF_1(p)}{dp} = F_1(p)\left[-\frac{1}{p} - \frac{2}{p - p_2} + \frac{2}{p + 2\zeta} + \tau\right].$$

This expression can be simplified by means of Eq. (4–32), and we obtain

$$\frac{dF_1(p)}{dp}\bigg|_{p=p_1} = \frac{e^{j3\phi_1} e^{p_1\tau}}{16\zeta^2\beta^2\omega_n}\left[\frac{\zeta\sqrt{9 - 8\zeta^2}}{\beta} e^{j\phi_2} + \tau\right],$$

where

$$\cos \phi_1 = \zeta \qquad \text{and} \qquad \tan \phi_2 = \zeta/3\beta.$$

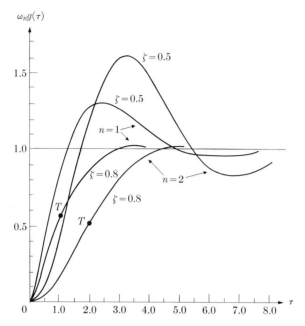

FIG. 4–11. Normalized step-responses for an n-stage shunt-peaked amplifier.

The final result, in normalized form, is

$$\frac{v_2(t)}{(g_m R)^2} = \omega_n g(\tau) = 1 + \frac{e^{-\zeta\tau}}{8\zeta^2(1 - \zeta^2)}$$

$$\times \left[\tau \cos(\beta\tau + 3\phi_1) + \zeta \sqrt{\frac{9 - 8\zeta^2}{1 - \zeta^2}} \cos(\beta\tau + 3\phi_1 + \phi_2) \right]. \blacktriangle \quad (4\text{–}34)$$

Equations (4–33) and (4–34) have been used to plot the results shown in Fig. 4–11. We see that the overshoot increases as ζ decreases and as the number of stages n increases. Figures 4–12 and 4–13 show the phase angle and magnitude characteristics for a single stage. The phase angle and magnitude for n similar stages are $n\beta$ and $|H(j\omega)|^n$, respectively. Note that the choice $\zeta = 0.8$ results in a reasonably linear phase and flat magnitude characteristics. Thus this case approximates the ideal transfer function given by Eq. (4–18).

The time delay, as computed from Eq. (4–21), is indicated in Fig. 4–11 by the points labeled T. It is evident that T can be used to estimate the time required for $\omega_n g(\tau)$ to rise to 50% of its final value, provided that the overshoot is small.

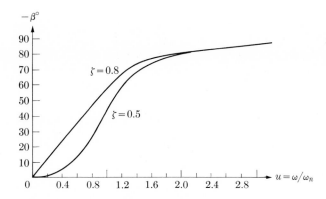

FIG. 4–12. Phase characteristic for a one-stage shunt-peaked amplifier.

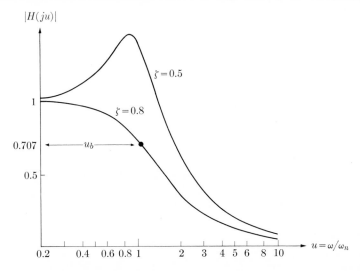

FIG. 4–13. Magnitude characteristic for a one-stage shunt-peaked amplifier.

It is of interest to discuss a more general form of the transfer function (4–29). This can be written as $G(p) = G_0 H(p)$, where

$$H(p) = \frac{1}{a} \frac{p + a}{p^2 + bp + 1} ; \qquad (4\text{–}35)$$

$G_0 = G(0)$ is the zero-frequency gain. In Eq. (4–29) we have $a = b = 2\zeta$, and

$$G_0 = -g_m R = - \frac{g_m}{C} \left(\frac{2\zeta}{\omega_n} \right). \qquad (4\text{–}36)$$

The *maximally flat* magnitude characteristic is defined by the conditions that make the greatest number of derivatives of $|H(ju)|^2$ equal to zero at $u = 0$. To determine the relation between a and b for the maximally flat case, we expand Eq. (4-35) in a power series in p and then substitute $p = ju$. This yields

$$H(ju) = 1 + j\,\frac{1 - ab}{a}\,u - \left(b^2 - 1 - \frac{b}{a}\right)u^2 + \cdots,$$

from which we obtain

$$|H(ju)|^2 = 1 + \left[\left(\frac{1 - ab}{a}\right)^2 - 2\left(b^2 - 1 - \frac{b}{a}\right)\right]u^2 + \cdots.$$

Equating the coefficient of u^2 to zero yields the condition for the maximally flat case:

$$b^2 = \frac{1}{a^2} + 2. \tag{4-37}$$

For Eq. (4-29), where $a = b = 2\zeta$, this equation yields $\zeta = 0.778$. Figure 4-11 shows that this value results in a good compromise between rise time and overshoot. Once ζ has been fixed by these considerations and ω_n specified by the bandwidth required, it follows from Eq. (4-36) that the zero-frequency gain is determined by the factor g_m/C which is taken as a *figure of merit* for the choice of pentode tubes.

The normalized bandwidth, u_b (see Fig. 4-13), is defined by

$$|H(ju_b)|^2 = \tfrac{1}{2}.$$

Using the substitution $u_b^2 = x$, we find that x satisfies the equation

$$x^2 + \left(b^2 - 2 - \frac{2}{a^2}\right)x - 1 = 0, \tag{4-38}$$

which, for the maximally flat case, yields

$$u_b = \frac{1}{a}\left(\frac{1 + \sqrt{1 + 4a^4}}{2}\right)^{1/2}. \tag{4-39}$$

For the maximally flat case of (4-29), where $a = 1.556$, we find that $u_b = 1.1$.

A quantity of interest in amplifier design is the *gain-bandwidth product* defined by $|G_0|\omega_n u_b$. The gain-bandwidth product is of considerable use as a figure of merit in comparing the performance of different coupling networks [2]. For the maximally flat case of (4-29), we find that $|G_0|\omega_n u_b = 1.72\,g_m/C$.

The *maximally linear* phase characteristic is defined by the conditions that make the greatest number of higher-order (greater than one) derivatives of $\beta(u)$ equal to zero at $u = 0$. In general, β is determined from a relation having the form

$$\tan \beta = \frac{a_1 u + a_3 u^3 + a_5 u^5 + \cdots}{a_0 + a_2 u^2 + a_4 u^4 + \cdots}. \tag{4–40}$$

If the expansion

$$\tan \beta = \beta + \tfrac{1}{3}\beta^3 + \tfrac{2}{15}\beta^5 + \tfrac{17}{315}\beta^7 + \cdots$$

is substituted into Eq. (4–40), we obtain

$$(a_1 u + a_3 u^3 + \cdots) = (a_0 + a_2 u^2 + a_4 u^4 + \cdots)(\beta + \tfrac{1}{3}\beta^3 + \tfrac{2}{15}\beta^5 + \cdots). \tag{4–41}$$

Neglecting the second- and higher-order powers of u, we find that

$$\beta = \frac{a_1}{a_0} u;$$

substituting this result back into Eq. (4–41) and equating the coefficients of like powers of u, we obtain

$$a_3 = \frac{a_0}{3}\left(\frac{a_1}{a_0}\right)^3 + \frac{a_1 a_2}{a_0},$$

$$a_5 = \frac{2a_0}{15}\left(\frac{a_1}{a_0}\right)^5 + \frac{a_2}{3}\left(\frac{a_1}{a_0}\right)^3 + a_4\left(\frac{a_1}{a_0}\right),$$

$$a_7 = \frac{17a_0}{315}\left(\frac{a_1}{a_0}\right)^7 + \frac{2a_2}{15}\left(\frac{a_1}{a_0}\right)^5 + \frac{a_4}{3}\left(\frac{a_1}{a_0}\right)^3 + a_6\left(\frac{a_1}{a_0}\right), \tag{4–42}$$
$$\vdots$$

These are the conditions for a maximally linear phase characteristic. As the conditions for a_3, a_5, ... are successively fulfilled, the linearity of the phase characteristic is successively improved.

If we substitute $p = ju$ into Eq. (4–35) and let θ_1 and θ_2 be the phase angles for the numerator and denominator, respectively, we find

$$\tan \theta_1 = \frac{u}{a} \quad \text{and} \quad \tan \theta_2 = \frac{bu}{1 - u^2}.$$

Since $\beta = \theta_1 - \theta_2$, we obtain

$$\tan \beta = \frac{[(1 - ab)/a]u - u^3/a}{1 + [(b - a)/a]u^2}.$$

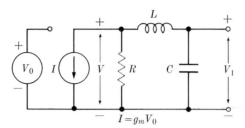

FIG. 4–14. A series-peaked circuit.

Comparing this result with Eq. (4–40), we see that

$$a_1 = \frac{1 - ab}{a}, \qquad a_0 = 1,$$

$$a_3 = -\frac{1}{a}, \qquad a_2 = \frac{b - a}{a},$$

$$\vdots \qquad\qquad \vdots$$

The condition (4–42) for a_3 yields

$$\frac{1}{ab} = \left(1 - \frac{3}{b^2}\right)^{1/3}. \tag{4–43}$$

If $a = b = 2\zeta$, we can solve this equation by substituting $x = 1/b^2$. The resulting cubic equation,

$$x^3 + 3x - 1 = 0,$$

has a root at $x = 0.32$. We then find $\zeta = 0.884$. For the maximally linear case of (4–29) we find from Eqs. (4–36) and (4–39) that $u_b = 0.87$ and $|G_0|\omega_n u_b = 1.57 \, g_m/C$.

EXAMPLE 6. The network shown in Fig. 4–14 is known as a *series-peaked circuit*. The impedance of this circuit is

$$Z = \frac{R(1 + LCs^2)}{LCs^2 + RCs + 1}.$$

The transfer function of a single stage can be determined from $V/V_0 = -g_m Z$, and

$$V_1 = V \frac{1/Cs}{Ls + 1/Cs},$$

which yields

$$H_1(s) = \frac{V_1}{V_0} = (-g_m R) \frac{\omega_n^2}{s^2 + 2\zeta\omega_n s + \omega_n^2}. \tag{4–44}$$

Consider two cascaded series-peaked stages having the same ω_n but different load resistors R_1 and R_2. The transfer fnction is

$$H_2(s) = (g_m R_1)(g_m R_2) \frac{\omega_n^4}{(s^2 + 2\zeta_1\omega_n s + \omega_n^2)(s^2 + 2\zeta_2\omega_n s + \omega_n^2)}.$$

If the input is a unit step, the output voltage transform can be written in the form

$$\frac{V_2(s)}{(g_m R_1)(g_m R_2)} = G(p) = \frac{1}{\omega_n p} \frac{1}{(p^2 + 2\zeta_1 p + 1)(p^2 + 2\zeta_2 p + 1)}.$$

The poles are at $p = 0$, p_1, p_1^*, p_2, p_2^*, where

$$p_1 = -\zeta_1 + j\beta_1, \qquad p_2 = -\zeta_2 + j\beta_2,$$

and

$$\beta_1 = \sqrt{1 - \zeta_1^2}, \qquad \beta_2 = \sqrt{1 - \zeta_2^2}.$$

The pole coefficients are

$$F_0(p) = \frac{1}{\omega_n} \frac{e^{p\tau}}{(p^2 + 2\zeta_1 p + 1)(p^2 + 2\zeta_2 p + 1)} \qquad \text{at} \qquad p = 0,$$

$$F_1(p) = \frac{1}{\omega_n} \frac{e^{p\tau}}{p(p - p_1^*)(p^2 + 2\zeta_2 p + 1)} \qquad \text{at} \qquad p = p_1,$$

$$F_2(p) = \frac{1}{\omega_n} \frac{e^{p\tau}}{p(p^2 + 2\zeta_1 p + 1)(p - p_2^*)} \qquad \text{at} \qquad p = p_2.$$

The response can be obtained from the Heaviside expansion

$$g(\tau) = F_0(0) + 2\,\text{Re}[F_1(p_1)] + 2\,\text{Re}[F_2(p_2)].$$

In evaluating $F_1(p_1)$, note that

$$(p_1^2 + 2\zeta_2 p_1 + 1)p_1^* = p_1 + 2\zeta_2 + p_1^* = 2(\zeta_2 - \zeta_1),$$

and hence

$$F_1(p_1) = \frac{1}{\omega_n} \frac{(p_1^*)^2 e^{p_1\tau}}{j4\beta_1(\zeta_2 - \zeta_1)} = \frac{1}{\omega_n} \frac{e^{j2\phi_1} e^{p_1\tau}}{j4\beta_1(\zeta_2 - \zeta_1)},$$

where $\cos\phi_1 = \zeta_1$. The final result is

$$\frac{v_2(t)}{(g_m R_1)(g_m R_2)} = \omega_n g(\tau)$$

$$= 1 - \frac{e^{-\zeta_1\tau} \sin(\beta_1\tau + 2\phi_1)}{2(\zeta_1 - \zeta_2)\beta_1} - \frac{e^{-\zeta_2\tau} \sin(\beta_2\tau + 2\phi_2)}{2(\zeta_2 - \zeta_1)\beta_2}. \; \blacktriangle$$

$$(4\text{--}45)$$

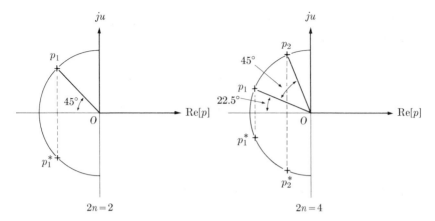

FIG. 4–15. Pole locations for Butterworth network functions where $2n$ is the number of poles.

The series-peaked circuit can be used in transistorized video amplifiers whose impedance levels are sufficiently low such that the stray capacitance shunting R can be neglected [3]. This is not the case with vacuum-tube amplifiers. However, it will be shown in Section 4–7 that the series-peaked circuit can be used in the analysis of the envelope response of narrow-band bandpass amplifiers.

The case where a cascade of series-peaked stages results in a transfer function with a maximally flat magnitude characteristic is of considerable importance.* All stages have the same ω_n but different damping ratios, ζ_k, so that, assuming no loading between stages, we find that the normalized transfer function of the kth stage [see Eq. (4–44)] is

$$H_k(p) = \frac{1}{p^2 + 2\zeta_k p + 1}. \tag{4–46}$$

The poles of this function are located on the unit circle in the left-half of the p-plane (Fig. 4–15). For an n-stage amplifier with a transfer function $H(p)$ the maximally flat case occurs when

$$|H(ju)|^2 = \frac{1}{1 + x^{2n}}, \tag{4–47}$$

since the first $2n - 1$ derivatives with respect to $x = u^2$ are zero at $u = 0$. Using the substitution $p = ju$, we find that Eq. (4–47) takes the form

$$H(p)H(-p) = \frac{1}{1 + p^{4n}}.$$

---

* Networks of this type satisfying the maximally flat condition are also called *Butterworth* networks.

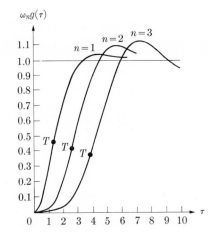

FIG. 4–16. Normalized step responses for a maximally flat n-stage series-peaked amplifier.

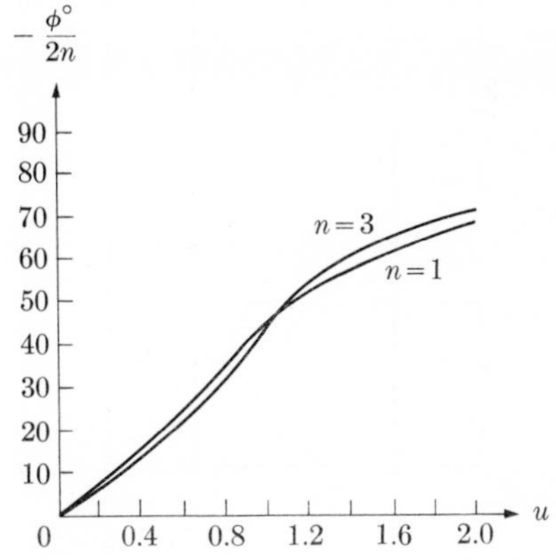

FIG. 4–17.   Phase characteristic for a maximally flat n-stage series-peaked amplifier.

The poles of this function are the roots of the equation

$$p^{4n} = -1. \tag{4–48}$$

It follows from Eq. (4–46) that the poles of $H(p) = H_1(p) \cdots H_n(p)$ are those roots of Eq. (4–48) which are in the left-half of the p-plane.

Figure 4–16 shows the normalized response to a unit-step input for the maximally flat case and $n = 1, 2, 3$. The response for $n = 2$ has been computed from Eq. (4–45), where $\zeta_1 = \beta_2 = 0.924$ and $\zeta_2 = \beta_1 = 0.383$. In each case, the normalized bandwidth is given by $u_b = 1$ [see Eq (4–47)]. Figure 4–17 shows the phase characteristic, which is reasonably linear. The time delay, as computed from the slope, is indicated by the points labeled T in Fig. 4–16.

EXAMPLE 7. In Fig. 4–18, n identical shunt-peaked amplifier stages are connected in cascade. Let us consider the problem of determining the output voltage response to an input voltage $v_i(t)$ whose source is in the first stage as indicated. This voltage will be taken to be a unit impulse so that $\mathcal{L}[v_i(t)] = 1$. The transform of the grid voltage of the first stage is

$$V_0(s) = \frac{1/Cs}{R + Ls + 1/Cs} = \frac{\omega_n^2}{s^2 + 2\zeta\omega_n s + \omega_n^2},$$

and the output voltage transform is

$$V_n(s) = (-g_m Z)^n V_0(s) = (-1)^n \left(\frac{g_m}{C}\right)^n \frac{\omega_n^2 (s + 2\zeta\omega_n)^n}{(s^2 + 2\zeta\omega_n s + \omega_n^2)^{n+1}},$$

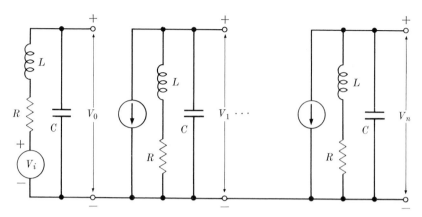

FIG. 4–18. An n-stage shunt-peaked amplifier.

which can be written in the form

$$\left(\frac{-2\zeta}{g_m R}\right)^n V_n(s) = H(p) = \frac{(p + 2\zeta)^n}{(p^2 + 2\zeta p + 1)^{n+1}}. \qquad (4\text{-}49)$$

This transform can be simplified by using the s-translation theorem (4–7) with $a = 2\zeta$:

$$\mathcal{L}^{-1}\left[\frac{(p + 2\zeta)^n}{(p^2 + 2\zeta p + 1)^{n+1}}\right] = e^{-2\zeta\tau}\mathcal{L}^{-1}\left[\frac{p^n}{[(p - \zeta)^2 + \beta^2]^{n+1}}\right].$$

Furthermore, since

$$\mathcal{L}\left[\frac{d^n f(\tau)}{d\tau^n}\right] = p^n F(p)$$

(note that all initial conditions are taken to be identically zero), we have

$$\mathcal{L}^{-1}[H(p)] = e^{-2\zeta\tau}\frac{d^n}{d\tau^n}\left\{\mathcal{L}^{-1}\left[\frac{1}{[(p - \zeta)^2 + \beta^2]^{n+1}}\right]\right\}.$$

A second application of the s-translation theorem, with $a = -\zeta$, yields

$$\mathcal{L}^{-1}[H(p)] = e^{-2\zeta\tau}\frac{d^n}{d\tau^n}\left\{e^{\zeta\tau}\mathcal{L}^{-1}\left[\frac{1}{(p^2 + \beta^2)^{n+1}}\right]\right\}.$$

The remaining transform can be evaluated with the aid of Eq. (D–16) given in Appendix D. Thus

$$\mathcal{L}^{-1}[H(p)] = e^{-2\zeta\tau}\frac{\sqrt{\pi}}{n!(2\beta)^{n+1/2}}\frac{d^n}{d\tau^n}\left(e^{\zeta\tau}\tau^{n+1/2}J_{n+1/2}(\beta\tau)\right), \qquad (4\text{-}50)$$

where $J_n(z)$ is the *Bessel function of the first kind of order* n. If $z = \beta\tau$ is large, we can use the asymptotic expansion [see Appendix, Eq. (D–53):

$$J_{n+1/2}(z) \cong \sqrt{2/\pi z} \cos [z - (n+1)(\pi/2)]. \qquad (4\text{–}51)$$

In Eq. (4–50) the dominant term for large τ is that with the largest power of τ, which is obtained by considering τ^n as a fixed factor in the bracket so that differentiation is carried out on $\cos \beta \tau$ alone. Since

$$\frac{d}{d\tau}\,[e^{\zeta \tau} \cos (\beta \tau - \alpha)] = e^{\zeta \tau} \cos (\beta \tau + \phi - \alpha),$$

where $\cos \phi = \zeta$ and α is a constant, we obtain the result

$$v_n(t) = \omega_n \left(\frac{-g_m R}{2\zeta}\right)^n h(\tau) \cong \frac{\omega_n}{\beta n!} \left(\frac{-g_m R}{2\zeta}\right)^n \left(\frac{\tau}{2\beta}\right)^n$$

$$\times e^{-\zeta \tau} \cos \left[\beta \tau + n\phi - (n+1)\,\frac{\pi}{2}\right]. \qquad (4\text{–}52)$$

It is of interest to solve the same problem by an alternative method. The poles of (4–49) are at $p = p_1,\ p_2$, and the pole coefficient at p_1 is

$$F_1(p) = \frac{(p + 2\zeta)^n}{(p - p_2)^{n+1}}\, e^{p\tau}.$$

Evaluating $h(\tau)$ yields

$$h(\tau) = 2 \operatorname{Re}\left[\frac{1}{n!}\frac{d^n}{dp^n}\left\{\frac{(p + 2\zeta)^n}{(p - p_2)^{n+1}}\, e^{p\tau}\right\}\right]_{p=p_1}.$$

This can be simplified by means of the substitution

$$p = p_2 + \frac{u}{\tau},$$

which yields

$$h(\tau) = \frac{2\tau^n}{n!} \operatorname{Re}\left[e^{p_2 \tau}\frac{d^n}{du^n}\left\{\frac{\tau}{u}\left(1 - \frac{\tau p_1}{u}\right)^n e^u\right\}\right]_{u=2j\beta\tau}. \qquad (4\text{–}53)$$

For large τ the dominant term in Eq. (4–53) is obtained by considering the first two terms inside the brackets as fixed factors. These factors yield

$$\frac{\tau}{u} = \frac{1}{2j\beta} = \frac{e^{-j(\pi/2)}}{2\beta}$$

and

$$\left(1 - \frac{\tau p_1}{u}\right) = \frac{e^{j(\phi - \pi/2)}}{2\beta}.$$

The result is identical with (4–52). ▲

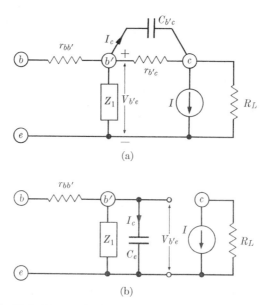

FIG. 4–19. Hybrid-π equivalent circuits for a transistor ($I = g_m V_{b'e}$).

4–6 Transistor video amplifiers. When transistors are the active element, the simple methods used to design vacuum-tube amplifiers are not directly applicable. Bruun [4] has shown that a simplified *hybrid-π* equivalent circuit can be used for design purposes. The hybrid-π equivalent circuit is shown in Fig. 4–19(a), where ⓑ,ⓔ, and ⓒ refer to the base, emitter, and collector terminals, respectively, and where

$$\frac{1}{Z_1} = \frac{1}{r_{b'e}} + C_{b'e}s. \tag{4–54}$$

The approximate equivalent circuit is obtained by neglecting $r_{b'c}$ and accounting for the interaction between collector and base by an equivalent impedance (Fig. 4–19b):

$$Z_e = \frac{V_{b'e}}{I_c} \cong \frac{1}{C_e s},$$

where

$$C_e = C_{b'c}(1 + g_m R_L). \tag{4–55}$$

In deriving this expression, we have assumed that

$$|R_L C_{b'c} s| \ll 1,$$

which is valid for the small load resistors used in video amplifiers. In effect, this means the total generator current i flows through the load R_L.

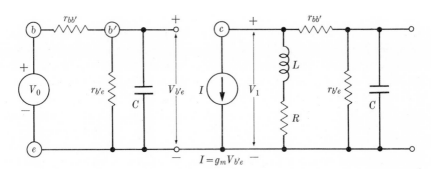

FIG. 4–20. Hybrid-π equivalent circuit for one-stage of a shunt-peaked transistor video amplifier.

Figure 4–20 shows the simplified hybrid-π equivalent circuit for one stage of a shunt-peaked video amplifier, where $C = C_{b'e} + C_e$. The load for this stage is not a constant. However, in Eq. (4–55), it can be reasonably well approximated by its zero-frequency value which is taken as R_L. This approximation is valid for the video amplifier for which the load is relatively small. The transfer function $H = V_1/V_0$ for this stage takes the form

$$H(s) = -\frac{g_m}{C}\frac{s + a\omega_n}{s^2 + b\omega_n s + \omega_n^2},$$ (4–56a)

where

$$\omega_n^2 = \frac{R + r_{be'} + r_{bb'}}{r_{be'}}\frac{1}{LC},$$ (4–56b)

$$b\omega_n = \frac{1}{r_{be'}C} + \frac{R + r_{bb'}}{L},$$ (4–56c)

and

$$a = \frac{R}{\omega_n L}.$$ (4–56d)

The function $H(s)$ can be written in the normalized form, $G_0 H[p]$, where $H[p]$ is given by Eq. (4–35) and

$$G_0 = -\frac{g_m a}{C\omega_n} = -g_m\frac{Rr_{be'}}{R + r_{bb'} + r_{be'}}$$ (4–57)

is the zero-frequency gain expressed in the same form as given by Eq. (4–36). However, the method of realizing specified values of a, b and ω_n (or G_0) is more complicated for a transistor. This can be seen from equations (4–56b) through (4–56d) since the transistor parameters enter into all these relations. In general, graphical or iterative methods are required for a practical design [3, 5, 6, 7].

In summary it can be stated that the design of video amplifiers involves the following considerations. The gain-bandwidth product for a fixed amplifier configuration is used as a design parameter to ascertain whether the gain and bandwidth specifications can be met. The choice of a suitable amplifier configuration is based on the normalized transfer function. The parameters in the normalized transfer function are chosen to produce pole-zero locations that are known to yield a good compromise between rise time and overshoot for the response to a unit step. In the examples discussed, where the coupling networks were either shunt or series peaked, the parameters were a, b, and ζ, which can be selected to yield a maximally flat magnitude characteristic or a maximally linear phase characteristic. The selection made fixes the form of the response. The remaining selection involves a compromise between ω_n and G_0. Both the bandwidth and time scale for the response are fixed by ω_n. A large value of ω_n will result in a small rise time and a large bandwidth. However, it follows from Eq. (4–57) that G_0 is decreased as ω_n is increased.

4–7 Bandpass networks. In amplitude-modulated carrier systems, a carrier signal $\sin \omega_c t$ is modulated to give a signal of the form

$$v(t) = m(t) \sin \omega_c t,$$

where ω_c is the angular frequency of the carrier and

$$m(t) = m_0 + v'(t)$$

is the modulating signal. Since m_0 is a constant, we can restrict the discussion of system responses to the case of carrier-suppressed modulation, where $m_0 = 0$. If desired, the response so obtained can be added to the steady response due to m_0, to give the total response. If $m_0 = 0$, the signal $v'(t)$ represents the *envelope* of the modulated carrier. In systems of this type it is desirable to consider the envelope alone and define an *envelope transfer function* of the form*

$$\frac{\mathcal{L}[v'_o(t)]}{\mathcal{L}[v'_i(t)]} = \frac{V'_o(s')}{V'_i(s')} = H_e(s'), \tag{4–58}$$

where $v'_i(t)$ and $v'_o(t)$ are the envelopes of the input and output signals, respectively, and s' is the complex frequency of the spectral terms of the envelope signal. A representation of the form (4–58) is possible for a narrow-band system. This case is illustrated by the following example.

---

* The index e is used to indicate an envelope transfer function.

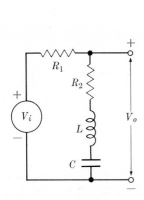

FIG. 4–21. A bandpass network.   FIG. 4–22. Pole-zero locations for the transfer function of a bandpass network.

EXAMPLE 8. Consider the network shown in Fig. 4–21 whose transfer function is

$$H(s) = \frac{\mathcal{L}[v_o(t)]}{\mathcal{L}[v_i(t)]} = \frac{s^2 + 2\zeta_1\omega_c s + \omega_c^2}{s^2 + 2\zeta_2\omega_c s + \omega_c^2}, \qquad (4\text{–}59)$$

where

$$\omega_c^2 LC = 1, \qquad 2\zeta_1\omega_c = \frac{R_2}{L}, \qquad \text{and} \qquad 2\zeta_2\omega_c = \frac{R_1 + R_2}{L}.$$

The transfer function can be factored into the form

$$H(s) = \frac{(s - s_1)(s - s_1^*)}{(s - s_2)(s - s_2^*)},$$

and its pole-zero locations are shown in Fig. 4–22. If $\zeta_2 \ll 1$, we have

$$s_1 \cong \omega_c(-\zeta_1 + j) \qquad \text{and} \qquad s_2 \cong \omega_c(-\zeta_2 + j).$$

Now let

$$s = j\omega_c + s'. \qquad (4\text{–}60)$$

For a narrow-band system,

$$|s'| \ll \omega_c$$

provided that ω_c is very large compared with the frequency range of the envelope. If ω_c is large, it is easily seen that

$$\frac{s - s_1^*}{s - s_2^*} \cong 1$$

and that

$$H(s) \cong \frac{s' + \omega_c\zeta_1}{s' + \omega_c\zeta_2} = H_e(s'). \; \blacktriangle \qquad (4\text{–}61)$$

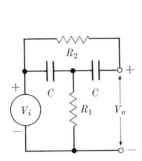

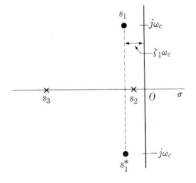

FIG. 4–23. A bridged-T bandpass network.

FIG. 4–24. Pole-zero locations for the transfer function of a bridged-T bandpass network when $\zeta_1 \ll 1$.

Equation (4–61) can be obtained by transforming the upper pole-zero cluster to the origin of the s'-plane. This is a bandpass to low-pass transformation yielding a transfer function of the form (4–58), which can then be treated by conventional methods.

A network having a transfer function of the form (4–61), where $\zeta_1 < \zeta_2$, is known as a phase-lead network and finds applications in control systems as a compensating network. For good performance it is essential that the carrier frequency be sufficiently stable. Since the network must be tuned to the carrier frequency, the L- or C-network elements must be adjustable. For this reason, the network shown in Fig. 4–21 may not always be practical. A network containing only RC-elements is more convenient from this point of view. Figure 4–23 shows a bridged-T RC-network which has a transfer function of the form (4–59), where

$$\omega_c^2 R_1 R_2 C^2 = 1, \qquad \zeta_1 \omega_c = \frac{1}{R_2 C}, \qquad \text{and} \qquad \zeta_2 = \zeta_1 + \frac{1}{2\zeta_1} \cong \frac{1}{2\zeta_1}.$$

The last equation is valid if $\zeta_1 \ll 1$ which is a necessary condition to realize a phase-lead network. It follows that $\zeta_2 \gg 1$. Under these conditions the poles and zeros (Fig. 4–24) are

$$s_2 \cong 0, \qquad s_3 \cong -2\zeta_2\omega_c, \qquad s_1 \cong -\zeta_1 w_c + j\omega_c.$$

Using the substitution (4–60) yields

$$H(s) = \frac{(s - s_1)(s - s_1^*)}{(s - s_2)(s - s_3)} \cong \frac{1}{\zeta_2\omega_c}\,(s' + \zeta_1\omega_c) = H_e(s'),$$

which is the transfer function of a lead network. However, since $\zeta_2 \gg \zeta_1$, the zero-frequency gain is extremely small so that an amplifier stage is essential.

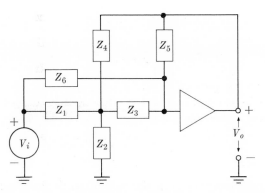

FIG. 4–25. An operational amplifier active network.

EXAMPLE 9. The need for an amplifier stage for the previous network makes the use of an active network more attractive. Consider the configuration shown in Fig. 4–25. The transfer function for this network is

$$H = -\frac{1/Z_1 + (Z_3/Z_6)(1/Z_1 + 1/Z_2 + 1/Z_3 + 1/Z_4)}{1/Z_4 + (Z_3/Z_5)(1/Z_1 + 1/Z_2 + 1/Z_3 + 1/Z_4)},$$

which can be expressed in the form

$$H = -\frac{R_4}{R_1}\frac{s^2 + 2\zeta_1\omega_c s + \omega_c^2}{s^2 + 2\zeta_2\omega_c s + \omega_c^2}$$

by choosing

$$\frac{1}{Z_1} = \frac{1}{R_1}, \qquad \frac{1}{Z_4} = C_4 s + \frac{1}{R_4},$$

$$\frac{1}{Z_2} = C_2 s, \qquad \frac{1}{Z_5} = C_5 s,$$

$$\frac{1}{Z_3} = \frac{1}{R_3}, \qquad \frac{1}{Z_6} = C_6 s.$$

We then have

$$\frac{1}{\omega_c^2} = R_1 R_3 C_6 (C_2 + C_4) = R_4 R_3 C_5 (C_2 + C_4),$$

$$\frac{2\zeta_1}{\omega_c} = R_1 R_3 C_6 \left(\frac{1}{R_1} + \frac{1}{R_3} + \frac{1}{R_4}\right), \qquad (4\text{--}62)$$

$$\frac{2\zeta_2}{\omega_c} = R_4 C_4 + \frac{2\zeta_1}{\omega_c}.$$

Since $\zeta_2 > \zeta_1$, the resulting network is a lead network. By choosing

$$\frac{1}{Z_1} = C_1 s + \frac{1}{R_1}, \qquad \frac{1}{Z_4} = \frac{1}{R_4},$$

one can realize a lag network, where $\zeta_2 < \zeta_1$.

To give a numerical example, let us suppose that we wish to obtain the transfer function representing a lead network,

$$H_e(s') = -\frac{1}{3} \frac{s' + 57}{s' + 309}, \qquad (4\text{--}63)$$

where the carrier frequency f_c is 400 cps. Equations (4–62) yield the following possible values:

$$R_1 = 48 \text{ k}\Omega, \qquad C_2 = 1 \text{ }\mu\text{f},$$
$$R_3 = 33 \text{ k}\Omega, \qquad C_4 = 0.005 \text{ }\mu\text{f},$$
$$R_4 = 16 \text{ k}\Omega, \qquad C_5 = 300 \text{ }\mu\mu\text{f},$$
$$C_6 = 100 \text{ }\mu\mu\text{f}.$$

In determining the envelope response of this bandpass network to different inputs, one can use the envelope transfer function (4–63) and thus achieve considerable simplification. ▲

Analytically a bandpass to low-pass transformation is obtained by means of the equation

$$p' = \tfrac{1}{2}\left(p + \frac{1}{p}\right). \qquad (4\text{--}64)$$

Solving this equation for p yields

$$p = p' + j\sqrt{1 - p'^2} = j + p' - \frac{j}{2} p'^2 + \cdots$$

It is seen that the error introduced by the use of Eq. (4–60) in deriving envelope transfer functions is of second order. However, the exact transformation (4–64) may not always be applicable. Such is the case with the double-tuned transformer.

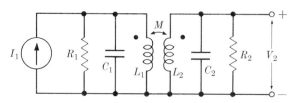

FIG. 4–26. A double-tuned transformer-coupled network.

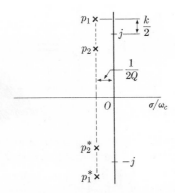

FIG. 4–27. Pole-zero locations for the transfer function of a double-tuned network when k and $1/Q$ are small.

An important type of bandpass network is the transformer-coupled circuit shown in Fig. 4–26. The transfer function is

$$\frac{V_2(s)}{I_1(s)} = \frac{M\omega_c/(1 - k^2) \cdot p}{[p^2 + (1/Q)p + (1/1 - k)][p^2 + (1/Q)p + (1/1 + k)]}, \quad (4\text{–}65)$$

where

$$s = \omega_c p, \qquad\qquad Q = \frac{R_1}{\omega_c L_1} = \frac{R_2}{\omega_c L_2},$$

$$k = \frac{M}{\sqrt{L_1 L_2}}, \qquad \omega_c^2 L_1 C_1 = \omega_c^2 L_2 C_2 = 1.$$

If k is small and Q large the poles p_1, p_1^*, p_2, p_2^* are given by (see Fig. 4–27)

$$p_1 \cong -\frac{1}{2Q} + j\frac{k}{2} + j,$$

$$p_2 \cong -\frac{1}{2Q} - j\frac{k}{2} + j.$$

By factoring the denominator terms of Eq. (4–65) and substituting $p = j + p'$, we obtain the envelope transfer function

$$H_e(p') = \frac{-jM\omega_c/4(1 - k^2)}{p'^2 + (1/Q)p' + (1/4)(1/Q^2 + k^2)}. \quad (4\text{–}66)$$

This result has the same form as that obtained for the series-peaked circuit [see Eq. (4–44)]. To realize a maximally flat magnitude characteristic, the poles of $He(p')$ must be located at an angle of 45° with respect to the negative real axis in the p'-plane. One thus obtains *critical coupling* with $k = 1/Q$. If more than one double-tuned stage is used, the circuit Q's

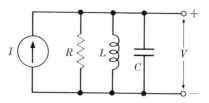

FIG. 4–28. A parallel RLC-network.

and k's can be individually adjusted to realize an overall maximally flat envelope transfer function. The normalized envelope step response is shown in Fig. 4–16 for $n = 1, 2, 3$.

The denominator factors of Eq. (4–65) can also be realized by *stagger-tuning* two stages of parallel-RLC networks* (Fig. 4–28). The impedance of this network is

$$Z(s) = \frac{V}{I} = \frac{1}{C} \frac{s}{s^2 + 2\zeta\omega_0 s + \omega_0^2}, \qquad (4\text{–}67)$$

where

$$\omega_0^2 LC = 1, \qquad 2\zeta = \frac{\omega_0 L}{R}.$$

In the case of stagger-tuning, the factor k in Eq. (4–65) represents the degree to which the two cascaded circuits are adjusted above and below the center frequency, respectively.

4–8 The response of networks to frequency-modulated signals. Frequency modulation is a special case of angle modulation in which the signals are considered to be the real part of

$$\begin{aligned} v_i(t) &= e^{j\phi_i} \\ &= m(t)e^{j\omega_c t}, \end{aligned} \qquad (4\text{–}68)$$

where $\phi_i = \omega_c t + \phi(t)$ is the *instantaneous phase* and $m(t)$ is the complex modulating signal. The *instantaneous angular velocity* is defined to be

$$\omega_i = \frac{d\phi_i}{dt} = \omega_c + \frac{d\phi}{dt}.$$

This equation illustrates the principle of frequency modulation where the instantaneous frequency is varied by means of the rate of change of the phase ϕ. The response of networks to inputs of the form (4–68) is difficult

---

* It is assumed that there is no loading between stages.

to evaluate. We now consider some cases of interest for which useful solutions are possible.

EXAMPLE 10. Let us consider the parallel-RLC network shown in Fig. 4–28. If $i = 1 \cdot e^{j\omega_1 t}$, the steady-state voltage response is

$$v_1(t) = 1 \cdot Z_1 e^{j\omega_1 t}, \qquad t < 0,$$

where $Z_1 = Z(j\omega_1)$. At $t = 0$ we consider an instantaneous change in frequency so that $i = 1 \cdot e^{j\omega_2 t}$ for $t > 0$. This problem involves the consideration of the initial conditions at $t = 0$. The simplest method of deriving the solution $v_2(t)$ is to note that it consists of the steady-state response plus a transient response which arises due to the poles of $Z(s)$ [see Eq. (4–67)]. For small ζ, these are $-\omega_0\zeta \pm j\omega_0$. Thus $v_2(t)$ has the form

$$v_2(t) = (Z_1 - Z_2 + jB)e^{-\zeta\omega_0 t}e^{j\omega_0 t} + Z_2 e^{j\omega t_2}, \qquad t > 0,$$

where $Z_2 = Z(j\omega_2)$ and B is a real constant. At $t = 0$, physical considerations require that the voltage and rate of change of voltage be continuous. Since the physical solution is the real part of v_1 and v_2, we must have

$$\mathrm{Re}[v_1(0)] = \mathrm{Re}[v_2(0)], \qquad \mathrm{Re}\left[\frac{dv_1(t)}{dt}\right]_{t=0} = \mathrm{Re}\left[\frac{dv_2(t)}{dt}\right]_{t=0}$$

which yields

$$B = \mathrm{Re}\left[(Z_1 - Z_2)(-\zeta + j) + j\left(\frac{\omega_2}{\omega_0}Z_2 - \frac{\omega_1}{\omega_0}Z_1\right)\right].$$

When $\omega_1 = \omega_0$ it can be shown that $B \cong 0$.

To determine the instantaneous frequency we write

$$v_2(t) = Z_2 e^{j\omega_2 t}e^{j\alpha},$$

where

$$e^{j\alpha} = 1 + \left(\frac{Z_1 - Z_2}{Z_2} + j\frac{B}{Z_2}\right)e^{-\zeta\omega_0 t}e^{j(\omega_0 - \omega_2)t}. \qquad (4\text{–}69)$$

The instantaneous frequency for $v_2(t)$ is the rate of change of arg $v_2(t)$. Thus

$$\omega_i = \omega_2 + \mathrm{Re}\left[\frac{d\alpha}{dt}\right]. \qquad (4\text{–}70)$$

It follows from Eq. (4–69) that

$$\frac{1}{\zeta\omega_0}\frac{d\alpha}{dt} = (-x_2 + j)(1 - e^{-j\alpha}), \qquad (4\text{–}71)$$

where

$$x_2 = \frac{\omega_2 - \omega_0}{\omega_0\zeta}.$$

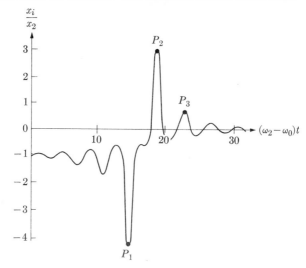

FIG. 4–29. Instantaneous frequency deviation for a parallel RLC-network.

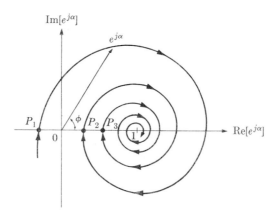

FIG. 4–30. Instantaneous phase deviation for a parallel RLC-network.

Equation (4–70) can be expressed in the normalized form

$$x_i = \frac{\omega_i - \omega_2}{\omega_0 \zeta} = \frac{1}{\zeta \omega_0} \operatorname{Re}\left[\frac{d\alpha}{dt}\right],$$

which can be evaluated by means of Eq. (4–71). Figure 4–29 is a plot of x_i/x_2 for the case where $\omega_1 = \omega_0$ and $x_2 = 11$. The curve shows the form of the transient response of the instantaneous frequency deviation from its final steady-state value ω_2. The understanding of this figure is facilitated by considering Fig. 4–30, which is a polar plot of Eq. (4–69).

The instantaneous phase deviation is arg $e^{j\alpha}$. At P_1, there is a rapid negative rate of change of phase, while at P_2 and P_3 the rate of change is positive. ▲

We now discuss the possibility of a more general representation of network responses to signals of the form (4–68). Let

$$M(s) = \int_0^\infty e^{j\phi}e^{-st}\,dt$$

be the Laplace transform of the complex modulating signal. It follows that the Laplace transform of Eq. (4–68) is

$$V_i(s) = \int_0^\infty e^{j(\omega_c t + \phi)}e^{-st}\,dt = M(s - j\omega_c).$$

If the system transfer function is $H(s)$, the output response can be found from

$$V_o(s) = H(s)V_i(s) = H(s)M(s - j\omega_c).$$

We now apply the s-translation theorem and obtain

$$v_o(t) = e^{j\omega_c t}\mathcal{L}^{-1}[H(s + j\omega_c)M(s)]. \tag{4–72}$$

This equation gives the exact output response. However, the desired response is often of the form

$$v_d(t) = e^{j\phi_i}H(j\omega_i), \tag{4–73}$$

which is a quasi-stationary response where the instantaneous phase and frequency are considered to be changing slowly so that steady-state phasor analysis is applicable. One wishes to obtain a response of this type in networks that are being tested with the aid of sweep-frequency generators. We now determine under what conditions $v_o(t) \cong v_d(t)$. We first substitute $\omega_c t = \phi_i - \phi$ and $\omega_c = \omega_i - d\phi/dt$ in Eq. (4–72). Thus

$$v_o(t) = e^{j\phi_i}e^{-j\phi}\mathcal{L}^{-1}\left[H\left(s + j\omega_i - j\frac{d\phi}{dt}\right)M(s)\right].$$

We now let $p = s - j(d\phi/dt)$, expand $H(p + j\omega_i)$ in a power series in p, and obtain

$$v_o(t) = e^{j\phi_i}e^{-j\phi}\mathcal{L}^{-1}\left[\sum_{n=0}^\infty \frac{1}{n!}H^{(n)}(j\omega_i)p^n M(s)\right]$$

$$= e^{j\phi_i}e^{-j\phi}\sum_{n=0}^\infty \frac{1}{n!}H^{(n)}(j\omega_i)\left(\frac{d}{dt} - j\frac{d\phi}{dt}\right)^n m(t). \tag{4–74}$$

The latter result follows from the fact that $\mathcal{L}^{-1}[s^n M(s)] = d^n m(t)/dt^n$. Equation (4–74) can be written in the form

$$v_o(t) = e^{j\phi_i} H(j\omega_i)[1 + \epsilon(t)],$$

where

$$\epsilon(t) = \frac{e^{-j\phi}}{H(j\omega_i)} \sum_{n=2}^{\infty} \frac{1}{n!} H^{(n)}(j\omega_i) \left(\frac{d}{dt} - j\frac{d\phi}{dt}\right)^n e^{j\phi}.$$

If we consider only the first term of this series, we obtain (note that the term for $n = 1$ vanishes)

$$\epsilon(t) \cong \frac{j}{2} \frac{H^{(2)}(j\omega_i)}{H(j\omega_i)} \frac{d^2\phi}{dt^2}. \tag{4–75}$$

This equation can be used to determine the conditions under which a quasi-stationary response is obtained. Consider once more the impedance function (4–67). If we substitute $s = j\omega_i = j(1 + u)\omega_0$ and if u is small, we obtain

$$H(j\omega) = Z(j\omega) \cong \frac{1}{2\omega_0 c} \frac{1}{\zeta + ju}.$$

It follows that

$$\left| \frac{H^{(2)}(j\omega_i)}{H(j\omega_i)} \right| \leqq \frac{2}{(\zeta\omega_0)^2}.$$

Suppose that the phase is modulated according to the equation

$$\phi = \delta \sin \omega_m t,$$

so that

$$\frac{d\phi}{dt} = \delta\omega_m \cos \omega_m t$$

is the frequency deviation. Substituting this result into Eq. (4–75) yields the condition

$$\frac{\Delta\Omega\omega_m}{(\zeta\omega_0)^2} \ll 1,$$

where $\Delta\Omega = \delta\omega_m$ is the maximum frequency deviation.

PROBLEMS

4–1. Suppose that the transfer function of an operational amplifier is

$$G(s) = \frac{K}{1 + T_a s},$$

where $K \gg 1$ and $T_a \ll 1$. If $Z_1 = R$, $Z_2 = 1/Cs$, $RC = 1$ (see Fig. 4–1) show that

$$H(s) = \frac{V_o}{V_i} = -\frac{K}{(1 + T_1 s)(1 + T_2 s)},$$

where $T_1 \cong K$ and $T_2 \cong T_a/K$. The function $H(s)$ is the transfer function of an operational integrator. Compute the response to a unit-step input and compare the result with that obtained from a perfect integrator.

4–2. Suppose that $Z_1 = R$, $1/Z_2 = 1/R + Cs$, and that three identical operational amplifiers are connected in cascade. Determine the response to a unit-step input.

4–3. An operational amplifier is connected as shown in Fig. 4–31. (a) Show that the transfer function is

$$H(s) = \frac{V_2}{V_1} = -\frac{1/Z_1}{1/Z_4 + (Z_3/Z_5)(1/Z_1 + 1/Z_2 + 1/Z_3 + 1/Z_4)}.$$

If

$$Z_1 = R_1, \qquad Z_2 = \frac{1}{C_2 s}, \qquad Z_3 = R_3, \qquad Z_4 = R_4, \qquad Z_5 = \frac{1}{C_5 s}$$

show that

$$H[p] = -\frac{R_4}{R_1} \frac{1}{p^2 + 2\zeta p + 1},$$

where

$$s = \omega_n p, \qquad \omega_n^2 R_3 C_5 R_4 C_2 = 1, \qquad 2\zeta\omega_n = \frac{1}{C_2}\left(\frac{1}{R_1} + \frac{1}{R_3} + \frac{1}{R_4}\right).$$

(b) Two similar amplifiers having the same ω_n but different values for ζ are connected in cascade. The output of the last stage has an RC-network as shown in the figure, where $\omega_n RC = 1$. Determine the output response $v_3(t)$ of the cascaded network to a unit-step input.

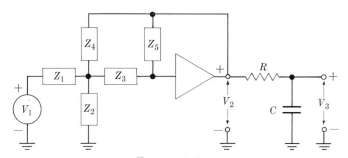

FIGURE 4–31

4-4. Suppose that the transfer function (4-19), which is used to approximate a delay operation, is modified to

$$H(s) = \frac{s^2 - 2\zeta\omega_0 s + \omega_0^2}{s^2 + 2\zeta\omega_0 s + \omega_0^2}\frac{s - a}{s + a}.$$

Compute the response to a unit-step. Determine the additional amplifiers and connections required in Fig. 4-5 to realize this transfer function.

4-5. An improvement to the approximation for a delay operation can be obtained by cascading two networks of the type shown in Fig. 4-5. The transfer function of this combined network has the form given by Eq. (4-20). Compute the response of this network to a unit-step input (see Fig. 4-6).

4-6. Consider a system having the transfer function

$$H(p) = \frac{1}{(p+1)^{n+1}}.$$

(a) Show that the response to a unit-impulse input is $h(\tau) = \tau^n e^{-\tau}/n!$. (b) Show that the time delay for a unit-step input, as computed from Eq. (4-21), is $T = n + 1$. (c) Show that $h(\tau)$ has a maximum at $\tau = \tau_m = n$. It is seen that τ_m approximates T for large n. For the type of response shown in Fig. 4-8, which is the case here, the maximum slope $h(\tau_m)$ of the unit-step response $g(\tau)$ can be used to estimate the rise time τ_R. Show that for large n,

$$\frac{1}{\tau_R} = \frac{n^n e^{-n}}{n!} \cong \frac{1}{\sqrt{2\pi n}},$$

where the latter result follows from the Stirling expansion [8]. (d) Show that the bandwidth u_b can be found from the equation

$$\frac{1}{n}\ln 2 = \ln(1 + u_b^2) \cong u_b^2$$

and that

$$u_b\tau_R \cong 2.1,$$

so that the bandwidth rise-time product is independent of n.

4-7. Consider the network shown in Fig. 4-32, which represents a high-frequency approximation for an RC-coupled amplifier, taking into account the stray capacitance C. (a) For a cascade of $n + 1$ identical stages show that the

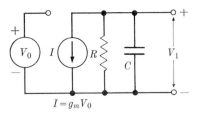

$$I = g_m V_0$$

FIGURE 4-32

normalized unit-step and unit-impulse responses are given by

$$\frac{g(t)}{(-g_m R)^{n+1}} = 1 + \frac{(-1)^{n+1}t^{n+1}}{n!} \frac{d^n}{dt^n}\left(\frac{e^{-at}}{t}\right)$$

and

$$\frac{h(t)}{(-g_m R)^{n+1}} = a\frac{(at)^n}{n!}e^{-at},$$

respectively, where $a = 1/RC$. (b) Use the results of Problem 4–6 to show that the rise time is given by $\tau_R \cong (2.5/a)\sqrt{n}$ if n is large.

4–8. The network shown in Fig. 4–33 finds application in video amplifiers as a means of improving the low-frequency response. (a) Show that the transfer function $V/I = H$ has the form

$$H(s) = \frac{R R_1}{R + R_1}\frac{(1 + a/s)}{(1 + b/s + c/s^2)},$$

where

$$a = \frac{R + R_2}{R R_2}\frac{1}{C_2}, \qquad b = \frac{(R + R_1 + R_2)C_1 + R_2 C_2}{(R_1 + R)R_2 C_1 C_2},$$

and

$$c = \frac{1}{(R_1 + R)R_2 C_1 C_2}.$$

(b) Suppose that the input current is a unit step. By expanding $H(s)$ into a power series in $1/s$ and taking the inverse Laplace transform show that

$$v(t) = \frac{R R_1}{R + R_1}\left[1 - (b - a)t - (c - b^2 + ab)\frac{t^2}{2} + \cdots\right].$$

(c) The case $a = b$ results in a flat-topped response to a unit step. Show that this condition yields $R_1 C_1 = R C_2$.

4–9. Consider the network shown in Fig. 4–34. Show that

$$\tan \beta = \frac{(a - b)u + (2b - a - a^2 b)u^3 - bu^5}{1 - 2u^2 + u^4},$$

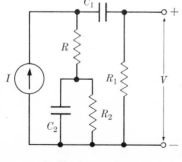

FIGURE 4–33

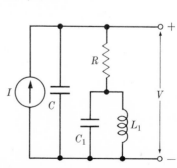

FIGURE 4–34

where β is the phase angle of $V(j\omega)/I(j\omega)$, $\omega = \omega_n u$, $\omega_n^2 L_1 C_1 = 1$, $a = \omega_n L_1/R$, and $b = \omega_n RC$. Show that the conditions (4–42) for a maximally linear phase characteristic can be put into the form

$$b = T(\tfrac{2}{15}T^4 - \tfrac{2}{3}T^2 + 1), \qquad 2a = b + \frac{1}{b} + \frac{T}{b}\left(\frac{T^2}{3b} - T - \frac{1}{b}\right)$$

where $T = b - a$ is the time delay. Solve these equations iteratively by assuming a value for b/T, evaluating T and a, and using these values to determine a new value for b/T.

4–10. Consider an all-pass transfer function of the form

$$H(p) = \frac{p^2 - 2\zeta p + 1}{p^2 + 2\zeta p + 1}.$$

Show that $\tan(\beta/2) = -2\zeta u/(1 - u^2)$, where β is the phase angle of $H(ju)$ and that the value $\zeta = \sqrt{3}/2$ results in a maximally linear phase characteristic, where $T = 2\sqrt{3}$. Determine the frequency range in which the deviation from linearity does not exceed a specified percentage error ϵ.

4–11. Consider an all-pass transfer function of the form

$$H(p) = \frac{p^2 - 2\zeta_1 p + 1}{p^2 + 2\zeta_1 p + 1}\frac{p^2 - 2\zeta_2 p + \alpha^2}{p^2 + 2\zeta_2 p + \alpha^2}.$$

Show that

$$\tan\frac{\beta}{2} = -\frac{(2\zeta_1\alpha^2 + 2\zeta_2)u - (2\zeta_1 + 2\zeta_2)u^3}{\alpha^2 - (1 + \alpha^2 + 4\zeta_1\zeta_2)u^2 + u^4}$$

and that the conditions (4–42) for a maximally linear phase characteristic can be put into the form $T^4 = 105/\alpha^2$, $(\zeta_1 + \zeta_2)T = 5$, $(1/\alpha^2)(4\zeta_1\zeta_2 + 1) = \tfrac{3}{7}T^2 - 1$, and $T = 2\zeta_1 + 2\zeta_2/\alpha^2$. Solve these equations iteratively by assuming a suitable value for $1/\alpha^2$ and ζ_1, evaluating T and ζ_2 from the first two equations, and determining new values for $1/\alpha^2$ and ζ_1 from the last two equations.

4–12. Consider a single-stage pentode amplifier with a series-peaked load (see Fig. 4–14). Show that the response to a unit-step input is

$$v_1(t) = (-g_m R)\left(1 - \frac{e^{-\zeta\tau}}{\beta}\sin(\beta\tau + \phi)\right),$$

where $\cos\phi = \zeta$ and the other quantities are as defined in the text.

4–13. Show that the response to a unit-step input of two identical cascaded series-peaked pentode stages is

$$v_2(t) = (g_m R)^2\left\{1 - \frac{e^{-\zeta\tau}}{2\beta^2}\left[\frac{\sqrt{4 - 3\zeta^2}}{\beta}\cos(\beta\tau - \phi_2) - \tau\cos(\beta\tau + \phi_1)\right]\right\},$$

where $\tan\phi_2 = \zeta(3 - 2\zeta^2)/2\beta^3$ and $\cos\phi_1 = \zeta$.

4–14. A single series-peaked stage is cascaded with a stage having a load as shown in Fig. 4–35. In both stages identical pentodes and resistors are used.

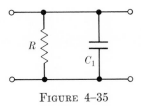

FIGURE 4–35

If $\omega_n R C_1 = 1$ and the input is a unit step show that

$$\frac{V_2(s)}{(g_m R)^2} = \frac{1}{\omega_n p} \frac{1}{p+1} \frac{1}{p^2 + 2\zeta p + 1}.$$

When $\zeta = \frac{1}{2}$, the result is a maximally flat transfer function. Determine the response to a unit-step input for this case.

4–15. Compute the response to a unit-step input for a three-stage series-peaked amplifier having different load resistors but the same ω_n. Assume that there is no loading between stages.

4–16. Consider an amplifier consisting of a cascade of n series-peaked stages where each stage has a transfer function of the type given by (4–46). Assume that there is no loading between stages. (a) Show that the time delay is $T = 2(\zeta_1 + \zeta_2 + \cdots + \zeta_n)$. (b) For the maximally flat case, show that $T = 1/[\sin{(\pi/4n)}]$. Use this result to compute the time delay for the unit-step responses illustrated in Fig. 4–16. Show that $T \cong 1.27n$ for large n.

4–17. Consider a system having the transfer function

$$H(p) = \frac{1}{(p^2 + 2\zeta p + 1)^n}.$$

(a) Show that $T = 2\zeta n$. (b) For τ large, show that the unit-impulse response is

$$h(\tau) \cong \frac{1}{\beta(n-1)!} \left(\frac{\tau}{2\beta}\right)^{n-1} e^{-\zeta\tau} \cos\left(\beta\tau - \frac{\pi n}{2}\right)$$

and that $h(\tau)$ has a maximum when $\tau = \tau_m \cong (n-1)/\zeta$. Prove that this agrees with the time delay T if n is large and $\zeta = 1/\sqrt{2}$. In this case, the overshoots are sufficiently small so that the considerations given in Problem 4–6 with respect to Fig. 4–8 are applicable. Show that the rise time is given by $\tau_R \cong \sqrt{\pi n}$. (c) By suitable choice of ζ the transfer function $H(p)$ can be made to approximate the maximally flat transfer function discussed in Problem 4–16(b). Show that the choice of $\zeta = 1/\sqrt{2}$ results in a reasonable agreement with the average value of the ζ_k's and between the respective time delays. Use the result of part (b) above to compute the rise time of the unit-step responses given in Fig. 4–16.

4–18. Consider a system whose transfer function $H(p)$ is given by

$$(2\zeta)^n H(p) = \left(\frac{p + 2\zeta}{p^2 + 2\zeta p + 1}\right)^n.$$

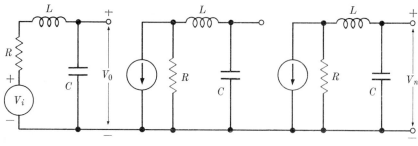

FIGURE 4–36

(a) Show that $T = (2\zeta - 1/2\zeta)n$. (b) For τ large, show that the unit-impulse response is

$$h(\tau) \cong \frac{1}{\beta(2\zeta)^n} \frac{1}{(n-1)!} \left(\frac{\tau}{2\beta}\right)^{n-1} e^{-\zeta\tau} \cos\left(\beta\tau + n\phi - \frac{\pi n}{2}\right),$$

where $\cos\phi = \zeta$, and that $h(\tau)$ has a maximum when $\tau = \tau_m = (n-1)/\zeta$. Prove that this agrees with the time delay T if n is large and $\zeta = \sqrt{3}/2$. In this case, the overshoots are sufficiently small so that the considerations given in Problem 4–6 with respect to Fig. 4–8 are applicable. Show that the rise time is given by $\tau_R \cong \beta(2\zeta)^n(2\beta\zeta)^{n-1}\sqrt{2\pi(n-1)}$. Apply this result to the unit-step response illustrated in Fig. 4–11 for $n = 2$ and $\zeta = 0.8$.

4–19. If $\zeta = 0.8$, the normalized rise time for a single shunt-peaked stage is approximately 2 (see Fig. 4–11). For the RC-coupled stage discussed in Problem 4–6, it is 2.5. However, the normalizing factor for the first case is $1/\omega_n$, while it is RC for the RC case. If the unit-step response of both cases is normalized with respect to RC, show that the shunt-peaked amplifier has a rise-time advantage of 2.

4–20. Consider a unit-impulse voltage whose source is in the first stage of an n-stage series-peaked amplifier as shown in Fig. 4–36. Determine an approximate solution for the output response, given that t is large.

4–21. Determine the envelope transfer function of the bandpass network shown in Fig. 4–37. Compute the response of this network to a unit-step carrier input.

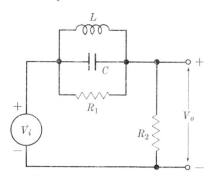

FIGURE 4–37

REFERENCES

1. W. CUNNINGHAM, "Time-delay networks for an analog computer," *Trans. IRE, PGEC,* **3**, 16–18 (December 1954).

2. G. VALLEY and H. WALLMAN, *Vacuum Tube Amplifiers*, McGraw-Hill, New York, 1948.

3. M. JOYCE and K. CLARKE, *Transistor Circuit Analysis*, Addison-Wesley, Reading, Mass., 1961.

4. G. BRUUN, "Common-emitter transistor video amplifiers," *Proc. IRE,* **44**, 1561–1572 (November 1956).

5. D. PEDERSON and R. PEPPER, "An evaluation of transistor lowpass broadbanding techniques," *IRE Wescon. Conv. Rec.,* pt. 2, 111–126 (1959).

6. V. GRINICH, "Stagger-tuned transistor video amplifiers," *IRE Trans. BTR,* **2**, 53–56 (October 1956).

7. P. HIRSCH, "Linear-phase transistor amplifiers," *Elec. Eng.* **78**, 1184–1189 (December 1959).

8. E. WHITTAKER and G. WATSON, *A Course of Modern Analysis*, Cambridge University Press, 1952, p. 253.

GENERAL REFERENCES

BAGHDADY, E., *Lectures on Communication System Theory*, McGraw-Hill, New York, 1961.

BLACK, H., *Modulation Theory*, D. Van Nostrand, New York, 1953.

PETTIT, J., and M. McWHORTER, *Electronic Amplifier Circuits*, McGraw-Hill, New York, 1961.

SCHWARTZ, M., *Information Transmission, Modulation, and Noise*, McGraw-Hill, New York, 1959.

CHAPTER 5

INITIAL CONDITIONS IN SYSTEMS

5–1 Introduction. In the examples discussed in the previous chapters all initial conditions were taken to be identically zero and the system was considered to be suddenly excited at $t = 0$. The definition of the transfer function [see Eq. (1–27)] is also based on the assumption that all initial conditions are zero. In discussing initial values, we must consider the condition

$$v(t) = 0 \quad \text{for} \quad t < 0. \tag{5–1}$$

This condition may not be satisfied, nor does it actually have to be. The state of the system is assumed known for $t < 0$ so that the initial values are also known at $t = 0$. At this instant a sudden change is applied to the system, and the response is to be determined. The Laplace transform method can be used to determine the response for $t > 0$. The fact that it yields the result (5–1) for $t < 0$ is evidently of no importance. It simply means that the mathematical model used to represent the system for $t < 0$ considers the system to be in a quiescent state and that suddenly, at $t = 0$, the initial conditions and sudden changes are applied.

Careful consideration must be given to the mathematical model used to represent the system. The initial value of $v(t)$ will be written

$$v(0) = \lim_{t \to 0} v(t), \tag{5–2}$$

which represents the initial value that a system response may have before sudden changes are applied. In an actual physical system a small but finite time interval ϵ is required to accomplish these changes. The instant of time after these changes have occurred will be called $t = 0^+$. We then have

$$v(0^+) = \lim_{\epsilon \to 0} v(\epsilon), \quad \epsilon > 0.$$

Evidently $v(0^+)$ does not have to equal $v(0)$ (see Fig. 5–1).

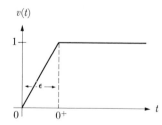

Fig. 5–1. A physical unit-step function.

86

5–2 Initial values in the Laplace transform. From Eq. (3–4) we have

$$\mathcal{L}\left[\frac{dv}{dt}\right] = s\mathcal{L}[v(t)] - v(0) = sV(s) - v(0), \qquad (5\text{–}3)$$

where $v(0)$ is to be interpreted in the sense given by Eq. (5–2). Applying Eq. (5–3) to $\mathcal{L}[d^2v/dt^2]$ yields

$$\mathcal{L}\left[\frac{d^2v}{dt^2}\right] = s\mathcal{L}\left[\frac{dv}{dt}\right] - v^{(1)}(0)$$

$$= s^2 V(s) - sv(0) - v^{(1)}(0).$$

This result is easily generalized:

$$\mathcal{L}\left[\frac{d^n v}{dt^n}\right] = s^n V(s) - s^{n-1}v(0) - s^{n-2}v^{(1)}(0) - \cdots - v^{(n-1)}(0), \qquad (5\text{–}4)$$

where the notation

$$\lim_{t\to 0} \frac{d^n v}{dt^n} = v^{(n)}(0)$$

has been used.

An important theorem is the *initial-value theorem*, which states that

$$v(0) = \lim_{t\to 0} v(t) = \lim_{s\to\infty} sV(s). \qquad (5\text{–}5)$$

We prove this result as follows. By definition

$$\mathcal{L}\left[\frac{dv}{dt}\right] = \int_0^\infty \frac{dv}{dt}\, e^{-st}\, dt. \qquad (5\text{–}6)$$

If $\text{Re}[s] > 0$ and if $s \to \infty$, the integral vanishes. The result (5–5) then follows from Eq. (5–3).

A further theorem is the *final-value theorem:*

$$v(\infty) = \lim_{t\to\infty} v(t) = \lim_{s\to 0} sV(s). \qquad (5\text{–}7)$$

The proof is easily established. If, in Eq. (5–6), $s \to 0$, we obtain

$$\lim_{s\to 0} \mathcal{L}\left[\frac{dv}{dt}\right] = \int_0^\infty \frac{dv}{dt}\, dt = v(\infty) - v(0). \qquad (5\text{–}8)$$

The result (5–7) then follows from Eqs. (5–3) and (5–8).

It is important to note that the theorem is valid only if both limits exist. If, for example, $v(t) = \sin \omega t$, then $v(\infty)$ does not exist, while

$$\lim_{s\to 0} s\, \frac{\omega}{s^2 + \omega^2} = 0.$$

Consider now Fig. 5–1 which illustrates a physically realizable unit-step function. The signal $v(t)$ rises to unity in a small time interval ϵ. Evidently,

$$v(0) = 0, \qquad v(0^+) = 1.$$

The transform of $v(t)$ is

$$V(s, \epsilon) = \frac{1 - e^{-\epsilon s}}{\epsilon s^2}, \tag{5–9}$$

and the initial-value theorem yields

$$v(0) = \lim_{s \to \infty} sV(s, \epsilon) = 0. \tag{5–10}$$

If, in Eq. (5–9), $\epsilon \to 0$, we obtain the transform of an idealized unit-step function:

$$\lim_{\epsilon \to 0} V(s, \epsilon) = 1/s = V(s),$$

and the initial-value theorem now yields

$$v(0^+) = \lim_{s \to \infty} sV(s) = 1. \tag{5–11}$$

The difference between (5–10) and (5–11) is a result of the mathematical idealized approximation to a physical unit step. The same kind of result will apply to systems in general. The actual signals, being of a physical nature, will be continuous functions. We obtain the Laplace transform from (5–4) using the prescribed initial conditions. After the transforms have been so obtained, they can often be considerably simplified by letting ϵ, the time required to introduce the changes, approach zero. If the initial-value theorem is applied to this limiting transform, we obtain (5–11), i.e., the initial value of $v(t)$ is the value that it has immediately after the changes have occurred.

EXAMPLE 1. Consider the ballistic galvanometer, Eq. (3–24) whose equation of motion is

$$\frac{d^2\theta}{dt^2} + 2\zeta\omega_n \frac{d\theta}{dt} + \omega_n^2\theta = \frac{BAN}{J} i(t). \tag{5–12}$$

Suppose that the initial conditions are

$$\theta(0) = 0, \qquad \theta^{(1)}(0) = K \tag{5–13}$$

and that there is no forcing term present, that is, $i(t) = 0$. Applying Eq. (5–4) yields

$$(s^2 + 2\zeta\omega_n s + \omega_n^2)\Theta(s) = K.$$

This equation can be solved for $\theta(t)$ by the previously developed methods. The initial-value theorem yields

$$\theta(0) = \lim_{s\to\infty} s\Theta(s) = 0,$$

$$\theta^{(1)}(0) = \lim_{s\to\infty} s^2\Theta(s) = K.$$

Let us suppose that the forcing term is a unit impulse of current and that the initial conditions are given by (5–13). The Laplace transform of (5–12) is now

$$(s^2 + 2\zeta\omega_n s + \omega_n^2)\Theta(s) = K + G$$

[for the definition of G, see Eq. (3–26)]. In applying the initial-value theorem one should note that the transform of $i(t)$ has been simplified by letting $\epsilon \to 0$ [see Eq. (3–25)] so that the initial values obtained will be $\theta(0^+)$ and $\theta^{(1)}(0^+)$. We have

$$\theta(0^+) = \lim_{s\to\infty} s\Theta(s) = 0$$

and

$$\theta^{(1)}(0^+) = \lim_{s\to\infty} s^2\Theta(s) = K + G. \tag{5–14}$$

The result (5–14) shows that the angular velocity at $t = 0^+$ consists of the initial angular velocity at $t = 0$ plus G, the increment in angular velocity due to the impulse. ▲

EXAMPLE 2. Consider the network shown in Fig. 3–1. The sinusoidal steady-state current responses due to the input voltage $v_i(t) = \cos 2t$ are obtained from Eqs. (3–15), (3–16), and (3–17). At $t = 0$ the sinusoidal steady-state terms yield

$$i_1(0) = \tfrac{9}{25}, \qquad i_2(0) = \tfrac{4}{25}, \qquad i_3(0) = -\tfrac{7}{100}.$$

After the network reaches the sinusoidal steady-state, the input voltage is suddenly short circuited at $t = 0$. The current responses to this sudden change are to be found. The voltage constraint at the input, $v_i(t) = 0$, requires that

$$i_1(t) = i_2(t) \qquad \text{for} \quad t > 0.$$

The inductors prevent any instantaneous changes in the currents $i_2(t)$ and $i_3(t)$. Thus

$$i_2(0^+) = i_2(0) = \tfrac{4}{25},$$

$$i_3(0^+) = i_3(0) = -\tfrac{7}{100},$$

$$i_1(0^+) = \tfrac{4}{25}. \tag{5–15}$$

These are the initial values after the change. There is no need to distinguish between $t = 0$ and $t = 0^+$ for the currents $i_2(t)$ and $i_3(t)$. If the equations (3–6) are written in differential equation form and (5–4) is used to introduce the initial conditions (5–15), we obtain

$$I_2(s) = \frac{4}{5\Delta} (9 + 4s),$$

$$(5\text{–}16)$$

$$I_3(s) = \frac{1}{5\Delta} (3 - 7s),$$

where Δ is defined by (3–7). The initial-value theorem can be used to check the conditions (5–15). We have

$$i_2(0) = \lim_{s \to \infty} sI_2(s) = \tfrac{4}{25},$$

$$i_3(0) = \lim_{s \to \infty} sI_3(s) = -\tfrac{7}{100}.$$

The responses are readily determined from (5–16):

$$i_2(t) = \tfrac{1}{25}[e^{-t} + 3e^{-6t}],$$

$$i_3(t) = \tfrac{1}{100}[2e^{-t} - 9e^{-6t}]. \ \blacktriangle$$

5–3 The equivalent-source representation of initial conditions. Suppose that the initial voltage of a capacitor is $v_c(0)$. We then have (Fig. 5–2)

$$\frac{dv_c(t)}{dt} = \frac{1}{C} i(t),$$

and, from Eq. (5–3)

$$\mathcal{L}\left[\frac{dv_c}{dt}\right] = \frac{I(s)}{C} = sV_c(s) - v_c(0),$$

which can be rearranged:

$$V_c(s) = \frac{I(s)}{Cs} + \frac{v_c(0)}{s}. \tag{5–17}$$

The last term in (5–17) can be interpreted as a voltage step $v_c(0)u(t)$

Fig. 5–2. Equivalent-source representation of initial conditions.

applied at $t = 0$, where $u(t)$ is the unit-step function. This voltage source is in series with the capacitor.

For an inductor with an initial current $i(0)$, we have

$$v(t) = L \frac{di}{dt}, \quad \text{and} \quad V(s) = LsI(s) - Li(0),$$

which can be rearranged:

$$I(s) = \frac{V(s)}{Ls} + \frac{i(0)}{s}. \tag{5–18}$$

The last term in (5–18) can be interpreted as an ideal current source $i(0)u(t)$ which is connected in parallel with the inductor.

The two results (5–17) and (5–18) illustrate the statement made in Section 5–1 that the initial conditions in the Laplace transform method are considered to be suddenly applied at $t = 0$.

5–4 The solution of ordinary linear differential equations. Let us consider the differential equation

$$\left(\frac{d^3}{dt^3} + a_2 \frac{d^2}{dt^2} + a_1 \frac{d}{dt} + a_0 \right) v(t) = 0 \tag{5–19}$$

and suppose that we are to determine the solution $v(t)$ which has the specified initial conditions $v(0)$, $v^{(1)}(0)$, $v^{(2)}(0)$. Taking the Laplace transform of Eq. (5–19) yields

$$D(s)V(s) = D_1(s)v(0) + D_2(s)v^{(1)}(0) + D_3(s)v^{(2)}(0) = N(s), \tag{5–20}$$

where

$$\begin{aligned}
D(s) &= s^3 + a_2 s^2 + a_1 s + a_0, \\
D_1(s) &= s^2 + a_2 s + a_1, \\
D_2(s) &= s + a_2, \\
D_3(s) &= 1.
\end{aligned} \tag{5–21}$$

The polynomials (5–21) will be called the *derived polynomials*. They are obtained from $D(s)$ by successively eliminating the constant term and dividing by s. The generalization of these results to an nth-order equation is obvious. $D(s)$ now has the form

$$\begin{aligned}
D(s) &= s^n + a_{n-1}s^{n-1} + \cdots + a_0 \\
&= (s - s_1)(s - s_2) \cdots (s - s_n). \tag{5–22}
\end{aligned}$$

The zeros of $D(s)$ are

$$s_1, s_2, s_3, \ldots, s_n,$$

and these are the poles of $V(s)$. If these poles are simple, we can write

$$D(s) = (s - s_k)Q_k(s),$$

so that the pole coefficient at s_k is

$$F_k(s) = \frac{N(s)}{Q_k(s)} e^{st}.$$

The solution is then

$$v(t) = \sum_{k=1}^{n} \frac{N(s_k)}{Q_k(s_k)} e^{s_k t}. \tag{5-23}$$

To determine $Q_k(s_k)$ note that $D(s_k) = 0$; hence

$$\frac{D(s) - D(s_k)}{s - s_k} = Q_k(s), \tag{5-24}$$

and therefore

$$Q_k(s_k) = \lim_{s \to s_k} \frac{D(s) - D(s_k)}{s - s_k} = D^{(1)}(s_k).$$

Equation (5-23) now has the form

$$v(t) = \sum_{k=1}^{n} \frac{N(s_k)}{D^{(1)}(s_k)} e^{s_k t}. \tag{5-25}$$

The term $N(s_k)$ can be computed from (5-20), and this approach will be called the *direct method*. There is an *alternative technique* which has some advantages. To understand this method let

$$P \equiv \frac{d}{dt}$$

be the differential operator and let

$$P_0^k v(0) \equiv \frac{d^k v(t)}{dt^k} \bigg]_{t=0}$$

represent the initial value of the kth derivative. It follows from (5-22) that the differential equation can be written in operator form as

$$D(P)v(t) = (P - s_1)(P - s_2) \cdots (P - s_n)v(t) = 0.$$

Consider now the function

$$u_m(t) = \frac{D(P)}{P - s_m} v(t) = Q_m(P)v(t). \tag{5-26}$$

Substituting (5–23) yields

$$u_m(t) = \sum_{k=1}^{n} \frac{D(P)}{P - s_m} \frac{N(s_k)}{Q(s_k)} e^{s_k t}$$

$$= \frac{N(s_m)}{Q(s_m)} Q(s_m) e^{s_m t}$$

$$= N(s_m) e^{s_m t}. \tag{5–27}$$

The latter result follows from the fact that $(P - s_k)e^{s_k t} = 0$. Thus all terms vanish except the mth term, since $Q_m(P)$ does not contain the factor $P - s_m$.

From Eqs. (5–26) and (5–27) we obtain, for $t = 0$,

$$u_m(0) = Q_m(P_0)v(0) = N(s_m).$$

EXAMPLE 3. Consider the differential equation

$$\left(\frac{d^3}{dt^3} + 6 \frac{d^2}{dt^2} + 11 \frac{d}{dt} + 6\right) v(t) = 0,$$

where

$$v(0) = 1,$$
$$v^{(1)}(0) = P_0 v(0) = 1,$$
$$v^{(2)}(0) = P_0^2 v(0) = 2.$$

We have

$$D(s) = s^3 + 6s^2 + 11s + 6 = (s + 1)(s + 2)(s + 3).$$

The zeros are $-1, -2, -3$, and the derived polynomials are

$$D_1(s) = s^2 + 6s + 11,$$
$$D_2(s) = s + 6,$$
$$D_3(s) = 1.$$

Using the direct method, we obtain from Eq. (5–20)

$$N(s) = D_1(s)v(0) + D_2(s)v^{(1)}(0) + D_3(s)v^{(2)}(0)$$
$$= s^2 + 7s + 19.$$

Thus $N(s_1) = 13$, $N(s_2) = 9$, and $N(s_3) = 7$. Since $D^{(1)}(s) = 3s^2 + 12s + 11$, we have

$$D^{(1)}(s_1) = 2, \qquad D^{(1)}(s_2) = -1, \qquad D^{(1)}(s_3) = 2.$$

Substituting these values into Eq. (5–25) yields the result

$$v(t) = \tfrac{13}{2}e^{-t} - 9e^{-2t} + \tfrac{7}{2}e^{-3t}.$$

If the alternative method is used to evaluate $N(s_k)$, we have

$$D(P_0) = (P_0 - s_1)(P_0 - s_2)(P_0 - s_3)$$

and

$$Q_1(P_0)v(0) = (P_0 + 2)(P_0 + 3)v(0)$$
$$= P_0^2 v(0) + 5P_0 v(0) + 6v(0)$$
$$= 13 = N(s_1).$$

Similarly,

$$Q_2(P_0)v(0) = (P_0 + 1)(P_0 + 3)v(0) = 9 = N(s_2)$$

and

$$Q_3(P_0)v(0) = (P_0 + 1)(P_0 + 2)v(0) = 7 = N(s_3).$$

The possible advantage of the alternative method is that in the case of complex zeros, it leads immediately to a separation of $N(s_k)$ into its real and imaginary parts. The numerical evaluation of $N(s_k)$ by the direct method is more difficult if s_k is complex but can be carried out with the aid of the remainder theorem (7–4). ▲

If all the poles are no longer simple, the result (5–25) must be suitably modified. Let us consider the pole s_k to be of second order to illustrate the procedure. We now have

$$D(s) = (s - s_k)^2 Q_k(s).$$

The pole coefficient is

$$F_k(s) = \frac{N(s)}{Q_k(s)} e^{st},$$

and the contribution of this one pole will be

$$v_k(t) = \frac{dF_k(s)}{ds}\bigg]_{s=s_k}. \tag{5–28}$$

Equation (5–28) yields

$$v_k(t) = \frac{N(s_k)e^{s_k t}}{Q_k(s_k)}\left[t + \frac{N^{(1)}(s_k)}{N(s_k)} - \frac{Q_k^{(1)}(s_k)}{Q_k(s_k)}\right]. \tag{5–29}$$

The quantities $N(s_k)$ and $N^{(1)}(s_k)$ can also be evaluated by the alternative method. Consider the function

$$u_k(t) = \frac{D(P)}{(P - s_k)^2} v(t) = Q_k(P)v(t) = Q_k(P)v_k(t), \tag{5–30}$$

where all terms in $v(t)$ have dropped out with the exception of $v_k(t)$ for the reason stated previously [see Eq. (5–27)]. Substituting $v_k(t)$ in the form given by (5–28) into (5–30) yields

$$u_k(t) = \frac{d}{ds}\left[\frac{N(s)}{Q_k(s)}Q_k(P)e^{st}\right]_{s=s_k} = \frac{d}{ds}[N(s)e^{st}]_{s=s_k},$$

from which we obtain

$$u_k(0) = N^{(1)}(s_k)$$

and

$$u_k^{(1)}(0) = s_k N^{(1)}(s_k) + N(s_k).$$

EXAMPLE 4. Consider the differential equation

$$\left(\frac{d^4}{dt^4} + 7\frac{d^3}{dt^3} + 17\frac{d^2}{dt^2} + 17\frac{d}{dt} + 6\right)v(t) = 0,$$

where

$$v(0) = 1, \qquad\qquad v^{(2)}(0) = P_0^2 v(0) = -1,$$
$$v^{(1)}(0) = P_0 v(0) = 1, \qquad v^{(3)}(0) = P_0^3 v(0) = -1.$$

We have

$$D(s) = s^4 + 7s^3 + 17s^2 + 17s + 6$$
$$= (s+1)^2(s+2)(s+3), \tag{5–31}$$

and the zeros are

$$s_1 = -1 \quad \text{(double zero)},$$
$$s_2 = -2,$$
$$s_3 = -3.$$

The derived polynomials are

$$D_1(s) = s^3 + 7s^2 + 17s + 17,$$
$$D_2(s) = s^2 + 7s + 17,$$
$$D_3(s) = s + 7,$$
$$D_4(s) = 1.$$

Generalizing Eq. (5–20) for $n = 4$, we have

$$N(s) = D_1(s)v(0) + D_2(s)v^{(1)}(0) + D_3(s)v^{(2)}(0) + D_4(s)v^{(3)}(0)$$
$$= s^3 + 8s^2 + 23s + 26.$$

From Eq. (5–31) we obtain

$$D^{(1)}(s) = 4s^3 + 21s^2 + 34s + 17.$$

The contribution of the simple poles can now be evaluated:

$$v_2(t) = \frac{N(s_2)}{D^{(1)}(s_2)} e^{s_2 t} = 4e^{-2t},$$

$$v_3(t) = \frac{N(s_3)}{D^{(1)}(s_3)} e^{s_3 t} = -\tfrac{1}{2} e^{-3t}.$$

The contribution of the double pole can be found by evaluating

$$Q_1(s_1) = (s_1 + 2)(s_1 + 3) = s_1^2 + 5s_1 + 6 = 2,$$

$$Q_1^{(1)}(s_1) = 2s_1 + 5 = 3,$$

$$N^{(1)}(s_1) = 3s_1^2 + 16s_1 + 23 = 10.$$

Substituting these results into Eq. (5–29) yields

$$v_1(t) = -\tfrac{5}{2} e^{-t} + 5t e^{-t},$$

and the final answer is

$$v(t) = -\tfrac{5}{2} e^{-t} + 5t e^{-t} + 4e^{-2t} - \tfrac{1}{2} e^{-3t}.$$

The alternative method may also be used. We have

$$N(s_2) = \frac{D(P_0)}{P_0 + 2} v(0) = (P_0 + 1)^2 (P_0 + 3) v(0) = 4,$$

$$N(s_3) = \frac{D(P_0)}{P_0 + 3} v(0) = (P_0 + 1)^2 (P_0 + 2) v(0) = 2,$$

$$u_1(0) = N^{(1)}(s_1) = \frac{D(P_0)}{(P_0 + 1)^2} v(0) = (P_0 + 2)(P_0 + 3) v(0) = 10,$$

$$P_0 u_1(0) = s_1 N^{(1)}(s_1) + N(s_1) = P_0(P_0 + 2)(P_0 + 3) v(0) = 0.$$

The latter two equations yield $N(s_1) = N'(s_1) = 10$. ▲

In mathematical terminology, Eq. (5–19) is a homogeneous linear differential equation. The general solution is called the *complementary function* and has the form (5–25), which can be written

$$v_c(t) = \sum_{k=1}^{n} c_k e^{s_k t}. \tag{5–32}$$

The zeros of $D(s)$ are called the *characteristic roots*. These are the poles of $V(s)$. Associated with each pole s_k is a *characteristic exponential* $e^{s_k t}$. The complementary function is thus a linear combination of all characteristic exponentials. The coefficients c_k depend on the specified initial conditions.

5–5 The nonhomogeneous equation. The nonhomogeneous equation is

$$\left(\frac{d^n}{dt^n} + a_{n-1}\frac{d^{n-1}}{dt^{n-1}} + \cdots + a_0\right)v_p(t) = f(t), \tag{5–33}$$

where $f(t)$ represents the forcing term in the physical system. Any solution of Eq. (5–33) is called a *particular integral*. To make the solution unique it can be specified that the initial values are

$$v_p^{(k)}(0) = 0, \qquad k = 0, 1, \ldots, n - 1. \tag{5–34}$$

Taking the Laplace transform of Eq. (5–33) yields

$$V_p(s) = \frac{F(s)}{D(s)}, \tag{5–35}$$

where $D(s)$ is defined by Eq. (5–22). The solution of Eq. (5–35) can be determined by the convolution theorem and is

$$v_p(t) = \int_0^t h(t - \tau)f(\tau)\,d\tau,$$

where

$$h(t) = \mathcal{L}^{-1}\left[\frac{1}{D(s)}\right]$$

is the impulse response of the system, i.e., the solution of (5–33) when $f(t) = \delta(t)$.

The initial-value theorem can be employed to verify the vanishing of the initial conditions (5–34). We have

$$v_p(0) = \lim_{s\to\infty} s\,\frac{F(s)}{D(s)} = \lim_{s\to\infty}\frac{f(0)}{s^n} = 0,$$

where the initial-value theorem has been used to introduce $f(0)$ into the numerator. Continuing, we have

$$v_p^{(1)}(0) = \lim_{s\to\infty} s\mathcal{L}\left[\frac{dv}{dt}\right] = \lim_{s\to\infty} s\,\frac{f(0)}{s^n} = 0,$$

$$\vdots$$

$$v_p^{(k)}(0) = \lim_{s\to\infty}\frac{s^k f(0)}{s^n} = 0, \qquad k < n,$$

and finally

$$v_p^{(n)}(0) = f(0).$$

The last result verifies that Eq. (5–33) is satisfied at $t = 0$.

The general solution of Eq. (5–33) consists of the sum of the complementary function and a particular integral:

$$v(t) = v_c(t) + v_p(t)$$

An interesting interpretation of the general solution is possible in terms of the poles of $V(s)$, which consist of the combined poles of $V_c(s)$ and $V_p(s)$. These poles are the characteristic roots of the system plus the additional poles due to $F(s)$.* Associated with each pole is an exponential, so that the general solution consists of a linear combination of all characteristic exponentials, i.e., the general solution has the form (5–32), with the summation extended to include the poles of $F(s)$. These exponentials can still be designated as characteristic exponentials, since they characterize the forced response of the system. A general response of the system can then be interpreted as an excitation of the characteristic exponentials due to the sudden application of the initial conditions and the forcing term at $t = 0$. The exponential term $c_k e^{s_k t}$ is the residue of $V(s)e^{st}$ at the pole $s = s_k$, which can be determined with the aid of the pole coefficient. The summation of all exponential terms yields the response. This is a restatement of the Heaviside expansion theorem (2–25).

---

* We restrict the discussion to that class of functions whose only singularities are poles.

PROBLEMS

5-1. Apply the initial-value theorem to $V(s)$ [see Eq. (5-20)] and prove that $v(t)$ has the prescribed initial values $v(0)$, $v^{(1)}(0)$, and $v^{(2)}(0)$.

5-2. Apply the initial-value theorem to $\mathcal{L}[\sin \omega t] = \omega/s^2 + \omega^2$ and determine the initial values of

$$\sin \omega t, \quad \frac{d \sin \omega t}{dt}, \quad \frac{d^2 \sin \omega t}{dt^2}, \quad \text{and} \quad \frac{d^3 \sin \omega t}{dt^3}.$$

5-3. Determine the solution of the differential equation

$$\left(\frac{d^4}{dt^4} + 3 \frac{d^3}{dt^3} + 3 \frac{d^2}{dt^2} + 3 \frac{d}{dt} + 2 \right) v(t) = f(t),$$

which satisfies the initial conditions $v(0) = 1$, $v^{(1)}(0) = -1$, $v^{(2)}(0) = 0$, $v^{(3)}(0) = 1$ if (a) $f(t) = 0$, (b) $f(t) = e^{-3t}$.

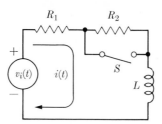

FIGURE 5-3

5-4. A voltage, $v_i(t) = 1$ volt, is applied to the network shown in Fig. 5-3. After the steady state is reached, the switch S is closed, short-circuiting the resistor R_2. Compute the current response $i(t)$.

5-5. Consider that the network shown in Fig. 3-13 [see Problem 3-7(b)] has reached the sinusoidal steady state, the input voltage being $v_i(t) = \sin \omega_n t$, where $\omega_n^2 LC = 1$. At $t = 0$, the input voltage is suddenly open-circuited. Compute the current response $i_2(t)$.

5-6. Consider Problem 3-5(b). After the sinusoidal steady state is reached, the input is suddenly short-circuited at $t = 0$. Compute the output-voltage response.

CHAPTER 6

FEEDBACK SYSTEMS

6-1 Introduction. Active networks are often designed to contain feedback paths. Examples of these have already been introduced in the discussion of operational amplifiers. A more general type of feedback system is shown in Fig. 6–1. The transfer functions for the networks in the forward and feedback paths are G and F, respectively. We then have the following relations:

$$E = V_i - FV_o, \quad \text{and} \quad V_o = GE,$$

from which we obtain the closed-loop transfer function

$$H = \frac{V_o}{V_i} = \frac{G}{1 + FG}. \tag{6-1}$$

A very important example of a feedback system is a feedback control system or *servosystem*. In this case, the output signal must follow the input signal very accurately. The difference,

$$\epsilon(t) = v_i(t) - v_o(t),$$

which is called the error signal, is to be kept small. In a servosystem a signal $v_o(t)$ is obtained from the output member by means of an electromechanical transducer and is subtracted from the input. The error signal is then amplified and drives a servomotor which moves the output member. In the majority of simple servosystems, $F = 1$.

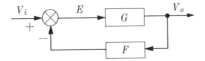

FIG. 6–1. A feedback system.

6-2 Stability. The response of a feedback system to applied initial conditions has the form (5–32), where $s_k = \sigma_k + j\omega_k$ are the poles of $H(s)$. If the system is to be stable, all the characteristic exponentials must be damped. This requires that $\sigma_k < 0$, i.e., all poles must be located in the left half of the s-plane. The poles of $H(s)$ are the zeros of $1 + GF$. Thus, if the system is to be stable, all roots of

$$R(s) = 1 + GF = 0 \tag{6-2}$$

must be located in the left half of the s-plane.

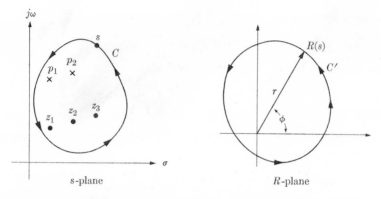

FIG. 6–2. The Nyquist stability condition $N = Z - P$.

We now discuss a theorem which can be used to determine whether this condition is fulfilled. Consider a closed path C in the s-plane (Fig. 6–2). The contour C is mapped by means of the analytic function $R(s)$ onto a contour C' in the R-plane. Within the contour C, $R(s)$ may have poles and zeros. The poles will be designated by p_k and their order by n_k, where $k = 1, 2, \ldots, u$. The zeros will be designated by z_k and their order by m_k, where $k = 1, 2, \ldots, v$. Let

$$P = \sum_{k=1}^{u} n_k \quad \text{and} \quad Z = \sum_{k=1}^{v} m_k$$

be the sum of the number of poles and zeros, respectively. It should be noted that a pole and zero of higher order are to be counted with the corresponding multiplicity. The theorem to be proved states that

$$N = Z - P, \tag{6–3}$$

where N is the number of mathematically positive revolutions made by the radius vector R in tracing through the contour C'.

The proof is established as follows. In the neighborhood of a zero z_k, $R(s)$ has the form

$$R(s) = (s - z_k)^{m_k} A_k(s),$$

where $A_k(z_k) \neq 0$. The logarithmic derivative,

$$\frac{d \ln R(s)}{ds} = \frac{m_k}{s - z_k} + \frac{1}{A_k} \frac{dA_k}{ds},$$

has a pole at $s = z_k$, and its residue is m_k.

In the neighborhood of a pole p_k, $R(s)$ has the form

$$R(s) = (s - p_k)^{-n_k} B_k(s),$$

where $B_k(p_k) \neq 0$. The logarithmic derivative,

$$\frac{d \ln R(s)}{ds} = \frac{-n_k}{s - p_k} + \frac{1}{B_k} \frac{dB_k}{ds},$$

has a pole at $s = p_k$ and its residue is $-n_k$. We now consider the integral

$$\frac{1}{2\pi j} \oint_C \frac{d \ln R(s)}{ds} = \frac{\Delta \ln R}{2\pi j} = \sum_{k=1}^{v} m_k + \sum_{k=1}^{u} -n_k. \qquad (6\text{-}4)$$

The extension to Cauchy's integral theorem (see Section 2–4) allows us to replace the contour C by a set of contours each of which encloses one pole. The contour integral around each pole can be evaluated with Cauchy's integral formula and yields the residue for the pole. The result is Eq. (6–4), which is the sum of the residues. The quantity $\Delta \ln R$ is the change that occurs in $\ln R$ in tracing through the contour C'. This can be determined by writing R in polar form as $R = re^{j\phi}$. We then obtain

$$\Delta \ln R = j2\pi N. \qquad (6\text{-}5)$$

Combining the results (6–4) and (6–5) yields Eq. (6–3).

The application of this theorem to the determination of the number of zeros of $R(s)$ in the right half of the s-plane is known as the *Nyquist criterion*. The contour C must now enclose the entire right half of the s-plane. If the system is to be stable, there must be no zeros of $R(s)$ within this contour, i.e., $Z = 0$, and thus

$$N = -P, \qquad (6\text{-}6)$$

where P is the number of poles of $R(s)$ within C. If the open-loop system is stable, GF will have no poles within C and therefore $P = 0$. In this case, the closed-loop system will be stable if $N = 0$. If $P > 0$, the open-loop system will be unstable. However, the closed-loop system can still be stable provided that the condition (6–6) is fulfilled.

EXAMPLE 1. Consider a system where $F = 1$ and

$$G(s) = \frac{K}{s(1 + T_1 s)(1 + T_2 s)}. \qquad (6\text{-}7)$$

The poles are at $s = 0$, $s = -1/T_1$, and $s = -1/T_2$. These poles can be taken outside the contour C as shown in Fig. 6–3. If $r_1 \to 0$ and $r_2 \to \infty$, the contour will enclose the entire right half of the s-plane as required. The

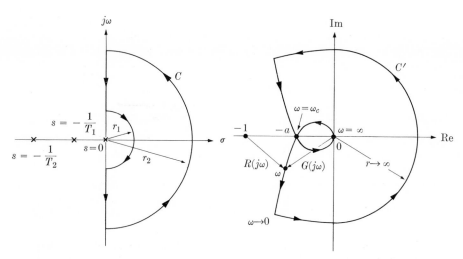

Fig. 6–3. A contour C enclosing the right half of the s-plane when $r_1 \to 0$ and $r_2 \to \infty$.

Fig. 6–4. Nyquist plot of $G(j\omega)$.

contour C is mapped onto the G-plane by means of $G(s)$ (see Fig. 6–4). The function $R(s)$ can then be obtained as indicated. It is evident from the plot that $N = 0$ if $a < 1$. The value of a can be obtained from Eq. (6–7) by substituting $s = j\omega_c$ and letting $G(j\omega_c) = -a$. This yields

$$\omega_c^2 T_1 T_2 = 1,$$

and

$$\frac{K}{\omega_c^2 (T_1 + T_2)} = a.$$

The closed-loop system is therefore stable if $K < (T_1 + T_2)/T_1 T_2$.

If $a > 1$, it is evident from the plot that $N = 2$. Hence there will be two zeros of $R(s)$ within C. This in turn means that there are two poles of $H(s)$ within C, and the system will be unstable. ▲

The value of N is obtained from the number of times that the contour C' encircles the point -1 in the G-plane.* This point is therefore referred to as the critical point, since the closed-loop transfer function has a pole on the $j\omega$-axis if C' passes through this point.

———————

* For physical reasons it is often more convenient to consider ω as increasing. The contour C' is then traced through in a clockwise sense. The theorem remains valid, provided that N is the number of clockwise revolutions of R.

6–3 Hurwitz polynomials. The transfer function of a network composed of lumped-parameter elements consists of the ratio of polynomials in s. In this case, the roots of Eq. (6–2) are determined by the zeros of a polynomial of the form

$$D(s) = a_n s^n + a_{n-1} s^{n-1} + \cdots + a_0, \qquad (6\text{--}8)$$

where all the coefficients a_k are real. For a stable system, all zeros must be in the left half of the s-plane. A polynomial having this property is known as a *Hurwitz polynomial*. To determine the conditions on the coefficients a_k which make $D(s)$ a Hurwitz polynomial, we consider the class of *positive real* (p.r.) functions, $F = F(s)$, which are defined by the conditions

$$F \text{ real for } s \text{ real} \qquad \text{and} \qquad \mathrm{Re}[F] > 0 \qquad \text{if} \quad \mathrm{Re}[s] > 0. \quad (6\text{--}9)$$

Evidently a p.r. function cannot have zeros in the right half of the s-plane, since the inequality (6–9) is no longer satisfied. We now prove several theorems dealing with p.r. functions.

THEOREM 1. If F is positive real, so is $1/F$.

Proof: Let $F = u + jv$. Since F is p.r., we have $\mathrm{Re}[F] = u > 0$ if $\mathrm{Re}[s] > 0$. It follows that

$$\mathrm{Re}\left[\frac{1}{F}\right] = \frac{u}{u^2 + v^2} > 0 \qquad \text{if} \qquad \mathrm{Re}[s] > 0.$$

A consequence of this theorem is that F can have no poles within the right half of the s-plane.

THEOREM 2. If F is a p.r. function which is odd, its poles are restricted to be on the $j\omega$-axis. These poles are simple and have real positive residues.

Proof: Due to its odd property, F can have no poles within the left half of the s-plane, since these would have to be accompanied by their negatives in the right half of the s-plane, which, according to Theorem 1, do not exist. For example, if F has a pole of order n at s_1, we must have n odd and

$$F = \frac{a_1}{(s - s_1)^n} + \frac{a_1}{(s + s_1)^n}$$

in order that $F(-s) = -F(s)$. Thus the poles of F are restricted to be on the $j\omega$-axis so that $s_1 = j\omega_1$. If $s \cong j\omega_1$, we have

$$F \cong \frac{a_1}{(s - j\omega_1)^n}.$$

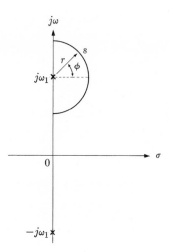

FIG. 6–5. s-plane poles of an odd positive-real function.

By substituting $s - j\omega_1 = re^{j\phi}$ (see Fig. 6–5) and using the fact that F is p.r., we obtain

$$\text{Re}[F] \cong \frac{a_1}{r^n} \cos n\phi > 0 \qquad \text{if} \qquad |\phi| < \frac{\pi}{2}.$$

This is possible only if $n = 1$ and if a_1 is real and positive. Since infinity is a point on the $j\omega$-axis, it follows that a pole at infinity must be simple and have a real positive residue.

THEOREM 3. An odd function F is positive real if its poles are restricted to be on the $j\omega$-axis and if these poles are simple with real positive residues.

Proof: If we include the possibility of a pole at infinity, F has the form

$$F = \sum_{k=1}^{n} c_k \left\{ \frac{1}{s - j\omega_k} + \frac{1}{s + j\omega_k} \right\} + c_0 s,$$

where the c_k's ($k = 0, 1, \ldots, n$) are real and positive. Using the substitutions $s = re^{j\phi}$, $s - j\omega_k = r_{k1}e^{j\phi_{k1}}$, $s + j\omega_k = r_{k2}e^{j\phi_{k2}}$, where

$$|\phi| < \frac{\pi}{2}, \qquad |\phi_{k1}| < \frac{\pi}{2}, \qquad |\phi_{k2}| < \frac{\pi}{2},$$

it can be seen that $\text{Re}[F] > 0$ if $\text{Re}[s] > 0$. The p.r. property of F then follows from the observation that F is real if s is real.

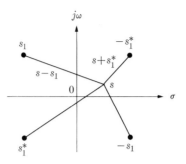

FIG. 6-6. s-plane zeros of a Hurwitz polynomial.

Let us consider now the polynomial (6-8) and suppose that it has two zeros s_1 and s_1^* (see Fig. 6-6). If $\text{Re}[s] > 0$, it is evident from the figure that

$$|s - s_1| > |s + s_1^*|. \tag{6-10}$$

Since $D(s) = (s - s_1)(s - s_1^*)$ and $D(-s) = (s + s_1)(s + s_1^*)$, it follows from (6-10) that

$$|D(s)| > |D(-s)| \quad \text{if} \quad \text{Re}[s] > 0. \tag{6-11}$$

The same inequality holds for the nth-order polynomial (6-8). This can be verified by considering the polynomial in factored form and showing that (6-10) holds for each of its factors.

We now consider the function

$$F = \frac{D(s) + D(-s)}{D(s) - D(-s)} = \frac{\text{even part of } D(s)}{\text{odd part of } D(s)}, \tag{6-12}$$

where the numerator and denominator consist of the even and odd powers of $D(s)$ respectively. It is seen that $F(-s) = -F(s)$ so that F is an odd function. Furthermore, if we set

$$\frac{D(s)}{D(-s)} = x + jy,$$

it follows from (6-11) that

$$\left| \frac{D(s)}{D(-s)} \right| = x^2 + y^2 > 1 \quad \text{if} \quad \text{Re}[s] > 0.$$

Using this inequality, we obtain from Eq. (6-12)

$$\text{Re}[F] = \frac{x^2 + y^2 - 1}{(x - 1)^2 + y^2} > 0 \quad \text{if} \quad \text{Re}[s] > 0.$$

Thus F is a p.r. function which is odd. From Theorem 2 it follows that its poles are restricted to be on the $j\omega$-axis and that these poles are simple with real positive residues. If n is even, it follows from Eq. (6–12) that

$$F = Z_1 = \frac{a_n s^n + a_{n-2} s^{n-2} + \cdots}{a_{n-1} s^{n-1} + a_{n-3} s^{n-3} + \cdots} = \frac{a_n}{a_{n-1}} s + Z_2. \qquad (6\text{–}13)$$

This is no restriction since, if n is odd we can take $Z_1 = 1/F$, which yields the same form as given by Eq. (6–13). Note that Z_1 is an odd p.r. function and has a simple pole at infinity. Theorem 2 requires that $a_n/a_{n-1} > 0$. It follows from Theorem 3 that the function Z_2, defined by (6–13), is positive real. Furthermore, $\lim_{s \to \infty} Z_2 = 0$ so that $Y_2 = 1/Z_2$ has a pole at infinity. We see that the function Y_2 has the same properties as the function Z_1 with the exception that both its numerator and denominator polynomials are one degree smaller. By continually removing the pole at infinity, we obtain a sequence of functions $Z_1, Y_2, Z_3, \ldots$ which have simple poles at infinity with real positive residues. Thus the condition that the function (6–8) be a Hurwitz polynomial, i.e., that the associated system be stable, leads to the condition that the sequence of poles at infinity be simple with real positive residues.* This is readily determined by successive divisions.

EXAMPLE 2(a). Consider the polynomial $D(s) = s^3 + s^2 + 4s + 2$. The function Z_1 is

$$Z_1 = \frac{s^3 + 4s}{s^2 + 2}.$$

Successive divisions yield

$$Z_1 = s + Z_2,$$

$$Y_2 = \frac{1}{Z_2} = \frac{s^2 + 2}{2s} = \frac{s}{2} + Y_3,$$

$$Z_3 = \frac{1}{Y_3} = s.$$

The poles at infinity are simple and the sequence of residues is 1, $\frac{1}{2}$, 1. Thus we have a Hurwitz polynomial. The functions $Z_1, Z_2, \ldots$ can be interpreted as the impedance functions of successive sections of a ladder network (see Fig. 6–7). If this ladder network is physically realizable with L- and C-elements alternating as shown, the function $D(s)$ is a Hurwitz polynomial. For the residues to be positive, it is essential that all the

---

* An equivalent criterion based on a sequence of determinants was derived by Routh and is referred to as the Routh-Hurwitz criterion.

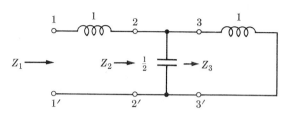

FIG. 6–7. The impedance functions Z_1, Z_2, Z_3 of an LC ladder network.

coefficients a_k have the same sign. If any coefficient is zero, not all the poles at infinity will be simple. In either case the system can be immediately judged to be unstable. ▲

EXAMPLE 2(b). If some of the zeros of $D(s)$ are on the $j\omega$-axis, then the division process will show up this fact by yielding, at some point, a zero remainder. Consider the polynomial

$$D(s) = (s^2 + 1)(s + 1)(s + 2) = s^4 + 3s^3 + 3s^2 + 3s + 2, \quad (6\text{–}14)$$

which gives

$$Z_1 = \frac{s^4 + 3s^2 + 2}{3s^3 + 3s}.$$

The successive divisions can be carried out by means of the following scheme:

$$
\begin{array}{r}
\frac{1}{3}s \\
3s^3 + 3s \,\overline{\big)\, s^4 + 3s^2 + 2} \\
\underline{s^4 + s^2} \qquad \frac{3}{2}s \\
2s^2 + 2 \,\overline{\big)\, 3s^3 + 3s} \\
\underline{3s^3 + 3s} \\
0 + 0
\end{array}
$$

The last step results in a zero remainder, which indicates the presence of zeros on the $j\omega$-axis. Note that these zeros are the zeros of the last divisor $2(s^2 + 1)$. This can be shown to be generally true. ▲

6–4 Gain and phase margins. The Nyquist criterion is of use in determining whether or not a system is stable. However, it gives no information about the degree of stability, which can only be obtained from a knowledge of the location of the zeros of $R(s)$. Equation (6–2), which determines these zeros, can be written in the alternative form

$$|F(s)G(s)| = 1 \qquad (6\text{–}15)$$

and

$$\arg \{F(s)G(s)\} = \pi + 2\pi n, \qquad (6\text{–}16)$$

where n is either zero or an integer. The real-frequency axis, $s = j\omega$, separates the region of stability (the left half of the s-plane) from the region of instability (the right half of the s-plane). If the two conditions (6–15) and (6–16) are satisfied for $s = j\omega_c$, the system can no longer be considered stable, since an undamped steady oscillation could result. A qualitative criterion for the degree of stability of a system can be obtained by specifying the degree to which one or the other of these conditions is not fulfilled on the $j\omega$-axis. If the phase condition is fulfilled at $s = j\omega_c$, we must have

$$|F(j\omega_c)G(j\omega_c)| = a < 1$$

to avoid having a zero of $R(s)$ on the $j\omega$-axis. The amount by which a is smaller than unity can be expressed on a decibel scale as

$$m = 20 \log_{10} \frac{1}{a} ;$$

this quantity is called the *gain margin*. For many feedback systems a gain margin of 10 db is considered sufficient for an adequate degree of stability.

If the magnitude condition is fulfilled at $s = j\omega_c$, we must have

$$|\arg \{F(j\omega_c)G(j\omega_c)\}| = \pi - \theta < \pi$$

to avoid satisfying the phase condition, which would lead to a zero of $R(s)$ on the $j\omega$-axis. Here θ is called the *phase margin*. A phase margin of 45° is considered sufficient for an adequate degree of stability in many feedback systems. Graphical methods for determining the gain and phase margins will be discussed in Section 6–6. It should be noted that these margins are of a qualitative nature only and cannot guarantee an adequate degree of stability in all systems. However, for many systems they are adequate and form a very convenient and simple design basis for feedback systems.

6–5 Error coefficients. It is evidently desirable to use the open-loop transfer function to obtain as much information as possible about the response characteristics of a feedback system. This approach eliminates the problem of obtaining the closed-loop transfer function and then evaluating the inverse Laplace transform. The criteria of phase and gain margins are qualitative means of attempting to achieve this objective. If we are interested in the steady-state response to particular kinds of inputs, the final-value theorem can be used to obtain quantitative results. This theorem, Eq. (5–7), applied to the error signal states that

$$\epsilon(\infty) = \lim_{s \to 0} sE(s),$$

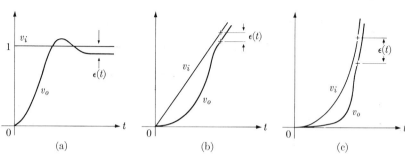

FIG. 6-8. Steady-state errors (a) position error, (b) velocity error, and (c) acceleration error.

where the error transform can be obtained from

$$E(s) = V_i(s) - \frac{FG}{1 + FG} V_i(s) = \frac{V_i(s)}{1 + FG}.$$

For a unit-step input we have $V_i = 1/s$ and

$$\epsilon(\infty) = \frac{1}{1 + K_p},$$

where

$$K_p = \lim_{s \to 0} FG$$

is defined to be the *position-error coefficient* [see Fig. 6-8(a)].

For a unit-ramp input, $v_i(t) = t$, we have $V_i = 1/s^2$ and

$$\epsilon(\infty) = \frac{1}{K_v}, \qquad (6\text{-}17)$$

where

$$K_v = \lim_{s \to 0} sFG$$

is defined to be the *velocity-error coefficient* [see Fig. 6-8(b)].

For an input of the form $v_i = \frac{1}{2}t^2$, we have $V_i = 1/s^3$ and

$$\epsilon(\infty) = \frac{1}{K_a},$$

where

$$K_a = \lim_{s \to 0} s^2 FG$$

is defined to be the *acceleration-error coefficient* (see Fig. 6-8(c)]. It is evident that these error coefficients may be extended to higher-order inputs. However, the higher-order error coefficients are seldom of any practical use and will not be discussed further. The steady-state errors for step, ramp, and acceleration inputs are referred to as position, velocity, and acceleration errors, respectively.

EXAMPLE 3(a). As an example of a system with a position error, consider an operational amplifier with a transfer function

$$G(s) = \frac{K}{(1 + T_1 s)(1 + T_2 s)(1 + T_3 s)} \qquad (6\text{–}18)$$

and take $F = 1$. The position-error coefficient is

$$\lim_{s \to 0} G(s) = K_p = K.$$

The physical significance of K_p is readily seen if we consider $v_i(t) = 1$ volt to be applied at the input of the closed-loop system. The steady-state error is $1/(1 + K_p)$ and the steady-state output is $K_p/(1 + K_p)$. If the error is to be kept small, it is evident that K_p must be very large. ▲

EXAMPLE 3(b). As an example of a system having zero position error, consider the transfer function

$$G(s) = \frac{K}{s(1 + T_1 s)}. \qquad (6\text{–}19)$$

For the position-error and the velocity-error coefficients we obtain $K_p = \infty$ and $K_v = K$, respectively. In Section 6–8 it will be seen that Eq. (6–19) is the transfer function of a simple amplifier driving a servomotor. If the input is a unit step, the error signal will drive the motor until the error is reduced to zero. If the input is a unit ramp, the steady-state error $1/K_v$ drives the motor and the steady-state output is $t - 1/K_v$. ▲

By modifying the transfer function (6–19) to the form

$$G(s) = \left(\frac{1}{s} + T_2 \right) \frac{K}{s(1 + T_1 s)} \qquad (6\text{–}20)$$

we obtain a system with zero velocity error. The acceleration-error coefficient is $K_a = K$. The physical significance of a system of this type can be seen by considering the response to a unit-ramp input where $V_i = 1/s^2$. The steady-state error is zero. However, using the final-value theorem, we find that the integral of the error is

$$\int_0^\infty \epsilon(t)\, dt = \lim_{s \to 0} s\, \frac{E(s)}{s} = \frac{1}{K},$$

and it is this signal that drives the motor. Note that this drive signal is the same as that discussed in Example 3(b), and the servomotor will run at the same rate. The factor, $(1/s + T_2)$, in Eq. (6–20) is the transfer function of a compensating network connected in cascade with the amplifier. The $(1/s)$-term in this factor represents an integration in the time domain. In the steady state the error is zero. However, the constant output of the integrator drives the servomotor at the required rate. The fact that there is no steady error can be seen by noting that this would be integrated to give an increasing drive signal for the servomotor.

6–6 Graphical methods. *The Nyquist locus.* When $s = j\omega$, the transfer function $G(s)$ represents the ordinary frequency response of the system, which can be written in polar form:

$$G(j\omega) = |G|e^{j\phi}. \qquad (6\text{–}21)$$

We now discuss suitable graphical representations for $G(j\omega)$, both for open-loop and closed-loop systems. As an example we consider $F = 1$ and

$$G(s) = \frac{K}{s(1 + T_1 s)(1 + T_2 s)}. \qquad (6\text{–}22)$$

The polar plot obtained by substituting $s = j\omega$ is called the *Nyquist locus*, which is shown in Fig. 6–9. The gain margin m and the phase margin θ can both be determined from this locus.

The locus for the closed-loop transfer function can be obtained from

$$H(s) = \frac{G(s)}{1 + G(s)} \qquad (6\text{–}23)$$

by noting that this equation is a bilinear transformation which maps the

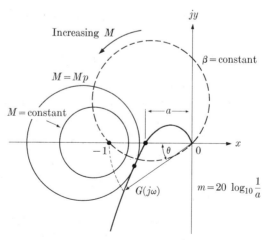

Fig. 6–9. The Nyquist locus in the $G(s)$-plane.

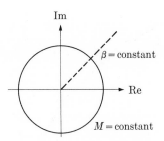

FIG. 6–10. The $H(s)$-plane.

G, or open-loop plane, onto H, the closed-loop plane. A bilinear transformation has the property of mapping circles in one plane onto circles in the other. If we set

$$H(j\omega) = Me^{j\beta}, \tag{6–24}$$

the families of circles, $M = $ constant, and $\beta = $ constant, will map onto circles in the G-plane. It should be noted that a straight line is considered to be a degenerate circle, i.e., a circle with an infinite radius. The family of circles, $\beta = $ constant, passes through the points $H = 0$ and $H = \infty$ (see Fig. 6–10). The corresponding points in the G-plane are $G = 0$ and $G = -1$. The equation for this family of circles can be obtained from Eqs. (6–21), (6–23), and (6–24) and is

$$(x + \tfrac{1}{2})^2 + \left(y - \frac{\cot\beta}{2}\right)^2 = \frac{1 + \cot^2\beta}{4}.$$

Due to the conformal nature of the mapping the circles $M = $ constant are orthogonal to the circles $\beta = $ constant. The equation for the M-circles can be shown to be

$$(x + \alpha)^2 + y^2 = \alpha(\alpha - 1),$$

where $\alpha = M^2/(M^2 - 1)$; M is called the *magnification* and the maximum value of M is the *peak magnification* M_p. This represents the resonant peak in the frequency response of the closed-loop system. From Fig. 6–9 we can see that small phase and gain margins indicate a large value of M_p. The degree of stability of the closed-loop system will then be small. Thus the value of M_p can be used as a qualitative measure of system stability.

The Bode diagram. The Bode diagram is a plot of $20 \log_{10} |G|$ and ϕ against $\log_{10} \omega$. The magnitude is expressed in terms of a decibel scale and the notation $|G| \text{ db} = 20 \log_{10} |G|$ will be adopted. For rapid plotting it is convenient to make use of asymptotic approximations. Where the poles and zeros are real, the transfer function contains factors of the type

$$F(s) = 1 + Ts.$$

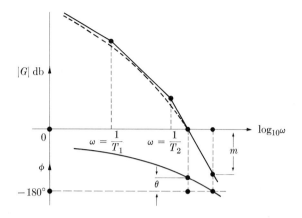

FIG. 6–11. The Bode diagram.

The asymptotic approximations for $s = j\omega$ are obtained by neglecting either ωT or 1, depending on whether $\omega T \ll 1$ or $\omega T \gg 1$. Thus

$$F(j\omega) \cong 1 \qquad \text{if} \qquad \omega \ll \frac{1}{T},$$

$$F(j\omega) \cong j\omega T \qquad \text{if} \qquad \omega \gg \frac{1}{T}.$$

When $\omega T = 1$, there is a transition from one extreme to the other. The frequency at which $\omega = 1/T$ is called a corner frequency. If we take Eq. (6–22) as an example, we have

$$|G| \text{ db} = \begin{cases} 20[\log_{10} K - \log_{10} \omega], & \omega < \frac{1}{T_1} < \frac{1}{T_2}, \\[2mm] 20[\log_{10} K - \log_{10} \omega - \log_{10} \omega T_1], & \frac{1}{T_1} < \omega < \frac{1}{T_2}, \\[2mm] 20[\log_{10} K - \log_{10} \omega - \log_{10} \omega T_1 \\ \qquad - \log_{10} \omega T_2], & \frac{1}{T_1} < \frac{1}{T_2} < \omega. \end{cases}$$

The plotting can be simplified by noting that these equations represent straight line segments intersecting at the corner frequencies and that an increase in ω of one octave yields a change in $20 \log_{10} \omega$ given by

$$20[\log_{10} 2\omega - \log_{10} \omega] = 20 \log_{10} 2 \cong 6 \text{ db/octave}.$$

Knowing the location of the corner frequencies and the slope of each line segment allows one to sketch the asymptotic Bode plot (see Fig. 6–11, where the exact plot is indicated by the dotted curve). The phase and gain margins can be obtained as shown.

The Nichols chart. The Nichols chart is based on the equation

$$Me^{j\beta} = \frac{|G|e^{j\phi}}{1 + |G|e^{j\phi}}.$$

(6-25)

Multiplying by $e^{-j\phi}$ and equating the imaginary parts of Eq. (6-25) yields

$$|G| = \frac{\sin(\phi - \beta)}{\sin \beta} = f_1(\phi, \beta).$$

(6-26)

The magnitude of (6-25) yields

$$|G| = -\alpha \cos \phi \pm \sqrt{\alpha^2 \cos^2 \phi - \alpha} = f_2(\phi, M).$$

(6-27)

The Nichols chart consists of plots of the two families of curves (6-26) and (6-27), considering β and M as parameters and using a decibel scale for $|G|$. By means of this chart, one can obtain the closed-loop frequency response from the Bode plot of the open-loop transfer function. The various qualitative measures of system stability, the gain margin m, the phase margin θ, and the peak magnification M_p, are easily determined from these plots (see Fig. 6-12). From the Bode plot the quantities $|G|$ db and ϕ are known as functions of ω. The locus of $G(j\omega)$ can then be plotted on the Nichols chart with ω as a parameter. The closed-loop parameters M and β can then be found as functions of ω. Note that the critical point is determined by $|G| = 1$ and $\phi = \pi + 2\pi n$. At this point the gain and phase margins vanish and M is infinite. If the gain of the open-loop system is increased, this results in an upward shift of the entire plot. The change in M_p, m, and θ, as well as the change in the frequency response characteristics of both the open-loop and closed-loop system, can then be found.

The root locus. The qualitative measures of system stability form a simple design basis for feedback systems. However, it is often desirable, or even necessary, to know the exact location of the *characteristic roots.* These are the values of s which simultaneously satisfy the magnitude condition (6-15) and the phase condition (6-16). The *root locus* consists of all values of s which satisfy the phase condition. Let us consider, for example, the transfer function (6-18). The root locus is determined by the values of s satisfying the condition

$$\arg \left\{ \left(s + \frac{1}{T_1} \right) \left(s + \frac{1}{T_2} \right) \left(s + \frac{1}{T_3} \right) \right\} = \pi + 2\pi n,$$

(6-28)

where n is either zero or an integer. The factors in (6-28) can be represented geometrically by vectors having phase angles ϕ_1, ϕ_2, and ϕ_3, re-

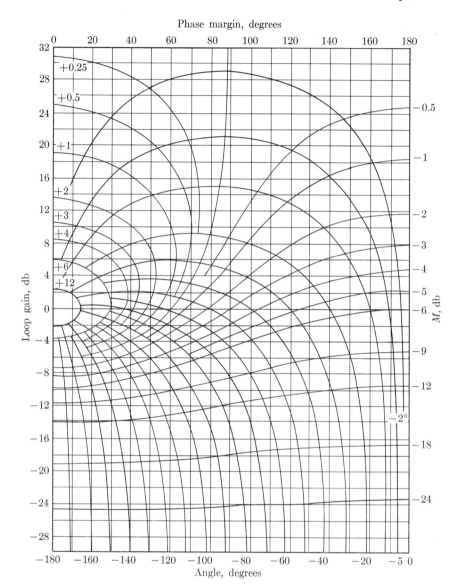

FIG. 6–12. The Nichols chart.

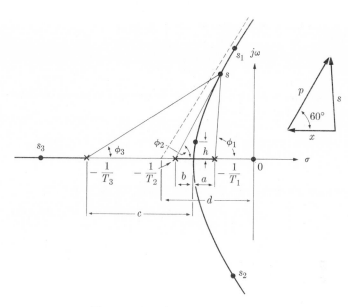

FIG. 6–13. The root-locus plot.

spectively (see Fig. 6–13). The condition (6–28) requires that

$$\phi_1 + \phi_2 + \phi_3 = \pi + 2\pi n. \tag{6–29}$$

For the segment of the real axis where

$$-\frac{1}{T_2} < \sigma < -\frac{1}{T_1},$$

we have $\phi_1 = \pi$, $\phi_2 = \phi_3 = 0$. Thus this segment forms part of the root locus where $n = 0$. For the segment of the real axis where

$$-\infty < \sigma < -\frac{1}{T_3},$$

we have $\phi_1 = \phi_2 = \phi_3 = \pi$. Thus this segment forms part of the root locus where $n = 1$. It is easily seen from (6–28) that the root locus has an asymptote for $s \to \infty$. This can be determined from the fact that we then have $\phi_1 = \phi_2 = \phi_3$. Thus $\phi_1 = \pi/3$ determines the direction of the asymptote. A further point of interest, that where the root locus breaks out into the complex plane from the real axis, can be determined in terms of the distances a, b, and c by considering an infinitesimal length of arc, h, along the locus. We have

$$(\pi - \phi_1)a = \phi_2 b = \phi_3 c = h.$$

The phase condition (6–29) yields, for $n = 0$,

$$\frac{1}{b} + \frac{1}{c} = \frac{1}{a}.$$

The intersection of the asymptote with the real axis can be obtained by substituting (see Fig. 6–13)

$$s = p + x,$$

where

$$\arg p^3 = \pi \tag{6–30}$$

into the phase condition (6–28) which yields, for $n = 0$,

$$\arg \left\{ p^3 \left(1 + \frac{x + 1/T_1}{p} \right) \left(1 + \frac{x + 1/T_2}{p} \right) \left(1 + \frac{x + 1/T_3}{p} \right) \right\} = \pi. \tag{6–31}$$

This equation can be written as

$$\arg \left\{ 1 + \frac{1}{p} \left[3x + \frac{1}{T_1} + \frac{1}{T_2} + \frac{1}{T_3} + O\left(\frac{1}{p}\right) \right] \right\} = 0, \tag{6–32}$$

where (6–30) has been used and where $O(p)$ indicates terms of the order of p. Equation (6–32) requires that the square bracket vanish. Thus

$$x = -\frac{1}{3}\left(\frac{1}{T_1} + \frac{1}{T_2} + \frac{1}{T_3} \right) - O\left(\frac{1}{p}\right).$$

Since $O(1/p) \to 0$ when $p \to \infty$, we obtain the result

$$\lim_{p \to \infty} x = d = -\frac{1}{3}\left(\frac{1}{T_1} + \frac{1}{T_2} + \frac{1}{T_3} \right),$$

which can be considered as the center of gravity of a system of unit masses located at the poles of $G(s)$.

The points on the root locus which satisfy the magnitude condition (6–15) determine the characteristic roots. This requires that

$$\frac{K}{r_1 r_2 r_3} = 1, \tag{6–33}$$

where r_1, r_2, and r_3 are the magnitudes of the factors in (6–18). If $K = 0$, (6–33) is satisfied for $r_1 = 0$, $r_2 = 0$, and $r_3 = 0$, that is, the characteristic roots are the poles of $G(s)$. If $K \to \infty$, we have $r_1 \to \infty$, $r_2 \to \infty$, $r_3 \to \infty$ and the characteristic roots approach the zeros of $G(s)$. With increasing gain K, the characteristic roots start at the poles and move out along the root locus to the zeros. For small K the three roots s_1, s_2, s_3

are all negative, real, and different. With increasing K the two roots s_1, s_2 become equal at the breakaway point. A further increase in gain moves s_1 and s_2 off the real axis and they become conjugate complex roots. The root s_3 remains negative real. When $K \geq K_m$, the roots s_1 and s_2 move into the right half of the s-plane. This value of gain is the maximum possible gain for a stable system.

The graphical methods discussed here are of great importance in the design and analysis of linear feedback systems. Special instruments have been developed for rapidly determining the required plots. A frequency-response slide rule is available to determine the Bode plot of complicated transfer functions.* The root locus can be obtained with the aid of a device called the *spirule* [1].

6–7 Compensating networks. By means of compensating networks the response properties of feedback systems can be modified. Let us consider, for example, the case of a high-gain d-c amplifier. For an uncompensated amplifier the required gain may lead to a small stability margin or even instability. A suitable interstage compensating network is shown in Fig. 6–14. The transfer function for this stage is

$$\frac{V_o}{V_g} = -g_m R_l G_c(s),$$

where

$$G_c(s) = \frac{1 + T_1 s}{1 + T_2 s} \tag{6–34}$$

and $T_1 = RC$, and $T_2 = (R + R_l)C$. The transfer function for the compensating network is considered to be $G_c(s)$, so that for the uncompensated system $G_c(s) = 1$. A Bode plot of $G_c(s)$ is shown in Fig. 6–15. Since the

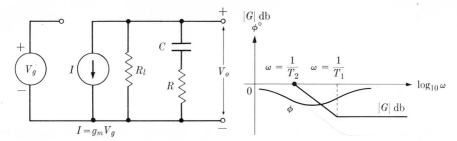

FIG. 6–14. An interstage compensating network.

FIG. 6–15. Bode plot for a lag network.

* *The Direct Reading Frequency Response Sliderule*, Boonshaft and Fuchs Inc., Huntingdon Valley, Pa., U.S.A.

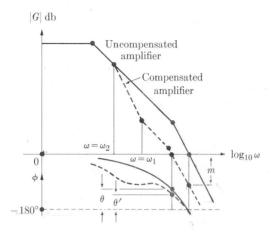

FIG. 6–16. Bode plot for a d-c operational amplifier.

phase shift of this network is negative, it is called a lag network. Figure 6–16 shows how a lag network can be used to stabilize a high-gain d-c amplifier. The uncompensated system is shown with zero gain and phase margin so that it would tend to oscillate. A lag network introduced into one of the amplifier stages will modify the plot in the manner indicated, increasing the gain and phase margins.

Lag networks are also used in servosystems to achieve a high gain at low frequencies. It was shown in Section (6–5) that a high zero-frequency gain is required to keep the velocity error small. In the discussion of (6–20) it was pointed out that a compensating network having a transfer function with a $(1/s)$-term, i.e., an integrator, gave a system with zero velocity error. The network represented by (6–34) will approximate an integrator if $|T_1s| \ll 1$ and $|T_2s| \gg 1$. A lag network is thus an integral-type network and can be used to reduce the velocity error.

The specifications on the performance of feedback systems are usually such that it is not possible to determine a unique design procedure. Trial and error methods are then very often convenient. The mid-band gain of feedback amplifiers or the velocity-error coefficient of servosystems are chosen to yield a sufficiently small error for the particular inputs considered. The gains required may lead to instability, making compensating networks essential.

A lag network will permit an increase in gain at low frequencies relative to the gain at high frequencies. For example, the lag network represented by (6–34) reduces the gain at high frequencies by a factor $T_1/T_2 = R/(R + R_l)$. This reduction in gain can result in stabilizing the system, and some convenient choice of this factor can be made. It is undesirable to have large time constants, since this can lead to a long settling time in

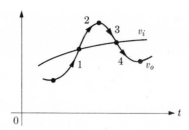

Fig. 6–17. Input and output signals.

response to transient inputs. On the other hand, T_1 and T_2 should not be too small, since the phase lag of this network decreases the available phase margin which would result from a simple overall decrease in gain. A compromise can be made by specifying the decrease in available phase margin that can be tolerated and choosing $T_1/T_2 > \frac{1}{10}$. Consideration must also be given to the effect of the network on the desired pass band. This is illustrated in Fig. 6–16, where θ is the available phase margin which results from a simple overall decrease in gain of m db, and θ' is the phase margin when a lag network is used to realize the gain reduction at high frequencies only.

Consider now Fig. 6–17, where v_i is the input signal, v_o the output signal, and where the error signal $\epsilon = v_i - v_o$ is to be kept small. For the four segments of arc shown, the error and error rate, $d\epsilon/dt$, have the following signs:

	ϵ	$d\epsilon/dt$	$|\epsilon_m|$
1	$+$	$-$	small
2	$-$	$-$	large
3	$-$	$+$	small
4	$+$	$+$	large

We consider the system to be driven by the error signal ϵ. Let ϵ_m be a modified drive signal by means of which an improved response is to be obtained. On arcs 1 and 3 the output is approaching the input as required. Thus a small drive signal ($|\epsilon_m| < |\epsilon|$) should be applied to avoid a large overshoot. On arcs 2 and 4 the output is moving away from the input. Thus a large drive signal ($|\epsilon_m| > |\epsilon|$) should be applied to bring the output to a rapid stop. A drive signal having the required properties is

$$\epsilon_m = \epsilon + a \frac{d\epsilon}{dt},$$

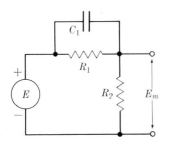

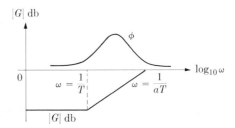

FIG. 6–18. A phase-lead network.   FIG. 6–19. Bode plot for a phase-lead network.

where $a > 0$ and the required transfer function is

$$\frac{E_m}{E} = 1 + as.$$

A network with this type of transfer function is called a derivative network. An approximation to this transfer function can be obtained with a passive RC-network of the type shown in Fig. 6–18, which has a transfer function

$$G_c(s) = a\,\frac{1 + Ts}{1 + aTs}, \tag{6–35}$$

where

$$T = R_1 C_1$$

and

$$a = \frac{R_2}{R_1 + R_2}.$$

The Bode plot for this network is shown in Fig. 6–19. Since the phase shift is always positive, the network is called a phase-lead network. If $a \ll 1$ then $G_c(s) \cong a(1 + Ts)$ and consequently a phase-lead network is a derivative-type network.

It can be shown that the maximum phase lead of (6–35), when $s = j\omega$, is determined by

$$\sin \phi_m = \frac{1 - a}{1 + a} \tag{6–36}$$

and the maximum occurs at $\omega_m = 1/T\sqrt{a}$. The maximum phase lead increases as a decreases, reaching an upper bound of 90° when $a = 0$. However, it is seen from (6–35) that a small value of a results in a small zero-frequency gain. In the case of a servosystem or d-c amplifier, this adversely affects the signal-to-noise ratio, since the transmission of high frequency noise is increased. A compromise between a large maximum phase lead and zero-frequency gain can be made by choosing $a > \frac{1}{10}$.

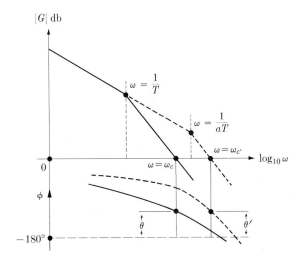

FIG. 6–20. System compensation with a phase-lead network.

After a has been fixed, there are numerous ways of determining T. Suppose that the uncompensated transfer function has a real pole at $s = -1/T_0$, which is the nearest pole to the origin. If the system is stable and a wide bandwidth is desired, we can choose $T = T_0$. This is known as pole-zero cancellation and results in replacing the pole at $s = -1/T$ by the pole at $s = -1/aT$, which would permit a more rapid system response. Figure 6–20 illustrates this for a servosystem where the amplifier gain has been increased by the factor $1/a$ to overcome the zero-frequency reduction of gain of the lead network. The zero-frequency gain of the compensated system remains, therefore, unchanged. The crossover angular frequency ω_c of the uncompensated system is increased to ω_c'. The phase and gain margins remain substantially the same. A higher crossover frequency means that the system bandwidth is increased so that the response for the high-frequency terms in the input signal is improved. Pole-zero cancellation is possible only if the system is sufficiently accurately represented by the transfer function used. If the system is marginally stable or unstable, the maximum phase lead is desired to improve the phase margin. In this case T should be chosen larger than T_0.

In RC-coupled amplifiers a lead network can be used for stabilization purposes at low frequencies where excessive phase lead can cause instability. Under these circumstances the phase condition for oscillation (6–16) requires that $n = 0$. A lead network can modify the phase and gain characteristics as illustrated in Fig. 6–21. Comparing this with Fig. 6–16 shows that the lead and lag networks complement each other and similar considerations are involved in determining the network parameters.

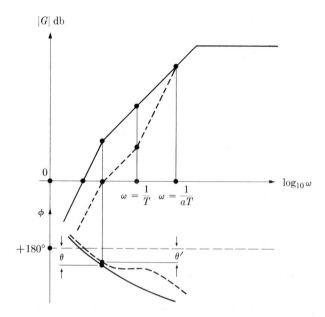

FIG. 6–21. Bode plot for an RC-coupled amplifier.

Simple lead and lag and combined lead-lag compensating networks are not adequate for all feedback systems. The interested reader is referred to the list of references at the end of the chapter for details concerning the design procedure and the discussion of more complex compensating networks.

6–8 The transfer functions of electromechanical components. The concept and physical significance of the term transfer function has been discussed in Chapter 1. The first step in the derivation of a transfer function is the determination of a suitable linear model of the actual system. This usually takes the form of linearized incremental equations about the operating point of the system. The linear model is further simplified by considering only those parameters which are significant over the frequency range of interest. It is important to note both of these points. Conclusions reached concerning system performance which are obtained from the linear model are no longer valid if the signals extend beyond the linear range of operation. Also, if the frequency range under consideration is extended, it is usually necessary to take additional parameters into account. An example is that of neglecting the effect of stray capacitances in the transfer functions of amplifiers at low frequencies. If a high gain is required over a wide bandwidth, it is essential to consider the effect of the stray capacitances in determining a suitable gain.

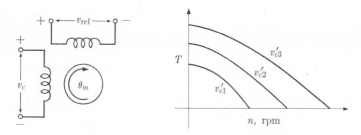

FIG. 6–22. Two-phase servomotor characteristics.

EXAMPLE 4.   Consider a two-phase a-c servomotor which is used in small instrument-type servosystems (see Fig. 6–22).   The dynamics of operation is determined by

$$J \frac{d^2\theta}{dt^2} + D \frac{d\theta}{dt} = T\left(v_c, \frac{d\theta}{dt}\right),$$

where

θ = motor shaft angle

J = moment of inertia

D = coefficient of mechanical viscous friction

$T\left(v_c, \dfrac{d\theta}{dt}\right) =$ motor torque due to the applied voltage v_c which is a carrier signal of the form

$$v_c = v'_c \sin \omega_c t. \tag{6–37}$$

The torque characteristics can be reasonably well approximated by a linear equation of the form

$$T\left(v_c, \frac{d\theta}{dt}\right) = av'_c - b \frac{d\theta}{dt}.$$

The transfer function is then

$$G(s) = \frac{\Theta(s)}{V'_c(s)} = \frac{a/(D+b)}{s(1+T_1 s)}, \tag{6–38}$$

where

$$T_1 = \frac{J}{D+b}.$$

The expression (6–38) is actually valid only at low frequencies.   At higher frequencies the effect of time delays associated with the rotor inductance and stray winding capacitance must be taken into account.   An example of an instrument-type servosystem is shown in Fig. 6–23.   The two-phase servomotor M drives the output shaft through a gear train having a ratio

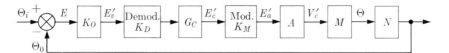

FIG. 6–23. Block diagram of an instrument-type servosystem.

N.　An electromechanical transducer converts the shaft angle into a
voltage. The voltage error transform is

$$E'_v(s) = K_0(\Theta_i(s) - \Theta_0(s)) = K_0 E(s),$$

where K_0 has the dimensions of volts per radian and represents the transducer gain. This error signal is usually in the form (6–37). If a compensation network is to be used, this should operate on the envelope $\epsilon'_v(t)$.
Suitable networks for this type of operation were briefly discussed in
Section 4–7. However, these require a very stable carrier frequency. If
the carrier is removed by means of a demodulator, the signal $K_D \epsilon'_v(t)$ is
obtained. A compensating network whose transfer function is $G_c(s)$ can
then be used, and the Laplace transform of the output signal is

$$E'_c(s) = K_D G_c(s) E'_v(s).$$

For convenience we consider G_c normalized so that $G_c(0) = 1$. A modula-
tor can be used to obtain

$$\epsilon_a(t) = \epsilon'_a(t) \sin \omega_c t = K_M \epsilon'_c(t) \sin \omega_c t,$$

which is a suitable signal for driving the servo-amplifier. Let $K_1 = K_D K_M$
be the gain associated with the demodulation-remodulation operation.
Then

$$E'_a = K_1 G_c E'_v = K_0 K_1 G_c E.$$

Suppose that the transfer function of the servomotor is

$$\frac{\Theta}{V'_c} = \frac{8.48}{s(1 + s/50)(1 + s/500)},$$

where θ is the motor shaft angle in radians and $v'_c(t)$ is the amplitude of the
control voltage. For a gear ratio of $N = 1/212$ we have

$$\frac{\Theta_0}{V'_o} = \frac{0.04}{s(1 + s/50)(1 + s/500)}.$$

The open-loop transfer function is

$$G(s) = \frac{\Theta_0}{E} = \frac{K_v G_c(s)}{s(1 + s/50)(1 + s/500)}, \tag{6–39}$$

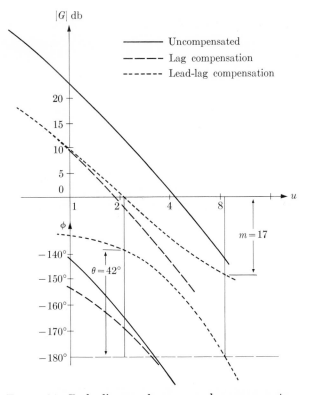

FIG. 6–24. Bode diagram for an open-loop servosystem.

where $K_v = 0.04\ K_0K_1A$ and A is the amplifier gain. Suppose that the velocity error is specified to be $\epsilon(\infty) = \frac{1}{10}°$ for a ramp input of 100°/sec. Since the velocity-error coefficient is K_v, we obtain with the aid of (6–17) (which applies for a unit-ramp input) $K_v = 1000$. By means of the substitution

$$s = 50p \qquad (6\text{--}40)$$

$G(s)$ takes the form

$$G[p] = G_c[p]\,\frac{20}{p(1 + p)(1 + 0.1p)}. \qquad (6\text{--}41)$$

For this choice of K_v, the uncompensated system is unstable (see Fig. 6–24). A suitable compensation network, shown in Fig. 6–25, is known as a lead-lag network, and its transfer function is

$$G_c(s) = \frac{(1 + T_1s)(1 + T_2s)}{1 + (T_1 + T_2 + T_3)s + T_1T_2s^2}, \qquad (6\text{--}42)$$

where $T_1 = R_1C_1$, $T_2 = R_2C_2$, $T_3 = R_1C_2$. If $T_1 = 0.01$, $T_2 = 0.08$,

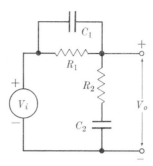

FIG. 6–25. Lead-lag compensating network.

$T_3 = 0.312$ and if the substitution (6–40) is used, the open-loop transfer function takes the form

$$G[p] = \frac{(1 + 4p)(1 + 0.5p)}{(1 + 20p)(1 + 0.1p)} \frac{20}{p(1 + p)(1 + 0.1p)}, \qquad (6\text{–}43)$$

and the closed-loop transfer function is

$$H[p] = \frac{100(2p^2 + 4.5p + 1)}{p^5 + 21.05p^4 + 121.1p^3 + 306p^2 + 455p + 100}. \qquad (6\text{–}44)$$

It should be noted that by suitable choice of time constants the transfer function (6–42) can be factored into a product of two transfer functions which represent a lead and a lag network, respectively. The lag network has a transfer function of the form

$$\frac{1 + a\tau_1 s}{1 + \tau_1 s},$$

where $a < 1$. To stabilize the system we can choose $a = \frac{1}{5}$. This decreases the high-frequency gain by a factor of 5 or 14 db, which results in a stable system. The time constant τ_1 is chosen so that the decrease in available phase margin does not exceed 6° (see Fig. 6–24). The transfer function of the lead network has the form

$$\frac{1 + \tau_2 s}{1 + a\tau_2 s}.$$

Suppose that the system bandwidth is judged to be adequate and an improvement in gain and phase margins is required. We choose $\tau_2 = 0.01$, which results in a slight increase in cross-over frequency and a considerable improvement in the gain and phase margins. The Bode and Nichols plots are shown in Figs. 6–24 and 6–26. It is seen that the peak magnification is $M_p = 1.45$ or 3.2 db and the phase and gain margins are 42° and 17 db, respectively. ▲

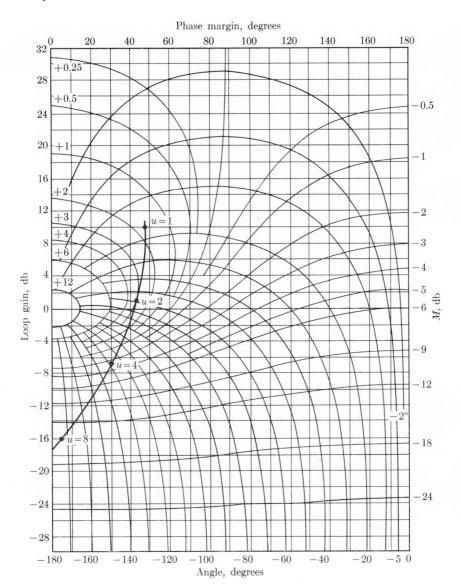

FIG. 6–26. Nichols plot for $G[p]$.

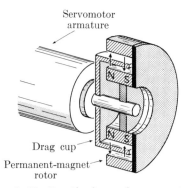

FIG. 6-27. Inertia-damped servomotor.

EXAMPLE 5. It is possible to design an electromechanical network having the transfer function of (6–43). This eliminates the necessity for the demodulation and remodulation operations of the previous example. The system to be discussed is known as an inertia-damped servomotor. The motor shaft is electromagnetically coupled to a permanent-magnet rotor (see Fig. 6–27). The torque equation for the servomotor now has the form

$$(J_m s^2 + D_m s)\Theta_m = aV_c' - D_r s(\Theta_m - \Theta_r), \qquad (6\text{–}45)$$

where the last term is due to the coupling. The relative angular velocity of the drag cup, which is attached to the servomotor armature causes induced currents to flow. These currents react back on the field to produce a retarding torque. The bearing friction for the rotor is very small, so that its equation of motion is

$$J_r s^2 \Theta_r = D_r s(\Theta_m - \Theta_r). \qquad (6\text{–}46)$$

By eliminating Θ_r from Eqs. (6–45) and (6–46), we obtain

$$\frac{\Theta_m}{V_c'} = \frac{a}{D_m} \frac{(1 + T_r s)}{s\{T_m T_r s^2 + [T_m + T_r(1 + D_r/D_m)] \cdot s + 1\}}, \qquad (6\text{–}47)$$

where

$$T_m = \frac{J_m}{D_m}, \qquad T_r = \frac{J_r}{D_r}.$$

The denominator term of (6–47) can be factored into the form $(1 + T_1 s)(1 + T_4 s)$, where

$$T_1 T_4 = T_m T_r, \qquad T_1 + T_4 = T_m + \left(1 + \frac{D_r}{D_m}\right)T_r. \qquad (6\text{–}48)$$

If $T_1 > T_4$, Eq. (6–48) yields

$$T_1 \cong \left(1 + \frac{D_r}{D_m}\right) T_r, \qquad T_4 \cong \frac{T_m}{1 + D_r/D_m}.$$

This will be the case if the motor parameters are chosen so that $T_2 = T_r > T_m = T_3$. If we let

$$G_m(s) = \frac{a}{D_m} \frac{1}{s(1 + T_3 s)}$$

be the transfer function of the motor with no inertia damping and let

$$G_c(s) = \frac{(1 + T_2 s)(1 + T_3 s)}{(1 + T_1 s)(1 + T_4 s)}$$

be the transfer function of the compensating network, Eq. (6–47) can be put into the form

$$G_c(s) G_m(s) = \frac{a}{D_m} \frac{(1 + T_2 s)}{s(1 + T_1 s)(1 + T_4 s)}.$$

The transfer function $G_c(s)$ has the same form as that for the lead-lag network as given in (6–42).

If A is the amplifier gain, so that $V_c' = AE$, where E is the error transform, the open-loop transfer function is

$$G(s) = \frac{K(1 + T_2 s)}{s(1 + T_1 s)(1 + T_4 s)},$$

where $K = Aa/D_m$. If we choose $K = 510$, $T_2 = 0.09804$, $T_1 = 0.5$, $T_4 = \frac{1}{98}$, and substitute $s = 10p$, we obtain

$$G[p] = \frac{100(0.9804p + 1)}{p(p + 0.2)(p + 9.8)}. \qquad (6\text{–}49)$$

The closed-loop transfer function is

$$H[p] = \frac{100(0.9804p + 1)}{p^3 + 10p^2 + 100p + 100}. \qquad (6\text{–}50)$$

The discussion of these transfer functions is left as an exercise (see Problem 6–10). ▲

For systems requiring large power amplification, rotary amplifiers are often used. The amplidyne (Fig. 6–28) illustrates the principles of this class of amplifier. There are essentially two independent stages of amplification in the amplidyne. The field winding of the first stage is excited by

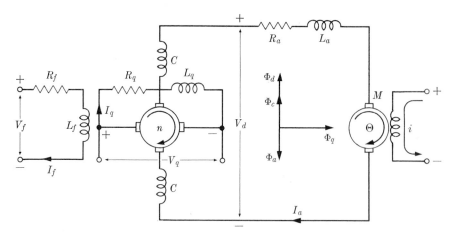

FIG. 6–28. Amplidyne and servomotor system.

the output of a low-power amplifier so that

$$V_f = K_a E = I_f R_f (1 + T_f s),$$ (6–51)

where

$$T_f = \frac{L_f}{R_f}$$

is the time constant of the field circuit, K_a is the amplifier gain, and E is the transform of the error signal driving the amplifier. The armature of the amplidyne is driven at a constant speed n by a separate drive motor. It is the available power from this drive motor which is controlled by the error signal. The field current i_f sets up a direct axis field flux ϕ_d. Thus

$$\Phi_d(s) = K_1 I_f(s).$$

Due to generator action, a voltage v_q is produced in the quadrature circuit so that

$$V_q(s) = K_2 n \Phi_d(s) = K_1 K_2 n I_f(s) = I_q R_q (1 + T_q s),$$ (6–52)

where

$$T_q = \frac{L_q}{R_q}$$

is the time constant of the quadrature circuit. The quadrature circuit is short circuited so that R_q is the resistance of the armature circuit as seen across the quadrature brushes. Since R_q is small, a large current i_q flows and sets up a large field flux ϕ_q along the quadrature axis. We have

$$\Phi_q(s) = K_3 I_q(s).$$ (6–53)

With the aid of Eqs. (6–51), (6–52), and (6–53), we obtain

$$\frac{\Phi_q}{E} = \frac{nK_1K_2K_3K_a}{R_qR_f} \frac{1}{(1 + T_fs)(1 + T_qs)}. \tag{6–54}$$

This transfer function represents the first stage of amplification. The second stage of amplification is due to the generator action between the armature and the large quadrature field flux ϕ_q. A large direct axis voltage v_d is generated causing the armature current i_a to flow. This provides the source of power for the servomotor M. We have

$$V_d(s) = nK_2\Phi_q(s) = I_aR_a(1 + T_as) + K_cs\Theta \tag{6–55}$$

where

$$T_a = \frac{L_a}{R_a}$$

and

$$(Js^2 + Ds)\Theta = K_MI_a. \tag{6–56}$$

In Eq. (6–55) the factor K_c arises due to the counter emf generated by the servomotor, J is the moment of inertia, and D the coefficient of mechanical viscous friction. In Eq. (6–56) it is assumed that the torque acting on the motor is proportional to the product of field flux and armature current. Since the field current is constant, the torque depends only on the armature current. Combining Eqs. (6–55) and (6–56), we obtain

$$\frac{\Theta}{\Phi_q} = \frac{K_MT_m}{R_aJ} \frac{nK_2}{s(1 + T_1s)(1 + T_2s)}, \tag{6–57}$$

where

$$T_m = \frac{J}{D + K_cK_m/R_a},$$

and $T_1T_2 = T_aT_m$, $T_1 + T_2 = T_m[1 + (D/J)T_a]$. If T_a is small, we have $T_1 \cong T_m$ and $T_2 \cong T_a$, so that T_1 is essentially the motor time constant, taking into account both the mechanical and electrical damping, and T_2 is essentially the armature circuit time constant.

The transfer function (6–57) represents the second stage of amplification. Combining Eqs. (6–54) and (6–57) yields

$$\frac{\Theta}{E} = \frac{K}{s(1 + T_fs)(1 + T_qs)(1 + T_1s)(1 + T_2s)}, \tag{6–58}$$

where

$$K = n^2 \frac{K_1K_2^2K_3K_aK_MT_m}{R_qR_f \cdot R_aJ}.$$

Equation (6–58) is the open-loop transfer function for the combined amplifier-amplidyne-servomotor system.

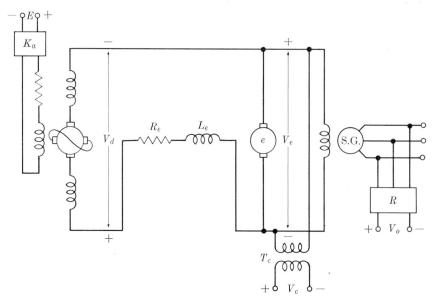

FIG. 6–29. Field excitation for a synchronous generator.

If the amplidyne is to drive an electrical network, the open-loop transfer function for the combined amplifier-amplidyne system up to the output voltage is of interest. This can be obtained from (6–54) and the first of Eqs. (6–55). Thus

$$\frac{V_d}{E} = \frac{K}{(1 + T_f s)(1 + T_q s)},$$ (6–59)

where

$$K = n^2 \frac{K_1 K_2^2 K_3 K_a}{R_q R_f}.$$

In the derivation of the transfer functions (6–58) and (6–59) it was assumed that the two stages of amplification could be considered independently. However, the armature current i_a sets up a flux ϕ_a in the armature opposing the original direct-axis field flux ϕ_d (Fig 6–28). To compensate for this, compensating windings C are wound on the stator. The current i_a sets up a flux ϕ_c in these windings which opposes ϕ_a. The amplidyne employs full compensation so that $\phi_a = \phi_c$. This usually results in L_a, and consequently T_a, being small. This can be seen by noting that the opposed winding sense of the compensating coils and armature windings results in a small inductance for this portion of the circuit. The inductance of the servomotor armature winding is also small. Thus, under these circumstances, it may be permissible to neglect $T_2 \cong T_a$ in (6–58).

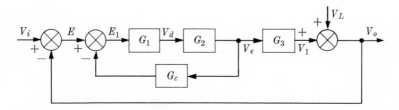

FIG. 6–30. Output voltage regulation of a synchronous generator.

EXAMPLE 6. Let us consider the application of an amplidyne to control the output voltage of a three-phase synchronous generator. Figure 6–29 shows the network connections. The exciter voltage aids the amplidyne output voltage in the exciter field circuit so that

$$V_e + V_d = (1 + T_e s) R_e I_e. \tag{6–60}$$

Due to generator action the exciter output voltage is proportional to the field current:

$$V_e = K_e I_e. \tag{6–61}$$

Combining Eqs. (6–60) and (6–61) yields

$$G_2 = \frac{V_e}{V_d} = \frac{1}{T_e} \frac{a}{b + s}, \tag{6–62}$$

where $a = K_e/R_e$ and $b = (1 - a)/T_e$. The transfer function for the amplifier-amplidyne system, given by Eq. (6–59), will be denoted by G_1. The transfer function for the synchronous generator, S.G., is

$$G_3 = \frac{V_o}{V_e} = \frac{K_3}{1 + T_3 s}.$$

It should be noted that v_o is obtained from the three-phase generator output by means of a rectifier R. A stabilizing transformer T_c is required, which has a transfer function

$$G_c = \frac{K_c s}{1 + T_c s}.$$

A block diagram of the closed-loop system is shown in Fig. 6–30, where v_i is the reference voltage and v_L represents the effect of a load disturbance. To determine the closed-loop transfer function, we have the following relations

$$\frac{V_e}{E_1} = \frac{V_d V_e}{E_1 V_d} = G_1 G_2 \quad \text{and} \quad \frac{V_e}{E} = \frac{G_1 G_2}{1 + G_1 G_2 G_c},$$

where Eq. (6–1) has been used with $G = G_1G_2$ and $F = G_c$. The open-loop transfer function $G = V_1/E$ is

$$G = \frac{G_1G_2G_3}{1 + G_i}$$

$$= \frac{K_{11}(1 + T_c s)}{s(1 + T_3 s)} \frac{1}{\{(1 + T_f s)(1 + T_q s)(1 + T_c s)[(b + s)/as] + K_{22}\}}, \tag{6–63}$$

where $K_{11} = KK_3/T_e$, $K_{22} = KK_c/T_e$ and

$$G_i = G_1G_2G_c = \left(\frac{as}{b + s}\right) \frac{K_{22}}{(1 + T_f s)(1 + T_q s)(1 + T_c s)}. \tag{6–64}$$

Since the system is a voltage regulator, the input is a fixed reference voltage. In this case we are interested in the system response due to load disturbances and the variables can then be taken to represent incremental deviations from a fixed operating point. Thus $V_i = 0$, and the closed-loop transfer function for load disturbances is

$$H_L = \frac{V_o}{V_L} = \frac{1}{1 + G}. \tag{6–65}$$

If the output voltage is to be relatively insensitive to load disturbances, it is essential that G be sufficiently large over the desired bandwidth. The system must be stable, and it is convenient to judge the stability in terms of the response to incremental inputs. The closed-loop transfer function to be considered is

$$H = \frac{V_o}{V_i} = \frac{G}{1 + G}.$$

Suppose that the choice $a = 1$ is made. This results in $b = 0$, which yields an infinite zero-frequency gain for the field circuit [see Eq. (6–62)]. If a sufficiently large value of K_{22} is chosen, the transfer function (6–63) takes the approximate form

$$G \simeq \frac{K_{11}(1 + T_c s)}{K_{22}s(1 + T_3 s)}$$

over a specified bandwidth. Thus it appears that by choosing K_{22} and T_c large, a very large gain K_{11} and phase margin are realizable. However, in this case, phase margin loses its significance. A large value of K_{22} will result in the inner loop, whose transfer function is $G_1G_2/(1 + G_i)$, being unstable. In this case G will have poles in the right half of the s-plane so that the stability criterion (6–3) must be used where $P > 0$.

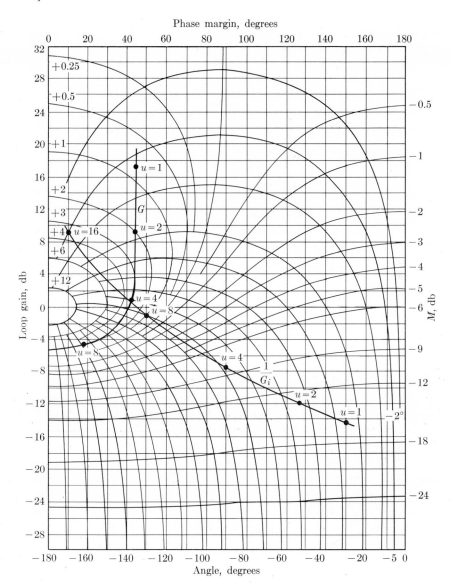

Fig. 6–31. Nichols plot for the functions G and G_i^{-1}.

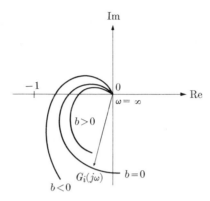

FIG. 6–32. Nyquist plots of $G_i(j\omega)$ with b as a parameter.

We will now discuss a design procedure based on the choice of a stable inner loop and $b = 0$. Suppose that the fixed values of the system parameters are $T_f = 0.04$, $T_q = 0.1$, $T_3 = 2$. By choosing $K_{22} = 5$ and $T_c = 0.4$, a stable inner loop results which has a phase margin of 45°. This completely determines G_i. The factor

$$\frac{1}{1 + G_i} = \frac{1/G_i}{1 + 1/G_i} \tag{6–66}$$

can be determined from a Nichols chart if we use $G = 1/G_i$. The value of $1/G_i$ is obtainable from a Bode plot of G_i by changing the sign of the log magnitude and phase angle. Figure 6–31 illustrates the Nichols plot. Note that since we are plotting $-\phi$, we must also change the sign of β and consider the β-values as $-\beta$. We see that the factor $1/(1 + G_i)$ results in a substantial phase lead which has a maximum of 75°. It is for this reason that the inner loop with the transformer feedback can be used as a compensating network. Once the factor (6–66) is known, the open-loop transfer function (6–63) can be plotted. Figure 6–31 shows the Nichols plot with $K_{11} = 100$ from which we obtain a peak magnification $M_p = 1.4$ or 3 db. The phase and gain margins are 40° and 5 db, respectively. These quantities serve as a means of judging the stability of the closed-loop. The closed-loop transfer function has the form

$$H[p] = \frac{10}{32} \frac{1 + 4p}{p^5 + 3.8p^4 + 3.563p^3 + 3.919p^2 + 1.438p + 0.3125}, \tag{6–67}$$

where the substitution $s = 10p$ has been used.

We will now discuss the choice $b = 0$ further. If b is small, the change in the Nyquist plot of G_i for nonzero ω is also small (see Fig. 6–32). Thus $N = 0$ for a range in values of b about $b = 0$. However, if $b < 0$, G_i has

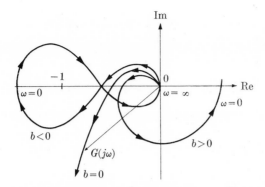

FIG. 6–32. Nyquist plots of $G(j\omega)$ with b as a parameter.

one pole in the right half of the s-plane [see Eq. (6–64)]. Thus, for this case, $Z = P = 1$. There is one zero of $1 + G_i$, and thus one pole of G in the right half of the s-plane.

The same result can be obtained by root-locus methods. We see that G_i has a zero at the origin and a pole at $s = -b$. The section of the real axis between this zero and pole is part of the root locus. If b is small, the root s_0 is small and can be found from Eq. (6–64). Thus

$$-1 = G_i \cong \frac{as_0}{b + s_0} K_{22},$$

which yields

$$s_0 \cong -\frac{b}{1 + aK_{22}}.$$

Since the pole and zero tend to cancel each other, the other roots are not appreciably affected.

Let us consider now the open-loop transfer function (6–63). It has been established that for $b < 0$, G has one pole in the right half of the s-plane. The open-loop system is then unstable. Figure 6–33 illustrates the Nyquist plots of G for different values of b. It is seen that if $b < 0$, $N = -1$. Thus $Z = N + P = (-1) + (1) = 0$ and the closed-loop system is stable. It is evident from this example that careful consideration must be given to the significance of phase and gain margins in the design of multiple loop feedback systems. ▲

EXAMPLE 7. A further example of the application of an amplidyne is in a positioning or tracking system. In the block diagram shown in Fig. 6–34, G_1 represents a filter used in the detection operation performed on the error signal. Its transfer function is taken to be

$$G_1 = \frac{K_d}{1 + T_d s}.$$

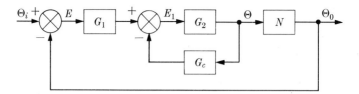

FIG. 6–34. A tracking system with amplidyne control.

The combined amplifier-amplidyne servomotor system is represented by

$$G_2 = \frac{K}{s(1 + T_f s)(1 + T_q s)(1 + T_1 s)}$$

[see (6–58)], where T_2 has been neglected. The compensating network consists of a tachometer attached to the servomotor shaft whose transfer function is

$$G_c = K_t s. \qquad (6\text{–}68)$$

The open-loop and closed-loop transfer functions are

$$G = \frac{\Theta_0}{E} = \frac{NG_1 G_2}{1 + G_2 G_c} \qquad (6\text{–}69)$$

and

$$H = \frac{\Theta_0}{\Theta_i} = \frac{NG_1 G_2}{1 + G_2 G_c + NG_1 G_2}, $$

respectively, where N is the gear ratio. The terms in the numerator and denominator of G and H can be found from

$$NG_1 G_2 = \frac{K_1}{s(1 + T_f s)(1 + T_q s)(1 + T_1 s)(1 + T_d s)} \qquad (6\text{–}70)$$

and

$$G_i = G_2 G_c = \frac{K_2}{(1 + T_f s)(1 + T_q s)(1 + T_1 s)}, \qquad (6\text{–}71)$$

respectively, where

$$K_1 = NK_d K, \qquad K_2 = K_t K.$$

Substituting the values

$$T_f = 0.002, \qquad K_1 = 320,$$
$$T_q = 0.02, \qquad K_2 = 30,$$
$$T_d = 0.04, \qquad T_1 = 0.25,$$

and using the substitution $s = 10p$ yields

$$H[p] = \frac{8000}{p^5 + 57.9p^4 + 410.5p^3 + 3780p^2 + 7750p + 8000} . \qquad (6\text{--}72)$$

The discussion of these transfer functions is left as an exercise (see Problems 6–13 and 6–14). ▲

PROBLEMS

6–1. Consider a feedback system where the open-loop transfer function is

$$G(s) = \frac{K}{s(1 + T_1 s)(1 + T_2 s)(1 + T_3 s)} .$$

(a) Show that the Nyquist plot approaches an asymptote for $\omega \to 0$. Determine d (see Fig. 6–35). (b) Determine the angular frequency ω_c at which $G(j\omega)$ crosses the real axis and find the condition on K for a stable closed-loop system.

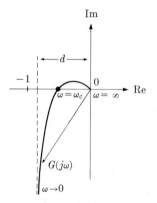

FIGURE 6–35

6–2. A feedback system has the open-loop transfer function

$$G(s) = \frac{K}{(1 + T_1 s)(1 + T_2 s)(1 + T_3 s)} .$$

(a) Sketch the Nyquist plot of $G(j\omega)$. (b) Determine the angular frequency ω_c at which $G(j\omega)$ crosses the negative real axis. Determine the condition on K for a stable closed-loop system.

6–3. Determine which of the following functions are Hurwitz polynomials.

(a) $s^6 + 3s^4 + 2s^3 + 8s^2 + 6s + 10$
(b) $s^3 + 3s^2 - s + 1$
(c) $s^4 + 4s^3 + 5s^2 + 8s + 6$
(d) $32s^5 + 120s^4 + 92s^3 + 120s^2 + 34s + 15$

6-4. In the discussion of Example 2(b) it was shown that the polynomial (6–14) has zeros on the $j\omega$-axis which were the zeros of the final divisor. Consider a polynomial which has the form $D(s) = D_1(s)D_2(s)$, where $D_1(s)$ is a Hurwitz polynomial and $D_2(s)$ has all its zeros on the $j\omega$-axis. Prove that the successive division process results in a zero remainder and that the final divisor has the form $cD_2(s)$, where c is a constant.

6-5. Consider a closed-loop transfer function of the form

$$H = \frac{G}{1 + G} = \frac{(1 + \tau_1 s)(1 + \tau_2 s) \cdots (1 + \tau_n s)}{(1 + T_1 s)(1 + T_2 s) \cdots (1 + T_m s)}$$

where G is the open-loop transfer function. Determine the integral of the error $I = \int_0^\infty \epsilon(t)\, dt$ for a unit-step input. [*Hint:* Determine the error transform in terms of G and the input and then apply the final-value theorem.]

6-6. Consider the closed-loop transfer function (6–1) and take $F = 1$. (a) If the position-error coefficient as defined by $K_p = \lim_{s \to 0} G(s)$ exists, use the Taylor series $H(s) = H(0) + H^{(1)}(0)s + H^{(2)}(0)(s^2/2) + \cdots$ to show that $H(0) = K_p/(1 + K_p)$. (b) If the velocity-error coefficient as defined by $K_v = \lim_{s \to 0} sG(s)$ exists, show that $H(0) = 1$ and $H^{(1)}(0) = -1/K_v$. (c) If the acceleration-error coefficient as defined by $K_a = \lim_{s \to 0} s^2 G(s)$ exists, show that $H(0) = 1$, $H^{(1)}(0) = 0$ and $H^{(2)}(0) = -2/K_a$. (d) By differentiating $H(s) = \mathcal{L}[h(t)]$ with respect to s prove that $(-1)^n H^{(n)}(0) = \int_0^\infty t^n h(t)\, dt$. Use this formula to show that

$$\frac{K_p}{1 + K_p} = \int_0^\infty h(t)\, dt, \qquad \frac{1}{K_v} = \int_0^\infty t h(t)\, dt, \qquad -\frac{2}{K_a} = \int_0^\infty t^2 h(t)\, dt.$$

These results show that a general definition of the error coefficients can be given in terms of $H^{(n)}(0)$, and that these coefficients are in turn related to the moments of the impulse response.

6-7. A feedback control system has the open-loop transfer function

$$G(s) = \frac{K}{s^2(1 + Ts)}.$$

Discuss the stability of the closed-loop system (a) by means of a Nyquist plot, (b) by means of a root-locus plot. Discuss the stabilizing effect of a lead-compensating network of the form

$$G_c(s) = \frac{1 + T_1 s}{1 + a T_1 s}.$$

6-8. The transfer function (6–35) is a bilinear transformation which maps circles in the s-plane onto circles in the G-plane. Use this fact to determine the Nyquist plot. Prove formula (6–36) for the maximum phase lead and show that $\omega_m = 1/T\sqrt{a}$.

6-9. The open-loop transfer function of a feedback system is

$$G(s) = \frac{42}{(1 + 2s)(1 + 0.1s)(1 + 0.05s)}.$$

Use a Bode plot to determine a lag-compensating network which yields a 10-db gain margin. A condition is imposed on the network by the requirement that the additional phase lag for $\omega \leq 0.2$ should not exceed 10°. Determine the phase margin. From a Nichols plot determine the closed-loop frequency response and the peak magnification. What is the steady-state error for a unit-step input?

6-10. From a Nyquist plot of (6-49) determine the phase margin for this system. Find the peak magnification and bandwidth from a Nichols plot.

6-11. The open-loop transfer function of an RC-coupled amplifier is represented by

$$G(s) = \frac{50Ks^3}{(1 + s/2)(1 + 10s)^2}.$$

(a) Determine the value of K which results in a 10-db gain margin. (b) It is desired to double the gain by means of a lead-compensating network. The gain margin is to remain unchanged and a condition is imposed on the lead network by the requirement that the additional phase lead is to be less than 10° for $\omega \geq 4$. Determine the compensating network parameters and the phase margin of the compensated system.

6-12. Consider Example 6 and the transfer function (6-65). Show that the steady-state output response due to a unit-step load disturbance is

$$v_o(\infty) = \frac{b}{b + aK_{11}}.$$

6-13. From a Bode plot of the inner-loop transfer function (6-71) determine the phase and gain margins for the closed inner loop. Determine the Bode plot of the factor $1/(1 + G_i)$ occurring in (6-69) by means of the Nichols chart. What is the maximum phase lead due to this factor? What are the gain and phase margins for the closed-loop system? Determine the steady-state error in degrees for a unit-ramp input of 10°/sec. Find the peak magnification and bandwidth from a Nichols plot.

6-14. Consider the tracking system discussed in Example 7. The transfer function (6-68) is modified to include a high-pass network so that

$$G_c(s) = \frac{Ts}{1 + Ts} K_t s.$$

Determine the improvement in steady-state tracking accuracy for ramp inputs. Discuss the considerations entering into a choice of the time constant T.

REFERENCE

1. W. R. EVANS, *Control-System Dynamics*, McGraw-Hill, New York, 1954.

GENERAL REFERENCES

D'AZZO, J. J., and C. H. HOUPIS, *Control System Analysis and Synthesis*, McGraw-Hill, New York, 1960.

GILLE, J. C., M. J. PELEGRIN, and P. DECAULNE, *Feedback Control Systems*, McGraw-Hill, New York, 1959.

KUO, B. C., *Automatic Control Systems*, Prentice-Hall, Englewood Cliffs, N.J., 1962.

THALER, G. J., and R. G. BROWN, *Analysis and Design of Feedback Control Systems*, McGraw-Hill, New York, 1960.

TRUXAL, J. G., *Control System Synthesis*, McGRAW-Hill, New York, 1955.

CHAPTER 7

THE NUMERICAL EVALUATION OF THE ZEROS AND VALUES OF POLYNOMIALS

7–1 Introduction. The determination of the poles of the transfer functions and response characteristics of closed-loop feedback systems usually involves solving for the zeros and the numerical values of polynomials of high order. This and the following chapter deal with a number of suitable numerical methods for problems of this kind.

7–2 The numerical values of polynomials. The numerical value of a polynomial can be determined by means of the *remainder theorem*. Let

$$F(x) = a_n x^n + a_{n-1} x^{n-1} + \cdots + a_0$$

be a polynomial of order n. If this polynomial is divided by a polynomial $D(x)$ of lower order, we obtain

$$F(x) = Q(x)D(x) + R(x), \tag{7-1}$$

where $Q(x)$ is the quotient and $R(x)$ the remainder. Consider the case where

$$D(x) = x - x_0$$

and x_0 is a real number. It follows from Eq. (7–1) that

$$F(x_0) = R(x_0) = R, \tag{7-2}$$

that is, the value $F(x_0)$ is the remainder R obtained by dividing $F(x)$ by $x - x_0$. For complex values, $x_0 = u + jv$, we choose

$$D(x) = (x - x_0)(x - x_0^*) = x^2 - 2ux + u^2 + v^2. \tag{7-3}$$

It follows from Eq. (7–1) that

$$F(u + jv) = R(u + jv), \tag{7-4}$$

that is, the value $F(u + jv)$ is obtained by dividing $F(x)$ by (7–3) and substituting $u + jv$ in the remainder, which is a linear function of x. The results (7–2) and (7–4) are referred to as the remainder theorem.

The division can be accomplished by a long-division process:

$$
\begin{array}{r}
a_n x^{n-1} + \cdots + a_1 \qquad\qquad = Q(x) \\
D(x) = x - x_0 \overline{)\ a_n x^n + a_{n-1} x^{n-1} + \cdots + a_0} = F(x) \\
\underline{a_n x^n - a_n x_0 x^{n-1}\qquad\qquad} \\
a'_{n-1} x^{n-1} + \cdots + a_0 \\
\cdots \\
\overline{a'_1 x + a_0} \\
\underline{a'_1 x - a'_1 x_0} \\
a_0 + a'_1 x_0 = R
\end{array}
$$

A simpler arrangement is that of synthetic division:

$$
\begin{array}{cccccc}
F(x) = a_n & a_{n-1} & a_{n-2} & \cdots & a_0 & \big| x_0 \\
& a_n x_0 & a'_{n-1} x_0 & \cdots & a'_1 x_0 & \\
\hline
Q(x) = a_n & a'_{n-1} & a'_{n-2} & \cdots & | a_0 + a'_1 x_0 = R &
\end{array}
$$

where $a'_{k-1} = a_{k-1} + a'_k x_0$ and $a'_n = a_n$.

The coefficients obtained by synthetic division are the same as those obtained by long division. However, synthetic division is more convenient for numerical work. In the case of a quadratic divisor (7–3), the long-division method must be used. Some simplification can be obtained by not explicitly writing down the powers of x, since these are implied by the position of the coefficients.

EXAMPLE 1. Consider

$$F(x) = x^3 - 2x^2 + x + 1,$$

and suppose that the value $F(2)$ is to be found. We have

$$
\begin{array}{ccccc}
F(x) = 1 & -2 & 1 & 1 & \big| 2 = x_0 \\
& 2 & 0 & 2 & \\
\hline
Q(x) = 1 & 0 & 1 & | \ 3 = R &
\end{array}
$$

The result is $F(2) = R = 3$. Suppose now that the value $F(1 + j2)$ is to be found. The divisor (7–3) is $D(x) = x^2 - 2x + 5$, and the division process yields

$$
\begin{array}{r}
1 \quad\ 0 \qquad\qquad\qquad = Q(x) \\
D(x) = 1 \quad -2 \quad 5 \ \overline{)\ 1 \quad -2 \quad\ 1 \quad\ 1} = F(x) \\
\underline{1 \quad -2 \quad\ 5 \qquad\quad} \\
0 \quad -4 \quad\ 1 = R(x)
\end{array}
$$

Thus $R(x) = -4x + 1$, and the remainder theorem yields

$$F(1 + j2) = R(1 + j2) = -3 - j8. \blacktriangle$$

7-3 The zeros of polynomials: Newton's method. A suitable method for determining the real zeros of a function is *Newton's method*. Consider the situation shown in Fig. 7-1, where y_0 is a zero of $F(x)$, and where x_0 is an approximate zero. The slope at x_0 is $F'(x_0)$. Extending the tangent at P_0 to the x-axis determines the point

$$x_1 = x_0 - \frac{F(x_0)}{F'(x_0)}, \tag{7-5}$$

which is a better approximation to y_0. The process is now repeated using x_1. If the sequence of values $x_0, x_1, \ldots$ converges, it will yield y_0.

EXAMPLE 2. Consider the polynomial

$$F(x) = x^3 + 10x^2 + 7x + 5, \tag{7-6}$$

where $F'(x) = 3x^2 + 20x + 7$. The remainder theorem can be used to obtain both $F(x)$ and $F'(x)$. As a first trial take $x_0 = -9$. Thus

$$
\begin{array}{llll|l}
F(x) = 1 & 10 & 7 & 5 & \underline{-9 = x_0} \\
 & -9 & -9 & 18 & \\
\hline
Q(x) = 1 & 1 & -2 & \;| \;23 = F(-9) \\
\end{array}
$$

$$
\begin{array}{lll|l}
F'(x) = 3 & 20 & 7 & \underline{-9} \\
 & -27 & 63 & \\
\hline
3 & -7 & \;|\; 70 = F'(-9) \\
\end{array}
$$

Substituting into Eq. (7-5) yields $x_1 = -9 - \frac{23}{70} \cong -9.33$. The process is now repeated using this as an improved approximation. After the fourth

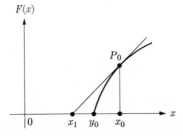

FIG. 7-1. Newton's method.

trial, we obtain $x_4 = -9.3055$ and

$$
\begin{array}{ccccc}
F(x) = 1 & 10 & 7 & 5 & \underline{|-9.3055} \\
 & -9.3055 & -6.46267 & -4.9998 & \\
\hline
Q(x) = 1 & 0.6945 & 0.5373 & \ 0.0002 = R
\end{array}
$$

The remainder is very small. The polynomial (7–6) can now be written in factored form:

$$
F(x) = (x + 9.3055)(x^2 + 0.6945x + 0.5373). \ \blacktriangle \qquad (7\text{--}7)
$$

7–4 Graeffe's root-squaring method. If $r_1, r_2, \ldots, r_n$ are the n roots of the equation

$$
F(x) = x^n + a_{n-1}x^{n-1} + \cdots + a_0 = 0, \qquad (7\text{--}8)
$$

we can write $F(x)$ in the factored form

$$
F(x) = (x - r_1)(x - r_2) \cdots (x - r_n). \qquad (7\text{--}9)
$$

Comparison of the coefficients of like powers of x in (7–8) and (7–9) yields

$$
-a_{n-1} = r_1 + r_2 + \cdots + r_n
$$

$$
a_{n-2} = r_1 r_2 + r_1 r_3 + \cdots + r_{n-1} r_n \qquad (7\text{--}10)
$$

$$
\vdots
$$

$$
(-1)^n a_0 = r_1 r_2 \ldots r_n.
$$

The right-hand sides of these expressions are easily remembered by noting that they are, respectively, the sum of the roots taken one at a time, the sum of the products of the roots taken two at a time, etc. *Graeffe's method* is based on transforming the polynomial (7–9) so that it becomes possible to use (7–10) to determine the roots. The transformations consist of a succession of steps, each of which yields a polynomial whose zeros are the squares of the zeros of the preceding polynomial. Let us consider the product

$$
F(x)F(-x)
$$
$$
= (x - r_1)(x - r_2) \cdots (x - r_n)(-x - r_1)(-x - r_2) \cdots (-x - r_n)
$$
$$
= (-1)^n(x^2 - r_1^2)(x^2 - r_2^2) \cdots (x^2 - r_n^2) = F_1(x^2).
$$

After substituting x for x^2 the product $F_1(x)F_1(-x)$ is formed to yield a polynomial $F_2(x^2)$. After repeating this process k times, we obtain

$$
(-1)^{nk}F_k(x) = (x - r_1^N)(x - r_2^N) \cdots (x - r_n^N)
$$
$$
= x^n - b_{n-1}x^{n-1} + b_{n-2}x^{n-2} + \cdots + (-1)^n b_0, \qquad (7\text{--}11)
$$

where $N = 2^k$.

Suppose now that the roots are real and that

$$|r_1| > |r_2| > \cdots > |r_n|.$$

By choosing a large N, we have

$$|r_1^N| \gg |r_2^N| \gg \cdots \gg |r_n^N|. \tag{7-12}$$

The relations (7–10) can now be applied to the polynomial (7–11). With the aid of (7–12) we obtain

$$b_{n-1} = r_1^N + \cdots + r_n^N \cong r_1^N$$

$$b_{n-2} \cong r_1^N r_2^N$$

$$\vdots$$

$$b_0 = r_1^N r_2^N \ldots r_n^N. \tag{7-13}$$

By taking the ratios of these quantities and using logarithms, the magnitudes of the roots can be found:

$$\log |r_1| \cong \frac{1}{N} \log b_{n-1}$$

$$\log |r_2| \cong \frac{1}{N} \log \frac{b_{n-2}}{b_{n-1}}$$

$$\vdots$$

$$\log |r_n| \cong \frac{1}{N} \log \frac{b_0}{b_1}.$$

When the coefficients start to obey a square-law it is an indication that the approximations (7–13) are valid and the root-squaring process can be terminated. This also indicates that the roots are all real and different.

Graeffe's method may also be applied when the roots are complex. In this case the coefficients obtained by the root-squaring process will not all obey a simple square law. Let us consider the case of a fifth-degree polynomial

$$F(x) = (x - r_1)(x - r_2 e^{j\phi_2})(x - r_2 e^{-j\phi_2})(x - r_3 e^{j\phi_3})(x - r_3 e^{-j\phi_3})$$

$$= x^5 + a_4 x^4 + \cdots + a_0 \tag{7-14}$$

and assume that

$$|r_1| > |r_2| > |r_3|. \tag{7-15}$$

The root-squaring process yields

$$(-1)^{nk} F_k(x)$$

$$= (x - r_1^N)(x - r_2^N e^{jN\phi_2})(x - r_2^N e^{-jN\phi_2})(x - r_3^N e^{jN\phi_3})(x - r_3^N e^{-jN\phi_3})$$

$$= x^5 - b_4 x^4 + b_3 x^3 - b_2 x^2 + b_1 x - b_0.$$

With the aid of the relations (7–10) and the conditions (7–15), we obtain

$$b_4 \cong r_1^N,$$

$$b_3 \cong r_1^N r_2^N e^{jN\phi_2} + r_1^N r_2^N e^{-jN\phi_2} = 2r_1^N r_2^N \cos N\phi_2,$$

$$b_2 \cong r_1^N r_2^N r_2^N = r_1^N (r_2^2)^N,$$

$$b_1 \cong 2r_1^N (r_2^2)^N r_3^N \cos N\phi_3,$$

$$b_0 = r_1^N (r_2^2)^N (r_3^2)^N.$$

Note that the coefficients b_0, b_2, and b_4 obey a simple square law. However, due to the cosine term, the coefficients b_1 and b_3 fluctuate in an apparently random manner. This behavior indicates the presence of complex roots, and the coefficients b_0, b_2, and b_4 can be used to determine the magnitudes:

$$\log |r_1| \cong \frac{1}{N} \log b_4,$$

$$\log r_2^2 \cong \frac{1}{N} \log \frac{b_2}{b_4}, \qquad (7\text{–}16)$$

$$\log r_3^2 \cong \frac{1}{N} \log \frac{b_0}{b_2}.$$

To determine the real and imaginary parts of the complex roots, we let

$$r_k e^{j\phi_k} = u_k + jv_k, \qquad k = 2, 3.$$

Equating the coefficients of x^4 and x of the two polynomial forms given by (7–14) yields

$$a_4 = -r_1 - 2u_2 - 2u_3,$$

$$a_1 = r_2^2 r_3^2 + 2r_1 r_2^2 u_3 + 2r_1 r_3^2 u_2, \qquad (7\text{–}17)$$

where the latter term is the sum of the products of the roots taken four at a time.

The linear equations (7–17) can be solved for the unknowns u_2 and u_3. Since the magnitudes of the roots are known, v_2 and v_3 can be easily found. It is evident from this discussion that Graeffe's method becomes difficult to apply when there are more than two pairs of complex roots. Alternative methods, such as Lin's method, should be used in these cases to factor the polynomial into simpler polynomials.

EXAMPLE 3. Consider the polynomial (7–6). Table 7–1 shows the root-squaring process. It should be noted that after the third step, the coefficient b_2 obeys a square law, indicating the presence of a real root. The coefficient b_1 fluctuates, indicating that the smaller roots are conjugate

TABLE 7–1

$F(x)$	1	10	7	5
$F(-x)$	-1	10	-7	5
	-1	100	-49	25
		-14	100	
$-F_1(x)$	-1	86	51	25
$-F_1(-x)$	1	86	-51	25
	-1	7396	-2601	625
		102	4300	
$F_2(x)$	-1	$7.498 \cdot 10^3$	$1.699 \cdot 10^3$	$6.25 \cdot 10^2$
$F_2(-x)$	1	$7.498 \cdot 10^3$	$-1.699 \cdot 10^3$	$6.25 \cdot 10^2$
	-1	$5.622 \cdot 10^7$	$-2.8866 \cdot 10^6$	$3.90625 \cdot 10^5$
		$0.0003 \cdot 10^7$	$9.3725 \cdot 10^6$	
$-F_3(x)$	-1	$5.6223 \cdot 10^7$	$6.4859 \cdot 10^6$	$3.90625 \cdot 10^5$

$$b_2 = 5.6223 \cdot 10^7 \qquad \log_{10}|r_1| = 0.96874 = \tfrac{1}{8}\log_{10} b_2$$

$$b_1 = 6.4859 \cdot 10^6 \qquad \log_{10} r_2^2 = -0.26977 = \tfrac{1}{8}\log_{10}\frac{b_0}{b_2}$$

$$b_0 = 3.90625 \cdot 10^5$$

$$k = 3$$
$$N = 8$$

complex. Thus equations of the form (7–16) apply, and we find

$$|r_1| = 9.3055, \qquad r_2^2 = 0.5374. \tag{7–18}$$

Since the coefficients of $F(x)$ are all positive, it is evident that r_1 must be negative. The real and imaginary parts of the root $r_2 e^{j\phi_2}$ can be found by considering the coefficient of x^2 which yields

$$10 = -(r_1 + 2u_2). \tag{7–19}$$

From (7–18) and (7–19), we obtain

$$u_2 = -0.3472, \qquad v_2 = 0.6455. \; \blacktriangle$$

In Graeffe's method, the manner in which the coefficients behave in the root-squaring process indicates the nature of the roots. It is best to keep the relations (7–10), upon which Graeffe's method depends, in mind. These relations and the behavior of the coefficients can be used to determine the nature of the roots. If, for example, the two largest roots are real and equal, it follows from (7–10) that the coefficient of x^{n-1} will eventually begin to double itself in the root-squaring process.

7–5 Lin's method. If x is small, the highest powers of x in (7–8) can be neglected so that

$$F(x) \cong a_2 x^2 + a_1 x + a_0.$$

The zeros of the quadratic expression

$$D_0(x) = x^2 + \frac{a_1}{a_2} x + \frac{a_0}{a_2}$$

can be easily found, and provided that they are small, will approximate the zeros of $F(x)$. *Lin's method* is a systematic means of obtaining more accurate quadratic factors of $F(x)$ starting with $D_0(x)$ as a zero-order approximation. If $D_0(x)$ is an exact quadratic factor of $F(x)$, there will be no remainder in the division of $F(x)$ by $D_0(x)$. This division process provides a means of obtaining a sequence of quadratic divisors $D_k(x)$. The polynomial $F(x)$ is divided by $D_k(x)$ to yield a quotient $Q_k(x)$ and a remainder $R_k(x)$. The remainder is obtained in the last step of the long-division process by a subtraction of the form

$$R_k(x) = c_2 x^2 + c_1 x + c_0 - c_2 D_k(x).$$

The quadratic expression

$$D_{k+1}(x) = x^2 + \frac{c_1}{c_2} x + \frac{c_0}{c_2}$$

is then chosen as a new divisor. The process is continued until the remainder is negligible.

EXAMPLE 4. As an example of Lin's method, consider once more the polynomial (7–6). The zero-order quadratic divisor is

$$D_0(x) = x^2 + \tfrac{7}{10}x + \tfrac{5}{10},$$

and the division process yields

		1	9.3		$= Q_0(x)$
$D_0(x) = 1$	0.7	0.5)1	10	7	5 $= F(x)$
		1	0.7	0.5	
			9.3	6.5	5 $= 9.3D_1(x)$

The new quadratic divisor is

$$D_1(x) = x^2 + \frac{6.5}{9.3} x + \frac{5}{9.3}$$

$$= x^2 + 0.6989x + 0.5376.$$

The process is now repeated, and after the third step yields

$$
\begin{array}{l}
1 \quad\ 9.3055 = Q_3(x) \\
D_3(x) = 1 \quad 0.6945 \quad 0.5373\,)1 \quad 10 7 5 = F(x) \\
\underline{1 \quad\ \ 0.6945 \quad 0.5373} \\
 9.3055 \quad 6.4627 \quad 5 = 9.3055 D_4(x) \\
 \underline{9.3055 \quad 6.4627 \quad 4.9998} \\
 0.0002 = R_4(x)
\end{array}
$$

The remainder is negligible; thus $F(x) = Q_3(x)D_3(x)$, which is the same as (7–7). ▲

Newton's, Graeffe's, and Lin's methods are suitable for obtaining roots with the aid of a hand calculator. However, these methods may not always yield convergent solutions. The problem of convergence and alternative root-finding methods are discussed in books on numerical methods.*

7–6 The root-locus method. Suppose that a polynomial $F(s)$ can be written in the form

$$F(s) = N(s) + D(s),$$

where the zeros of $N(s)$ and $D(s)$ are known. The zeros of $F(s)$ can then be determined by considering

$$1 + K\,\frac{N(s)}{D(s)} = 0$$

and determining the root-locus by means of the equation

$$\arg \frac{N(s)}{D(s)} = \pi + 2\pi n, \qquad n = 0, \pm 1, \pm 2, \ldots.$$

A simple means of choosing $D(s)$ is to take the three highest powers of $F(s)$. Thus, if

$$F(s) = s^5 + a_4 s^4 + a_3 s^3 + a_2 s^2 + a_1 s + a_0,$$

---

* F. Hildebrand, *Introduction to Numerical Analysis*, McGraw-Hill, New York, 1956.

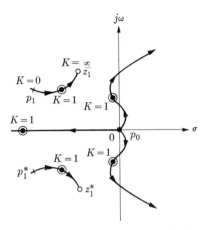

FIG. 7-2. The root-locus method.

we choose

$$D(s) = s^3(s^2 + a_4 s + a_3), \quad \text{and} \quad N(s) = a_2 s^2 + a_1 s + a_0.$$

The zeros of $D(s)$ and $N(s)$ are easily found. Let these be p_0, p_1, p_1^*, z_1 and z_1^*, respectively. The root-locus of

$$K \frac{a_2(s - z_1)(s - z_1^*)}{s^3(s - p_1)(s - p_1^*)}$$

is shown in Fig. 7-2. The zeros of $F(s)$ are those points on the root-locus where $K = 1$.

If $n > 5$, the zeros of the numerator polynomial can be found by the same procedure. The root-locus method is particularly well suited to problems where K can be identified with system parameters. The change in root location as the parameter K varies can then be conveniently found.

PROBLEMS

The following problems relate, in part, to the response of physical systems. These will be discussed further in Chapter 8. In each case the factors and zeros, x_k, of $D(x)$ and the values of $F(x_k)$ are to be found.

7-1. Amplidyne positioning system:

$$D(x) = x^5 + 57.9x^4 + 410.5x^3 + 3780x^2 + 7750x + 8000$$
$$F(x) = D'(x) = 5x^4 + 231.6x^3 + 1232x^2 + 7560x + 7750$$
$$x_1 = -51.28, \qquad x_2 = -2.147 + j7.357, \qquad x_3 = -1.163 + j1.142.$$

7-2. Linear-phase network:

$$D(x) = x^3 + 6.48x^2 + 14.67(x + 1)$$
$$F(x) = x^2 + 5.48x + 14.67$$
$$x_1 = -3.4712, \qquad x_2 = -1.5044 + j1.401.$$

7-3. Instrument servosystem:

$$D(x) = x^5 + 21.05x^4 + 121.1x^3 + 306x^2 + 455x + 100$$
$$F(x) = D'(x) = 5x^4 + 84.2x^3 + 363.3x^2 + 612x + 455$$
$$x_1 = -13.64, \qquad x_2 = -4.492, \qquad x_3 = -1.32 + j2.128, \qquad x_4 = -0.2611.$$

7-4. Amplidyne voltage control system:

$$D(x) = x^5 + 3.8x^4 + 3.563x^3 + 3.919x^2 + 1.438x + 0.3125$$
$$F(x) = 5x^4 + 15.2032x^3 + 10.6906x^2 + 7.84076x + 1.43814$$
$$x_1 = -2.999, \qquad x_2 = -0.1721 + j0.924, \qquad x_3 = -0.2287 + j0.2563.$$

7-5. Inertia-damped servomotor:

$$D(x) = x^3 + 10x^2 + 100x + 100$$
$$F(x) = D'(x) = 3x^2 + 20x + 100$$
$$x_1 = -1.1094, \qquad x_2 = -4.4453 + j8.839.$$

CHAPTER 8

THE NUMERICAL EVALUATION OF THE
RESPONSE OF LUMPED-PARAMETER SYSTEMS

8–1 Introduction. A general expression for the response of a lumped-parameter system has been given by Eq. (2–25), which has the form

$$v(t) = \sum_{k=1}^{n} F_k(s_k), \tag{8–1}$$

where $F_k(s)$ is the pole coefficient at the pole $s = s_k$, and $F_k(s_k)$ is the residue. The numerical evaluation of this sum requires the determination of the characteristic roots s_k, and the values of the residues. (In the above expression it is assumed that the roots are simple.) Suitable numerical methods have been discussed in the previous chapter. In general, the scaling theorem is required to obtain characteristic roots of the order of unity. Thus, if $H(s)$ is the system transfer function, and if the substitution $s = ap$ is used, we have

$$V_o(s) = V_o[p] = \frac{1}{ap} H[p],$$

where the input has been taken to be a unit step. Thus

$$v_o(t) = av[\tau] = \mathcal{L}^{-1} \left[\frac{H[p]}{p} \right],$$

where $\tau = at$.

If $H[p] = N(p)/D(p)$, where $N(p)$ and $D(p)$ are polynomials, the poles of $V_o[p]$ are given by $p = 0$ and by the roots of

$$D(p) = 0,$$

which will be designated by $p_1, p_2, p_3, \ldots, p_n$. Thus, using the Heaviside expansion in the form given by Eq. (5–25), we have

$$v_o(t) = \frac{N(0)}{D(0)} + \sum_{k=1}^{n} \frac{N(p_k)}{p_k D'(p_k)} e^{p_k \tau}. \tag{8–2}$$

We see that the problem consists of the numerical evaluation of the roots p_k, and in the determination of the numerical values of the polynomials $N(p_k)$ and $D'(p_k)$.

8-2 The numerical evaluation of the output response.

EXAMPLE 1. In Chapter 6, Example 7, an amplidyne-controlled positioning system is discussed. The closed-loop transfer function is given by Eq. (6–72), where the substitution $s = 10p$ has been used. We have $N(p) = 8000$ and

$$D(p) = p^5 + 57.9p^4 + 410.5p^3 + 3780p^2 + 7750p + 8000. \quad (8\text{--}3)$$

The zeros of this polynomial are given approximately by (see Problem 1, Chapter 7)

$$p_1 = -51.28,$$
$$p_2 = -2.147 + j7.357, \quad (8\text{--}4)$$
$$p_3 = -1.163 + j1.142.$$

These are actually the zeros of the polynomial

$$D(p) = p^5 + 57.9p^4 + 410.853p^3 + 3808.37p^2$$
$$+ 7746.81p + 8001.89. \quad (8\text{--}5)$$

The difference between the corresponding coefficients of (8–3), and (8–5) is small, and results from the insufficient numerical accuracy of (8–4). From a practical point of view these differences are insignificant. The values of system parameters are seldom known to this degree of accuracy. However, from the numerical point of view, these differences may not be entirely negligible. This is due to the fact that round-off errors may accumulate in an extensive sequence of numerical operations. A convenient check on this is afforded by means of the initial value, which can always be found from the initial-value theorem. Since all physical systems have a finite rise time, it will usually be the case, as it is in this example, that $v(0) = 0$. However, if the initial value is used as a check on the numerical computation, the polynomial (8–5) should be used and not (8–3). This may not always be necessary, but the difference between the coefficients of p^2 indicates the advisability of following this procedure in this example.

From (8–5) we obtain

$$D'(p) = 5p^4 + 231.6p^3 + 1232.56p^2 + 7616.74p + 7746.81.$$

The values of the polynomial $D'(p_k)$ are (see Problem 1, Chapter 7)

$$D'(p_1) = 6.15 \cdot 10^6,$$
$$D'(p_2) = (1.60807 - j3.59197) \cdot 10^4,$$
$$D'(p_3) = (-0.39755 + j6.15126) \cdot 10^3.$$

The residues, $F_k(p_k) = N(p_k)e^{p_k\tau}/p_k D'(p_k)$, can now be determined. We obtain

$$F_0(0) = 1,$$
$$F_1(p_1) = -2.5 \cdot 10^{-5}e^{p_1\tau},$$
$$F_2(p_2) = (2.02033 - j1.7186) \cdot 10^{-2}e^{p_2\tau},$$
$$F_3(p_3) = (-0.52008 + j0.60294)e^{p_3\tau}.$$

The resultant response is the sum of the residues. Thus

$$v_o(t) = F_0(0) + F_1(p_1) + 2\,\mathrm{Re}[F_2(p_2)] + 2\,\mathrm{Re}[F_3(p_3)]$$
$$= 1 - 2.5 \cdot 10^{-5}e^{-512.8t} + 4.04066 \cdot 10^{-2}e^{-21.47t}\cos 73.57t$$
$$+ 3.4372 \cdot 10^{-2}e^{-21.47t}\sin 73.57t - 1.04015e^{-11.63t}\cos 11.42t$$
$$- 1.20587e^{-11.63t}\sin 11.42t.$$

As a check on the numerical value of these coefficients, we have $v_o(0) = 0.00023$. ▲

EXAMPLE 2.   Consider the inertia-damped servomotor discussed in Chapter 6, Example 5.   The closed-loop transfer function is given by Eq. (6–50), where the substitution $s = 10p$ has been used. We have $N(p) = 100(0.9804p + 1)$ and $D(p) = p^3 + 10p^2 + 100p + 100$. The roots p_k and values $D'(p_k)$ are (see Problem 5, Chapter 7)

$$p_1 = -1.1094, \qquad\qquad D'(p_1) = 81.504,$$
$$p_2 = -4.4453 + j8.389, \qquad D'(p_2) = -140.752 - j55.97.$$

For a unit-step input the residues are

$$F_0(0) = 1,$$
$$F_1(p_1) = 0.096936e^{p_1\tau},$$
$$F_2(p_2) = (-0.5485 + j0.28425)e^{p_2\tau},$$

and the response is

$$v_o(t) = 1 + 0.097e^{-11.094t} - 1.097e^{-44.453t}\cos 83.89t$$
$$- 0.5685e^{-44.453t}\sin 83.89t. ▲$$

8–3 The case of higher-order poles.   Equation (8–1) is valid for the case of simple poles.   If one or more of the poles are of higher order, the corresponding pole coefficient must be differentiated.   Suppose, for example, that the pole s_k is of order m.   The contribution of this pole to the resultant response is

$$\frac{1}{m!}\,F_k^{(m)}(s_k).$$

The case of a second-order pole has been discussed in Chapter 5 (see Eq. 5–29). The evaluation of this term requires the determination of the values of the polynomials $N(s_k)$, $N'(s_k)$, $Q_k(s_k)$, and $Q_k'(s_k)$, where $D(s) = (s - s_k)^2 Q_k(s)$.

8–4 Graphical methods. It is possible to evaluate the factor

$$\frac{N(p_k)}{p_k D'(p_k)}$$

by graphical means, and thus all terms in the Heaviside expansion (8–2) can be found. The zeros of $D(p)$ have been designated by p_k. Thus

$$D(p) = \prod_{l=1}^{n} (p - p_l).$$

Since $D(p_k) = 0$, it follows that

$$D'(p_k) = \lim_{p \to p_k} \frac{D(p) - D(p_k)}{p - p_k} = \prod_{\substack{l=1 \\ l \neq k}}^{n} (p_k - p_l).$$

Let the zeros of $N(p)$ be designated by $z_1, z_2, \ldots, z_m$. Thus

$$N(p) = c \prod_{l=1}^{m} (p - z_l).$$

The magnitude and phase of the factors p_k, $p_k - p_l$, and $p_k - z_l$ can be determined graphically. The resultant magnitude and phase of the terms $N(p_k)$ and $p_k D'(p_k)$ are then easily found. The *spirule* [1] is a useful instrument for this purpose. If the poles are of higher order, suitable modifications can be determined [2].

8–5 Guillemin's method [3]. The impulse response of a system can be found by evaluating the inverse Laplace transform

$$h(t) = \frac{1}{2\pi j} \int_{c-j\infty}^{c+j\infty} H(s) e^{st}\, ds. \tag{8–6}$$

This integral is, however, not suitable for numerical computation, and must first be transformed into a real integral before it can be approximately evaluated by numerical methods. We consider all poles of $H(s)$ to lie in the left half of the s-plane, Substituting $s = j\omega$ and letting $R_h = \mathrm{Re}[H(j\omega)]$ and $I_h = \mathrm{Im}[H(j\omega)]$ denote the real and imaginary parts of $H(j\omega)$ so that

$$H(j\omega) = R_h + jI_h,$$

we obtain

$$h(t) = \frac{1}{2\pi} \int_{-\infty}^{+\infty} [R_h \cos \omega t - I_h \sin \omega t] \, d\omega, \qquad (8\text{-}7a)$$

and

$$0 = \frac{1}{2\pi} \int_{-\infty}^{+\infty} [R_h \sin \omega t + I_h \cos \omega t] \, d\omega. \qquad (8\text{-}7b)$$

The vanishing of the integral (8–7b) results from the fact that R_h is an even function and I_h an odd function of ω, so that $R_h(-\omega) = R_h(\omega)$ and $I_h(-\omega) = -I_h(\omega)$.* If $t < 0$, we have $h(t) = 0$. Thus, substituting $-t$ into (8–7a) yields

$$h(-t) = 0 = \frac{1}{2\pi} \int_{-\infty}^{+\infty} [R_h \cos \omega t + I_h \sin \omega t] \, d\omega. \qquad (8\text{-}8)$$

Adding Eqs. (8–7a) and (8–8) yields

$$h(t) = \frac{2}{\pi} \int_0^\infty R_h \cos \omega t \, d\omega, \qquad (8\text{-}9)$$

where we have used the fact that R_h is an even function of ω.

Similarly it can be shown that

$$h(t) = -\frac{2}{\pi} \int_0^\infty I_h \sin \omega t \, d\omega. \qquad (8\text{-}10)$$

The integral (8–9) has been used by Floyd [4] to determine $h(t)$ by approximating R_h by means of trapezoids. However, Guillemin's method is more convenient. It is based on applying the integrals (8–9) and (8–10) to a system whose transfer function $V(s)$ is related to $H(s)$ by means of $V(s) = d^n H(s)/ds^n$. It is shown in Appendix D–5 that the operation d/ds in the s-domain represents multiplication with $-t$ in the time domain. Thus

$$v(t) = (-1)^n t^n h(t). \qquad (8\text{-}11)$$

If we substitute $s = j\omega$ and let $V(j\omega) = R_v + jI_v$, we have

$$R_v + jI_v = \frac{1}{j^n} \left[\frac{d^n R_h}{d\omega^n} + j \frac{d^n I_h}{d\omega^n} \right].$$

Thus, if n is even,

$$R_v = (-1)^{n/2} \frac{d^n R_h}{d\omega^n}, \qquad I_v = (-1)^{n/2} \frac{d^n I_h}{d\omega^n}, \qquad (8\text{-}12)$$

---

* This follows from the fact that $H(s)$ can be expressed as the ratio of two polynomials with real coefficients.

and if n is odd

$$R_v = (-1)^{(n-1)/2} \frac{d^n I_h}{d\omega^n}, \qquad I_v = -(-1)^{(n-1)/2} \frac{d^n R_h}{d\omega^n}. \qquad (8\text{--}13)$$

If we now apply Eqs. (8–9) and (8–10) to the function $v(t)$ and use the relations (8–11), (8–12), and (8–13), we obtain, if n is even,

$$h(t) = \frac{2(-1)^{n/2}}{\pi t^n} \int_0^\infty \frac{d^n R_h}{d\omega^n} \cos \omega t \, d\omega, \qquad (8\text{--}14\text{a})$$

$$= -\frac{2(-1)^{n/2}}{\pi t^n} \int_0^\infty \frac{d^n I_h}{d\omega^n} \sin \omega t \, d\omega, \qquad (8\text{--}14\text{b})$$

and, if n is odd,

$$h(t) = \frac{2(-1)^{(n+1)/2}}{\pi t^n} \int_0^\infty \frac{d^n I_h}{d\omega^n} \cos \omega t \, d\omega$$

$$= \frac{2(-1)^{(n+1)/2}}{\pi t^n} \int_0^\infty \frac{d^n R_h}{d\omega^n} \sin \omega t \, d\omega.$$

To see how these integrals can be used to determine $h(t)$, we consider (8–14a) and choose $n = 2$ [5]. The function R_h is approximated by means of straight line segments (see Fig. 8–1). Thus $dR_h/d\omega$ has piecewise constant values which change abruptly by a_k at $\omega = \omega_k$, and $d^2 R_h/d\omega^2$ consists of impulses of area a_k at $\omega = \omega_k$. Thus

$$\frac{d^2 R_h}{d\omega^2} = \sum_{k=1}^n a_k \, \delta(\omega - \omega_k).$$

Substituting this equation into Eq. (8–14a) yields

$$h(t) = -\frac{2}{\pi t^2} \sum_{k=1}^n a_k \cos \omega_k t. \qquad (8\text{--}15)$$

If we restrict ourselves to systems where $h(t)$ is finite, it follows from Eq. (8–15) that

$$\sum_{k=1}^n a_k = 0. \qquad (8\text{--}16)$$

Multiplying (8–16) with $2/\pi t^2$ and adding this to (8–15) yields

$$h(t) = \sum_{k=1}^n a_k \omega_k^2 G_0(x_k), \qquad (8\text{--}17)$$

where

$$G_0(x) = \frac{2}{\pi} \cdot \frac{1 - \cos x}{x^2},$$

and $x_k = \omega_k t$.

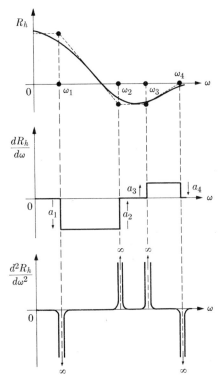

FIG. 8–1. Approximation of R_h by straight line segments.

To determine the response to a unit step input, we integrate (8–17) with respect to t and obtain

$$g(t) = \sum_{k=1}^{n} a_k \omega_k G_1(x_k),$$

where

$$G_1(x) = \frac{2}{\pi} \int_0^x \frac{1 - \cos u}{u^2} \, du = \frac{2}{\pi} \left[\text{Si } x - \frac{1 - \cos x}{x} \right],$$

and

$$\text{Si } x = \int_0^x \frac{\sin u}{u} \, du.$$

Similarly, the response to a unit ramp is found by integrating $g(t)$. Thus

$$\int_0^t g(u) \, du = \sum_{k=1}^{n} a_k G_2(x_k),$$

where

$$G_2(x) = \frac{2}{\pi} \int_0^x \left[\text{Si } u - \frac{1 - \cos u}{u} \right] du$$

$$= \frac{2}{\pi} \left[x \text{ Si } x - (1 - \cos x) - \text{Cin } x \right]$$

and

$$\text{Cin } x = \int_0^x \frac{1 - \cos u}{u} \, du.$$

The functions G_0, G_1, and G_2 are tabulated [5] and the values of Si x can be found in standard tables [6].

8–6 The approximation of transfer functions by means of ideal filter characteristics. It is often possible to approximate the frequency-response characteristics of a low-pass system by means of the ideal low-pass filter characteristics shown in Fig. 8–2. The system transfer function H is then approximated by the transfer function

$$H_a(j\omega) = \begin{cases} e^{-j\omega T} & 0 \le |\omega| < \omega_b, \\ 0 & |\omega| > \omega_b, \end{cases} \tag{8–18}$$

where ω_b is the bandwidth

If Eq. (8–9) is integrated with respect to t, the system response to a unit-step input is obtained:

$$g(t) = \frac{2}{\pi} \int_0^\infty R_h \frac{\sin \omega t}{\omega} \, d\omega. \tag{8–19}$$

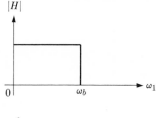

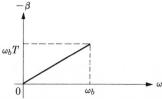

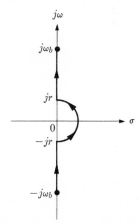

FIG. 8–2. Ideal low-pass filter characteristics.

FIG. 8–3. Integration path: ideal low-pass filter with step input.

Substituting (8–18) into (8–19) yields an approximation to $g(t)$:

$$g_a(t) = \frac{1}{\pi} \{\text{Si} [\omega_b(t + T)] + \text{Si} [\omega_b(t - T)]\}. \qquad (8\text{--}20)$$

A similar expression is obtainable from the inverse Laplace transform (8–6). If the input is a unit step, the integrand is approximated by

$$\frac{H_a(s)}{s} e^{st}.$$

Figure 8–3 shows the path of integration, which contains a small semicircle around the pole at the origin. The integral along the semicircle can be evaluated by noting that it is equal to one-half the integral around the complete circle, provided that the radius $r \to 0$. This yields

$$g_a(t) = \frac{1/2}{2\pi j} \oint_{s=0} \frac{H_a(s)}{s} e^{st} \, ds + 2 \, \text{Re} \left[\frac{1}{2\pi j} \int_0^{\omega_b} e^{j\omega(t-T)} \frac{d\omega}{\omega} \right]$$

$$= \frac{1}{2} + \frac{1}{\pi} \text{Si}[\omega_b(t - T)]. \qquad (8\text{--}21)$$

Equations (8–20) and (8–21) are both approximations to the unit-step response. The difference between these equations results from the fact that the approximation (8–18) has been used in different integrals. In these equations, T is the negative slope of the phase characteristic and represents the time delay. If $\omega_b \to \infty$, the transfer function (8–18) approaches the ideal delay function. This can be seen from both (8–20) and (8–21) by noting that Si $\infty = \pi/2$ and Si $(-x) = -\text{Si}\,(x)$. Thus we have

$$\lim_{\omega_b \to \infty} g_a(t) = \begin{cases} 0 & t < T, \\ \frac{1}{2} & t = T, \\ 1 & t > T. \end{cases}$$

Consider now the case of an all-pass transfer function of the type given by Eq. (4–20). The phase characteristic is shown in Fig. 4–7. This can be approximated by extending the linear portion until it intersects the asymptotic value of 4π, and yields an effective bandwidth of $\omega_b = 7.5$. If we neglect the contribution of all spectral terms above ω_b, we can use (8–20) or (8–21) to approximate the unit-step response. Figure 8–4 shows a plot of Eq. (8–21), where it is compared with the exact plot given in Fig. 4–6. It is seen that the approximation (8–21) gives a reasonable estimate of time delay, rise time, and overshoot. The fact that the high-frequency terms above ω_b have been neglected results in a poor approximation for

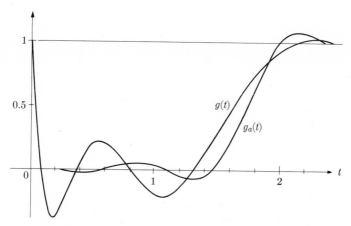

FIG. 8–4. Exact and approximate unit-step response.

small t. The rise time can be estimated from the maximum slope of (8–21), which occurs at $t = T$. This yields

$$\tau_R = \frac{\pi}{\omega_b}.$$

In the case of Eq. (4–20), we obtain $\tau_R = 0.42$.

If the input is a unit-step carrier, $\cos \omega_c t$, we can set $v_i(t) = e^{j\omega_c t}$ and take the input to be $\mathrm{Re}[v_i(t)]$. The integrand of the inverse Laplace transform is now approximated by

$$\frac{H_a(s)}{s - j\omega_c} e^{st}, \tag{8–22}$$

and a suitable path of integration, which contains a small semicircle around the pole at $s = j\omega_c$, is shown in Fig. 8–5. The integral along the semicircle can be evaluated by noting that it is equal to one-half the integral around the complete circle, provided that the radius, $r \to 0$. Thus

$$v_a(t) = \left[\frac{1}{2} + \frac{1}{2\pi j} \int_{-u_2}^{u_1} \frac{e^{ju}}{u}\, du\right] e^{j\omega_c(t-T)}$$

is the approximate system response to $v_i(t)$, and the approximate physical response is

$$\mathrm{Re}[v_a(t)] = \frac{1}{2}\left[1 + \frac{1}{\pi}\,(\mathrm{Si}\,u_1 + \mathrm{Si}\,u_2)\right] \cos \omega_c(t - T)$$

$$+ \frac{1}{2\pi}\,(\mathrm{Ci}\,u_1 - \mathrm{Ci}\,u_2) \sin \omega_c(t - T),$$

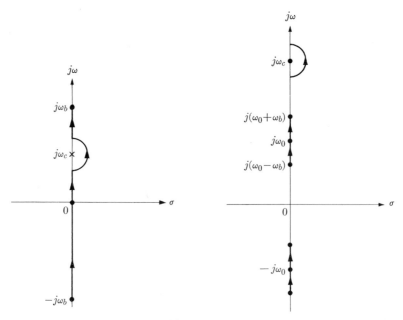

FIG. 8–5. Integration path: ideal low-pass filter with a step carrier input.

FIG. 8–6. Integration path: ideal bandpass filter with a step carrier input.

where $u_1 = (\omega_b - \omega_c)(t - T)$, $u_2 = (\omega_b + \omega_c)(t - T)$, and

$$\text{Ci } x = - \int_x^\infty \frac{\cos u}{u} \, du.$$

The transfer function of a bandpass network can often be approximated by the function

$$H_a(j\omega) = \begin{cases} e^{-j(\omega-\omega_0)T} & |\omega - \omega_0| < \omega_b, \\ e^{-j(\omega+\omega_0)T} & |\omega + \omega_0| < \omega_b, \\ 0 & \text{all other } \omega, \end{cases} \qquad (8\text{--}23)$$

where ω_0 is the band center and $2\omega_b$ the bandwidth. Let us consider a unit-step carrier input to a bandpass network. The integrand of the inverse Laplace transform is given approximately by (8–22). Figure 8–6 shows the path of integration for the case where $\omega_b < \omega_c - \omega_0 < \omega_c$. The integral along the negative $j\omega$-axis is then small, and can be neglected. The path along the semicircle yields $\frac{1}{2}H_a(j\omega_c)$, which is zero, since ω_c is outside the pass band. Thus

$$v_a(t) \cong \frac{e^{j\omega_0 T}}{2\pi j} \int_{\omega_0-\omega_b}^{\omega_0+\omega_b} \frac{e^{j\omega(t-T)}}{\omega - \omega_c} \, d\omega = v_a'(t) e^{j(\omega_0 t - \pi/2)},$$

where the approximation $\omega - \omega_c \cong \omega_0 - \omega_c$ is used to determine the approximate envelope response

$$v_a'(t) \cong \frac{1}{\pi} \frac{\omega_b}{\omega_0 - \omega_c} \frac{\sin \omega_b(t - T)}{\omega_b(t - T)}.$$

It should be noted that the carrier frequency for the output response is the band-center frequency $\omega_0/2\pi$.

PROBLEMS

For Problems 1–3, the system response to a unit-step input is to be determined.

8–1. (Instrument servosystem) The transfer function is given by Eq. (6–44). Thus $N(p) = 100(2p^2 + 4.5p + 1)$ and $D(p) = p^5 + 21.05p^4 + 121.1p^3 + 306p^2 + 455p + 100$, where the substitution $s = 50p$ has been used. The roots p_k and values of $D'(p_k)$ and $N(p_k)$ are (see Problem 3, Chapter 7)

$$p_1 = -13.64, \qquad p_2 = -4.492, \qquad p_3 = -1.32 + j2.128, \qquad p_4 = -0.2611,$$

$D'(p_1) = 1.91148 \cdot 10^4,$ $N(p_1) = 3.11719 \cdot 10^4,$

$D'(p_2) = -5.66442 \cdot 10^2,$ $N(p_2) = 21.1421 \cdot 10^2,$

$D'(p_3) = -(1.64108 + j4.5379)10^2,$ $N(p_3) = -(10.512 + j1.65984) \cdot 10^2,$

$D'(p_4) = 3.19791 \cdot 10^2,$ $N(p_4) = 3.86036.$

8–2. Figure 8–7 shows a linear-phase network, where the input is taken to be a unit-step current. If

$$C = 5.48C_1, \qquad T^2 = 14.67L_1C_1, \qquad \text{and} \qquad T = RC, \text{ show that}$$

$$\frac{Z[p]}{R} = \frac{p^2 + 5.48p + 14.67}{p^3 + 6.48p^2 + 14.67(p + 1)} = \frac{N(p)}{D(p)},$$

where $s = (1/T)p$. The poles of $Z[p]$ and the values of $N(p_k)$ and $D'(p_k)$ are

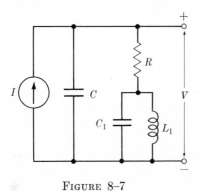

FIGURE 8–7

(see Problem 2, Chapter 7)

$$p_1 = -3.4712, \qquad p_2 = -1.5044 + j1.401,$$

$$D'(p_1) = 5.8309, \qquad\qquad N(p_1) = 7.697,$$
$$D'(p_2) = -3.9257 + j5.511, \qquad N(p_2) = 6.7263 + j3.4622.$$

8-3. (Amplidyne voltage-control system) The transfer function of this system is given by Eq. (6-67). Thus $N(p) = \frac{19}{32}(1 + 4p)$ and $D(p) = p^5 + 3.8p^4 + 3.563p^3 + 3.919p^2 + 1.438p + 0.3125$, where $s = 10p$. The roots p_k and values of $D'(p_k)$ are (see Problem 4, Chapter 7)

$$p_1 = -2.999, \qquad p_2 = -0.1721 + j0.924, \qquad p_3 = -0.2287 + j0.2563,$$

$$D'(p_1) = 68.4589,$$
$$D'(p_2) = 0.79352 - j4.27888,$$
$$D'(p_3) = -0.06253 + j1.12746.$$

Let $v_o(t)$ be the response to a unit-step input $v_i(t) = u(t)$. Show that the response to a unit-step load disturbance $v_L(t) = u(t)$ is given by $1 - v_o(t)$ (see Fig. 6-30).

8-4. (Inertia-damped servomotor) This system has been discussed in Chapter 6, Example 5 [see Eq. (6-50)]. If the initial conditions for the output are $v_o(0) = 0$, $v_o^{(1)}(0) = 10$, and the input $v_i(t)$ is zero, show that

$$V_o[p] = \frac{0.1p + 1}{p^3 + 10p^2 + 100p + 11},$$

where $s = 10p$. Determine the response. (For the roots p_k and the value of $D'(p_k)$ see Section 8-2, Example 2.

8-5. The magnitude and phase characteristics for the frequency response of a system are approximated as shown in Fig. 8-8, where $|H(j\omega)| = H_k$ and $\beta = -a_k\omega - b_k$, for $\omega_k \le \omega \le \omega_{k+1}$. Show that the system response to a unit-step input has the form

$$g(t) = \frac{1}{\pi} \sum_{k=1}^{n} [(\text{Si } u_{k+1} - \text{Si } u_k + \text{Si } v_{k+1} + \text{Si } v_k) \cos b_k$$
$$+ (\text{Ci } u_{k+1} - \text{Ci } u_k - \text{Ci } v_{k+1} + \text{Ci } v_k) \sin b_k]H_k,$$

where

$$u_k = (t + a_k)\omega_k, u_{k+1} = (t + a_k)\omega_{k+1}, v_k = (t - a_k)\omega_k, v_{k+1} = (t - a_k)\omega_{k+1}.$$

8-6. The function $R_h = \text{Re}[H(j\omega)]$ is approximated by straight line segments as shown in Fig. 8-9. Show that the impulse response for a system with the transfer function $H(s)$ can be approximated by

$$h_a(t) = \frac{2\Delta}{\pi} \left(\frac{\sin x}{x}\right)^2 \left[\frac{a_0}{2} + \sum_{k=1}^{n} a_k \cos 2kx\right],$$

where $x = \Delta t/2$.

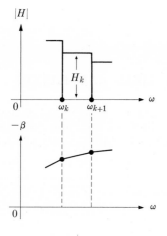

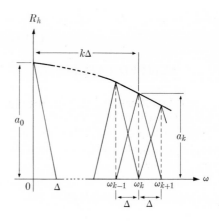

FIGURE 8-8   FIGURE 8-9

8–7. A unit-step carrier of the form $\cos \omega_c t$ is suddenly applied to a bandpass network whose transfer function can be approximated by Eq. (8–23). Show that the approximate envelope response is given by Eq. (8–21).

REFERENCES

1. See Ref. 1, Chapter 6.

2. D. S. BILLINGSLEY and M. G. REKOFF, "Evaluation of transient response coefficients, *Trans. IRE, PGAC*, Vol. AC–6, 80–83 (February 1961).

3. E. A. GUILLEMIN, "Computational techniques which simplify the correlation between steady-state and transient response of filters and networks," *Proc. National Electronics Conf.*, **9**, 513–532 (1954).

4. G. S. BROWN and D. P. CAMPBELL, *Principles of Servomechanisms*, Wiley and Sons, New York, 1948, pp. 332–350.

5. V. S. LEVADI, "Simplified method of determining transient responses of linear networks and systems," *IRE National Conv. Rec.*, pt. 4, 47–68 (1959).

6. E. JAHNKE and F. EMDE, *Tables of Functions*, Dover Publications, New York, 1945.

CHAPTER 9

LUMPED-PARAMETER DELAY LINES AND FILTERS

9–1 Introduction. In this chapter, two-terminal-pair lumped-parameter networks will be considered. A representation of a two-terminal network is shown in Fig. 9–1. One of the terminal pairs can be considered as the input, the other as the output. The cascade connection of two-terminal-pair network sections results in a class of networks designated as filters and delay lines. We shall consider the response of networks of this type to step and sinusoidal inputs.

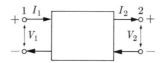

Fig. 9–1. A two-terminal-pair network.

9–2 Network parameters. For a linear network, the terminal voltages and currents are related to each other by linear equations. These take the form

$$V_1 = Z_{11}I_1 + Z_{12}(-I_2), \qquad V_2 = Z_{21}I_1 + Z_{22}(-I_2). \qquad (9\text{–}1)$$

It is convenient for the subsequent discussion to choose I_2 as the transform of the current leaving terminal pair 2, as shown in Fig. 9–1. Thus I_1 and $-I_2$ are the transforms of the currents entering the network at terminal pairs 1 and 2, respectively. An alternative form of these equations is

$$V_1 = AV_2 + BI_2, \qquad I_1 = CV_2 + DI_2. \qquad (9\text{–}2)$$

If all the elements are bilateral, the reciprocity theorem is valid. This requires that

$$Z_{12} = Z_{21}. \qquad (9\text{–}3)$$

Using (9–1) and (9–2), we obtain

$$\left(\frac{V_2}{I_1}\right)_{I_2=0} = Z_{21} = \frac{1}{C}, \quad \text{and} \quad \left(\frac{V_1}{-I_2}\right)_{I_1=0} = Z_{12} = \frac{AD - BC}{C}.$$

The condition (9–3) requires that

$$AD - BC = 1. \qquad (9\text{–}4)$$

170

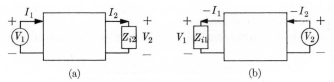

(a)   (b)

Fɪɢ. 9–2. Image impedances.

Using this relation, we can solve (9–2) for V_2 and I_2 in terms of V_1 and I_1. Thus

$$V_2 = DV_1 - BI_1, \qquad -I_2 = CV_1 - AI_1. \tag{9–5}$$

Consider now the case (a), where a voltage source V_1 is applied at terminal pair 1 with a load $Z_{i2} = V_2/I_2$ on terminal pair 2 [Fig. 9–2(a)], and the case (b), where a voltage source V_2 is applied at terminal pair 2 with a load $Z_{i1} = V_1/-I_1$ on terminal pair 1. The impedances Z_{i1} and Z_{i2} are designated as *image impedances*. From (9–2) we obtain, for case (a),

$$Z_{i1} = \frac{V_1}{I_1} = \frac{AZ_{i2} + B}{CZ_{i2} + D}, \tag{9–6}$$

and, for case (b),

$$Z_{i1} = \frac{V_1}{-I_1} = \frac{-AZ_{i2} + B}{CZ_{i2} - D}. \tag{9–7}$$

Equating (9–6) and (9–7) yields

$$Z_{i2} = \sqrt{BD/AC}\,.$$

Similarly from (9–5) we obtain, for case (a),

$$Z_{i2} = \frac{V_2}{I_2} = \frac{DZ_{i1} - B}{-CZ_{i1} + A}, \tag{9–8}$$

and, for case (b),

$$Z_{i2} = \frac{V_2}{-I_2} = \frac{DZ_{i1} + B}{CZ_{i1} + A}. \tag{9–9}$$

Equating (9–8) and (9–9) yields

$$Z_{i1} = \sqrt{AB/CD}.$$

From (9–2) we now obtain

$$\frac{V_1}{V_2} = A + \frac{B}{Z_{i2}} = \sqrt{A/D}\,(\sqrt{AD} + \sqrt{BC}), \tag{9–10}$$

and

$$\frac{I_1}{I_2} = CZ_{i2} + D = \sqrt{D/A}\,(\sqrt{AD} + \sqrt{BC}). \tag{9–11}$$

Equations (9–10) and (9–11) are valid, provided that terminal pair 2 is terminated in its image impedance.

It is convenient to represent these quantities in terms of other variables. Let

$$a = \sqrt{A/D} = \sqrt{Z_{i1}/Z_{i2}},$$

and

$$e^{\gamma} = \sqrt{AD} + \sqrt{BC}. \tag{9-12}$$

Equation (9–4) can be factored:

$$AD - BC = (\sqrt{AD} - \sqrt{BC})(\sqrt{AD} + \sqrt{BC}) = 1. \tag{9-13}$$

Substituting (9–12) into (9–13) yields

$$\sqrt{AD} - \sqrt{BC} = e^{-\gamma}. \tag{9-14}$$

From (9–12) and (9–14), we obtain

$$\cosh \gamma = \sqrt{AD}, \quad \text{and} \quad \sinh \gamma = \sqrt{BC}.$$

With the aid of these results the A, B, C, and D parameters can be expressed in terms of a, γ, and Z_{i2}. Thus

$$A = a \cosh \gamma,$$

$$B = a Z_{i2} \sinh \gamma,$$

$$C = \frac{1}{a Z_{i2}} \sinh \gamma, \tag{9-15}$$

$$D = \frac{1}{a} \cosh \gamma.$$

Substituting (9–15) into (9–2) yields

$$V_1 = a(V_2 \cosh \gamma + I_2 Z_{i2} \sinh \gamma),$$

$$I_1 = \frac{1}{a} \left(\frac{V_2}{Z_{i2}} \sinh \gamma + I_2 \cosh \gamma \right). \tag{9-16}$$

Equations (9–10) and (9–11) now have the form

$$\frac{V_1}{V_2} = a e^{\gamma}, \tag{9-17}$$

and

$$\frac{I_1}{I_2} = \frac{1}{a} e^{\gamma}. \tag{9-18}$$

The quantity γ is called the *propagation function*.

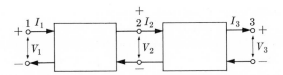

FIG. 9–3. Cascade connection of two similar symmetrical sections.

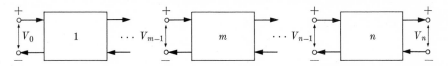

FIG. 9–4. Cascade connection of n identical symmetrical sections.

An important class of two-terminal-pair networks results from the condition $A = D$. It follows that $a = 1$ and

$$Z_{i1} = Z_{i2} = Z_0.$$

The network is then symmetrical with respect to the terminals. The common value of the image impedances Z_0 is called the *characteristic imped-ance*. If two identical symmetrical network sections are connected in cascade (see Fig. 9–3), we have, using matrix notation,

$$\begin{pmatrix} V_1 \\ I_1 \end{pmatrix} = \begin{pmatrix} A & B \\ C & D \end{pmatrix} \begin{pmatrix} V_2 \\ I_2 \end{pmatrix}$$

$$= \begin{pmatrix} A^2 + BC & 2AB \\ 2AC & A^2 + BC \end{pmatrix} \begin{pmatrix} V_3 \\ I_3 \end{pmatrix}$$

$$= \begin{pmatrix} \cosh 2\gamma & Z_0 \sinh 2\gamma \\ \dfrac{1}{Z_0} \sinh 2\gamma & \cosh 2\gamma \end{pmatrix} \begin{pmatrix} V_3 \\ I_3 \end{pmatrix}. \qquad (9\text{–}19)$$

The propagation function for the combined network is thus 2γ.

Consider now the cascade connections of n identical symmetrical two-terminal-pair network sections (Fig. 9–4). It follows from (9–19) that the propagation function for the combined network consisting of the mth to the nth sections is $(n - m)\gamma$. The characteristic impedance is Z_0. Equations (9–16) can be applied to this two-terminal-pair network where the inputs are V_m, I_m, and the outputs V_n, I_n. Thus

$$V_m = V_n \cosh (n - m)\gamma + I_n Z_0 \sinh (n - m)\gamma,$$

$$I_m = \frac{V_n}{Z_0} \sinh (n - m)\gamma + I_n \cosh (n - m)\gamma. \qquad (9\text{–}20)$$

9–3 Two-terminal-pair network sections. A filter, or delay line, is composed of a cascade connection of simple network sections, which we will now discuss. Figure 9–5 shows a symmetrical π-network section. The simplest method of obtaining the A, B, C parameters is to consider the open- and short-circuit conditions. Thus, if there is a short circuit at terminal pair 2, it follows from (9–2) that $V_1 = BI_2$ and $I_1 = AI_2$. From the voltage-current relations of the network, we obtain

$$I_2 = \frac{V_1}{Z_1},$$

and

$$I_1 = V_1 \left(\frac{1}{Z_1} + \frac{1}{2Z_2} \right).$$

Thus

$$A = 1 + \frac{Z_1}{2Z_2}, \quad \text{and} \quad B = Z_1.$$

Substituting these results into (9–15) yields (note $a = 1$ for a symmetrical network)

$$\cosh \gamma = 1 + \frac{Z_1}{2Z_2}, \tag{9–21a}$$

and

$$Z_0 = \frac{Z_1}{\sinh \gamma}. \tag{9–21b}$$

A symmetrical T-network is shown in Fig. 9–6. For an open circuit on terminal pair 2, we have $I_2 = 0$. Thus $V_1 = AV_2$ and $I_1 = CV_2$. The voltage-current relations for the network yield

$$\frac{V_2}{V_1} = \frac{Z_2}{Z_2 + Z_1/2},$$

and

$$I_1 = \frac{V_1}{Z_2 + Z_1/2}.$$

Thus

$$A = 1 + \frac{Z_1}{2Z_2}, \quad \text{and} \quad C = \frac{1}{Z_2}.$$

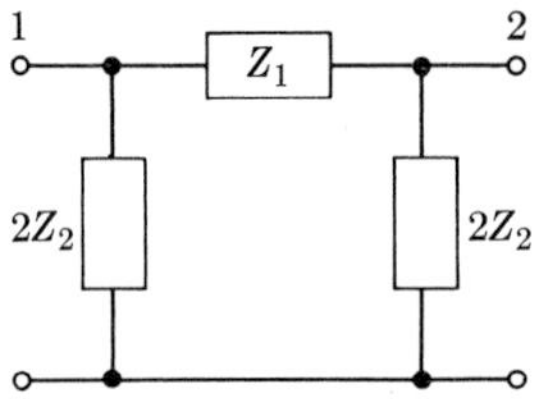

FIG. 9–5. π-network section.

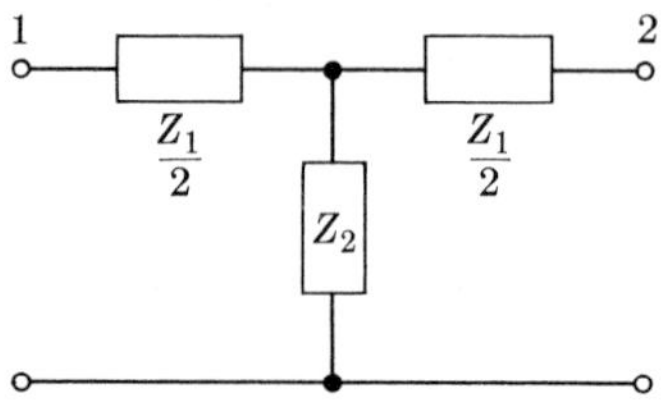

FIG. 9–6. T-network section.

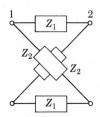

FIG. 9–7. Lattice network section.

Substituting these results into (9–15) yields

$$\cosh \gamma = 1 + \frac{Z_1}{2Z_2} \tag{9–22a}$$

and

$$Z_0 = Z_2 \sinh \gamma. \tag{9–22b}$$

Let us consider now the symmetrical lattice shown in Fig. 9–7. For an open-circuit constraint at terminal pair 2, we have $V_1 = A V_2$ and $I_1 = C V_2$; thus

$$V_1 = \frac{I_1}{2} (Z_2 + Z_1), \qquad V_2 = \frac{I_1}{2} (Z_2 - Z_1).$$

It follows from (9–15) that

$$A = \frac{V_1}{V_2} = \cosh \gamma = \frac{Z_2 + Z_1}{Z_2 - Z_1}, \tag{9–23a}$$

$$C = \frac{I_1}{V_2} = \frac{2}{Z_2 - Z_1},$$

and

$$Z_0 = \frac{Z_2 - Z_1}{2} \sinh \gamma. \tag{9–23b}$$

9–4 Response of filters to step inputs with open- and short-circuit terminations. If the nth section is terminated in an open circuit, this requires that $I_n = 0$. If, in addition, the first section is driven by a voltage source V_0, we have, using (9–20), with $m = 0$,

$$V_0 = V_n \cosh n\gamma.$$

This can be used to eliminate V_n in (9–20). Thus

$$V_m = V_0 \frac{\cosh (n - m)\gamma}{\cosh n\gamma}, \tag{9–24a}$$

and

$$I_m = \frac{V_0}{Z_0} \frac{\sinh (n - m)\gamma}{\cosh n\gamma}. \tag{9–24b}$$

If the nth section is terminated in a short circuit, this requires that $V_n = 0$. Equation (9–20) yields, with $m = 0$,

$$V_0 = I_n Z_0 \sinh n\gamma.$$

This can be used to eliminate I_n in (9–20). Thus

$$V_m = V_0 \frac{\sinh (n - m)\gamma}{\sinh n\gamma}, \tag{9–25a}$$

and

$$I_m = \frac{V_0}{Z_0} \frac{\cosh (n - m)\gamma}{\sinh n\gamma}. \tag{9–25b}$$

Note that both γ and Z_0 are, in general, functions of s.

Let us consider now (9–24) for the case of a unit step input $V_0 = 1/s$. The poles of V_m are determined by $s = 0$ and the roots of

$$\cosh n\gamma(s) = 0. \tag{9–26}$$

These roots are the complex natural frequencies of oscillation of the network, and will be designated by s_k. Equation (9–26) requires that $\gamma(s_k)$ be pure imaginary. Thus

$$\gamma(s_k) = \gamma_k = j\beta_k, \tag{9–27}$$

where

$$\cos n\beta_k = 0. \tag{9–28}$$

The roots of this equation are

$$\beta_k = (2k - 1) \frac{\pi}{2n}, \qquad k = 1, 2, \ldots, n. \tag{9–29}$$

The poles s_k are then found by solving [see Eq. (9–15)]

$$A(s_k) = \cosh \gamma_k = \cos \beta_k \tag{9–30}$$

for s_k. Values of k other than those indicated in (9–29) need not be considered, since they do not result in additional poles.

The inverse transform of V_m can be found by contour integration. The Heaviside expansion is valid, provided that it is possible to complete the path of integration in the left half of the s-plane so that all poles of V_m are enclosed by the contour. Assuming the poles to be simple, this yields

$$v_m(t) = \left[\frac{\cosh (n - m)\gamma}{\cosh n\gamma} \right]_{s=0} + \sum_{k=1}^{n} \frac{\cosh (n - m)\gamma_k}{[s(d \cosh n\gamma/ds)]_{s=s_k}} e^{s_k t}. \tag{9–31}$$

This expression can be simplified with the aid of (9–27) and (9–28). Thus

$$\cosh (n - m)\gamma_k = \cos (n - m)\beta_k = \sin n\beta_k \sin m\beta_k.$$

Also

$$\left[\frac{d\cosh n\gamma}{ds}\right]_{s=s_k} = \left[\frac{d\cosh n\gamma}{d\gamma}\frac{1}{d\cosh \gamma/d\gamma}\frac{d\cosh \gamma}{ds}\right]_{s=s_k}$$

$$= \left[\frac{n\sinh n\gamma}{\sinh \gamma}\frac{d\cosh \gamma}{ds}\right]_{s=s_k}$$

$$= \frac{n\sin n\beta_k}{\sin \beta_k}\left[\frac{d\cosh \gamma}{ds}\right]_{s=s_k}.$$

Substituting these results into (9–31) yields

$$v_m(t) = \left[\frac{\cosh (n-m)\gamma}{\cosh n\gamma}\right]_{s=0} + \frac{1}{n}\sum_{k=1}^{n}\frac{\sin \beta_k \sin m\beta_k}{[s(d\cosh \gamma/ds)]_{s=s_k}}e^{s_k t}. \qquad (9\text{--}32)$$

Similarly, (9–24b) yields the current response

$$i_m(t) = \left[\frac{\sinh (n-m)\gamma}{Z_0(s)\cosh n\gamma}\right]_{s=0} + \frac{1}{n}\sum_{k=1}^{n}\frac{j\sin \beta_k \cos m\beta_k}{Z_0(s_k)[s(d\cosh \gamma/ds)]_{s=s_k}}e^{s_k t}.$$

$$(9\text{--}33)$$

In deriving (9–33), it was assumed that $Z_0(s)$ contributes no additional poles to I_m. This can be seen by noting that the general solutions, for both the voltage and current responses, consist of linear combinations of the same characteristic exponentials $e^{s_k t}$.

EXAMPLE 1. As an application of (9–32) and (9–33), we consider the π-section, shown in Fig. 9–8, where $Z_1 = Ls$ and $Z_2 = 1/Cs$. The propagation function γ and the characteristic impedance Z_0 are determined from (9–21). We obtain

$$\cosh \gamma = 1 + \frac{LC}{2}s^2, \qquad (9\text{--}34)$$

and

$$Z_0 = \frac{Ls}{\sinh \gamma}. \qquad (9\text{--}35)$$

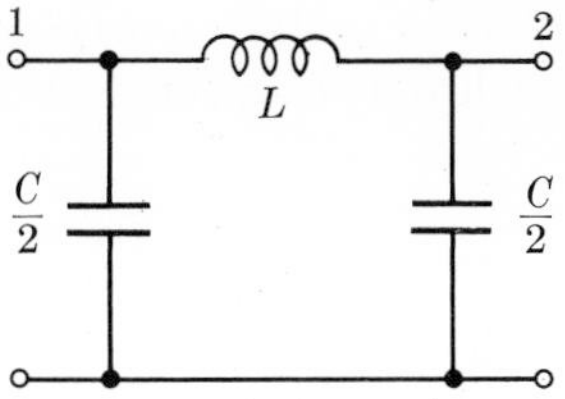

The poles s_k are the roots of (9–30). This yields

FIG. 9–8. Low-pass π-section.

$$1 + \frac{LC}{2}s_k^2 = \cos \beta_k = \cos 2\phi_k, \qquad (9\text{--}36)$$

where we have set

$$\phi_k = \frac{\beta_k}{2} = (2k-1)\frac{\pi}{4n}. \qquad (9\text{--}37)$$

Solving (9–36) for s_k yields

$$s_k = j\omega_k = \pm j \frac{2}{\sqrt{LC}} \sin \phi_k. \qquad (9\text{–}38)$$

In evaluating (9–32) it should be noted that $\gamma(0) = 0$ and also that

$$\left[s \frac{d \cosh \gamma}{ds} \right]_{s=s_k} = LCs_k^2 = -4 \sin^2 \phi_k. \qquad (9\text{–}39)$$

Substituting these results into (9–32) and noting that [see Eq. (9–38)] there are two poles for each value of k, we obtain

$$v_m(t) = 1 - \frac{1}{n} \sum_{k=1}^{n} \cot \phi_k \sin 2m\phi_k \cos \omega_k t. \qquad (9\text{–}40)$$

To evaluate $i_m(t)$ [see Eq. (9–33)], we use (9–35) and (9–38) to obtain

$$Z_0(s_k) = \frac{Ls_k}{\sinh \gamma_k} = \frac{Ls_k}{j \sin 2\phi_k} = \pm \sqrt{\frac{L}{C}} \frac{1}{\cos \phi_k} . \qquad (9\text{–}41)$$

Substituting (9–39) and (9–41) into (9–33) yields

$$i_m(t) = \frac{1}{n} \sqrt{\frac{C}{L}} \sum_{k=1}^{n} \frac{\cos^2 \phi_k \cos 2m\phi_k \sin \omega_k t}{\sin \phi_k}, \quad m = 1, 2, \ldots, n. \; \blacktriangle \; (9\text{–}42)$$

In the derivation of (9–32) and (9–33), it has been assumed that it is possible to complete the path of integration in the left half of the s-plane. It is for this reason that (9–42) is not valid for $m = 0$. This can be seen from Fig. 9–8. The first network element is a capacitor. If a step voltage is applied at the input, an infinite current pulse is required to charge the capacitor to the required voltage. This term can be obtained by considering the current transform (9–24b). Substituting (9–35) yields

$$I_m = \frac{1}{Ls^2} \frac{\sinh (n - m)\gamma \sinh \gamma}{\cosh n\gamma} .$$

It follows from (9–34) that $e^\gamma \cong LCs^2$, for $s \to \infty$. Thus

$$I_m \cong \frac{1}{2Ls^2} e^{(1-m)\gamma} \cong \frac{1}{2Ls^2} \left(\frac{1}{LCs^2} \right)^{m-1} .$$

If $m \geq 1$, it can be seen that I_m satisfies the conditions [see Eq. (2–20)] required to complete the path of integration in the left half of the s-plane. However, for $m = 0$, we obtain

$$\lim_{s \to \infty} I_0(s) = \frac{C}{2} . \qquad (9\text{–}43)$$

If we define $I_0'(s)$ by means of

$$I_0(s) = \frac{C}{2} + I_0'(s), \tag{9–44}$$

it follows from (9–43) that $\lim_{s \to \infty} I_0'(s) = 0$. Thus the path of integration required to evaluate $i_0'(t)$ can be completed in the left half of the s-plane. Since $I_0(s)$ and $I_0'(s)$ have the same poles, this leads to (9–42), with $m = 0$. The inverse transform of (9–44) is thus

$$i_0(t) = \frac{C}{2} \delta(t) + \frac{1}{n} \sqrt{\frac{C}{L}} \sum_{k=1}^{n} \frac{\cos^2 \phi_k \sin \omega_k t}{\sin \phi_k}.$$

The first term in this expression represents the current impulse required to charge the first capacitor to a voltage of 1 volt.

The fact that $Z_0(s)$ contributes no additional poles to I_m can be verified by considering (9–35). These additional poles would occur at the zeros of $Z_0(s)$. However, the apparent zero of $Z_0(s)$ at $s = 0$ is cancelled by the sinh γ term in the denominator. This can be seen from (9–34), which yields, for small s, $\gamma^2 \cong LCs^2$. Thus

$$Z_0(s) \cong \frac{Ls}{\sqrt{LC} \cdot s} = \sqrt{L/C}, \tag{9–45}$$

which is finite. This explains why the first term vanishes in (9–33).

The voltage-transfer function for the case where $n = m = 5$ is obtained from (9–24a) and has the form

$$H_5(s) = \frac{1}{\cosh 5\gamma}.$$

The frequency-response characteristics of H_5 are shown in Fig. 9–9. The poles are determined by (9–38). By substituting $s = j\omega$ into (9–34), it is seen that γ will be pure imaginary, provided that

$$|\omega| < \omega_c = \frac{2}{\sqrt{LC}},$$

which determines the *cut-off frequency* for this filter. If $|\omega| > \omega_c$, γ is real and $|H_5(j\omega)|$ decays rapidly to zero with increasing frequency. In the pass band, the phase changes by $-\pi$ each time ω passes through a pole. Figure 9–10 shows the voltage response $v_5(t)$ to a unit-step input. It is possible to interpret this response by comparing this filter with a lossless distributed-parameter transmission line with the same terminal conditions. The analysis of these lines is considered in Chapter 11. The dashed rectangular waveform in Fig. 9–10 illustrates the output response. This can

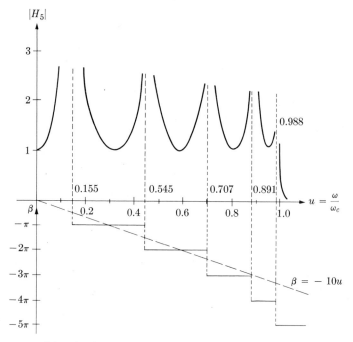

Fig. 9–9.   Magnitude and phase characteristics for the function $H_5 = (\cosh 5\gamma)^{-1}$.

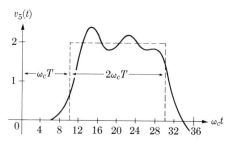

Fig. 9–10.   Unit-step output response for an open-circuited low-pass filter with five π-sections.

be interpreted in the following manner. The application of a unit-step voltage to the transmission line results in the propagation of a voltage wave of unit amplitude down the line. After a time T, this incident wave reaches the open-circuited output terminal, and a reflected wave of unit amplitude is generated. The output voltage consists of the superposition of both of these waves and has an amplitude of $+2$. This reflected wave takes a time T before it reaches the input, where it gives rise to a second incident wave with an amplitude of -1. When the second incident wave reaches the output terminal, it gives rise to a second reflected wave with an amplitude of -1. The output voltage is obtained by superimposing all these waves. Thus

$$v_o(t) = +1 + 1 - 1 - 1 = 0, \qquad 3T < t < 5T.$$

Since the line is lossless, there is an infinite sequence of incident and reflected waves. It is seen from Fig. 9–10 that the low-pass filter approximates this behavior. The time delay T has been computed from the formula

$$T = n\sqrt{LC} = \frac{10}{\omega_c}. \tag{9–46}$$

An explanation for this choice will be given in Section 9–5, which deals with infinite filters. However, it is sufficient to note that Eq. (9–46) results in a reasonable linear approximation to the phase characteristic of $H_5(j\omega)$ if it is taken as the negative slope.

EXAMPLE 2. Suppose that a filter is composed of n bandpass sections of the π-type shown in Fig. 9–11. We have $Z_1 = L_1 s + 1/C_1 s$ and $Z_2 = 1/C_2 s$. Substituting into (9–21a) yields

$$\cosh \gamma = 1 + \frac{1}{2}\frac{C_2}{C_1} + \frac{1}{2}C_2 L_1 s^2. \tag{9–47}$$

The poles s_k are determined by (9–30), which yields

$$\cosh \gamma_k = 1 + \frac{1}{2}\frac{C_2}{C_1} + \frac{1}{2}C_2 L_1 s_k^2 = \cos \beta_k = 1 - 2\sin^2 \phi_k, \tag{9–48}$$

where $\beta_k = 2\phi_k$, and ϕ_k is defined by (9–37). Solving (9–48) for s_k yields $s_k = j\omega_k$, where

$$\omega_k = \pm \sqrt{\frac{1}{L_1 C_1}\left(1 + 4\frac{C_1}{C_2}\sin^2 \phi_k\right)}.$$

From (9–47) we obtain

$$\left[s\frac{d\cosh \gamma}{ds}\right]_{s=s_k} = C_2 L_1 s_k^2 = -C_2 L_1 \omega_k^2.$$

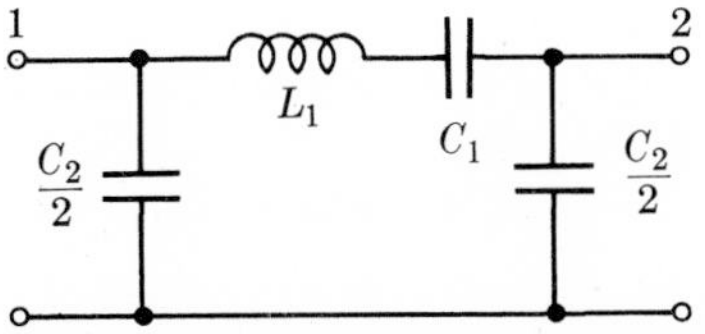

FIG. 9–11. Bandpass section with resonant series branch.

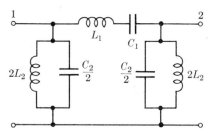

FIG. 9–12. Bandpass section with resonant series and antiresonant shunt branches.

Substituting these results into (9–32) yields

$$v_m(t) = \frac{\cosh(n-m)\gamma(0)}{\cosh n\gamma(0)} - \frac{2}{n}\sum_{k=1}^{n}\left(\frac{\omega_2}{\omega_k}\right)^2 \sin 2\phi_k \sin 2m\phi_k \cos \omega_k t,$$

where $\omega_2 = 1/\sqrt{L_1 C_2}$ and $\gamma(0)$ is determined by $\cosh\gamma(0) = 1 + \frac{1}{2}C_2/C_1$.▲

EXAMPLE 3. A band-pass filter composed of n π-sections of the type shown in Fig. 9–12 will now be considered. The elements are taken to satisfy the condition

$$\omega_1 = \frac{1}{\sqrt{L_1 C_1}} = \frac{1}{\sqrt{L_2 C_2}}.$$

We have

$$Z_1 = L_1\left(s + \frac{\omega_1^2}{s}\right),$$

$$\frac{1}{2Z_2} = \frac{C_2}{2}\left(s + \frac{\omega_1^2}{s}\right). \tag{9–49}$$

Thus

$$\cosh\gamma = 1 + \frac{2}{\omega_2^2}\left(s + \frac{\omega_1^2}{s}\right)^2, \tag{9–50}$$

where $\omega_2 = 2/\sqrt{L_1 C_2}$.

The poles s_k are found by using the substitutions (9–27) and (9–37) and solving

$$1 + \frac{2}{\omega_2^2}\left(s_k + \frac{\omega_1^2}{s_k}\right)^2 = 1 - 2\sin^2\phi_k \tag{9–51}$$

for $s_k = j\omega_k$. This yields

$$\omega_k = \pm a_k \pm b_k, \tag{9–52}$$

where

$$a_k = \frac{\omega_2}{2}\sin\phi_k \qquad b_k = \sqrt{\omega_1^2 + \left(\frac{\omega_2\sin\phi_k}{2}\right)^2}.$$

For each value of k there are thus four possible choices of sign in (9–52) leading to four different roots. These can be designated by $s_k = \pm j\omega_{k1}$, $\pm j\omega_{k2}$, where

$$\omega_{k1} = b_k - a_k, \qquad \omega_{k2} = b_k + a_k.$$

From (9–50) we obtain

$$\left[s \frac{d\cosh\gamma}{ds} \right]_{s=s_k} = \frac{4}{\omega_2^2} \left(s_k + \frac{\omega_1^2}{s_k} \right) \left(s_k - \frac{\omega_1^2}{s_k} \right) = -\frac{16}{\omega_2^2} (\pm a_k)(\pm b_k). \tag{9–53}$$

The final result in (9–53) follows from (9–51), which yields

$$s_k + \frac{\omega_1^2}{s_k} = \pm j\omega_2 \sin\phi_k = \pm j \cdot 2a_k,$$

and from (9–52), which yields

$$s_k - \frac{\omega_1^2}{s_k} = 2s_k - \left(s_k + \frac{\omega_1^2}{s_k} \right) = 2(s_k \mp ja_k) = \pm j2b_k.$$

It follows from (9–50) that $\gamma \to \infty$ for $s \to 0$. Thus

$$\frac{\cosh(n-m)\gamma}{\cosh n\gamma} \to 0.$$

Substituting these results into (9–32) yields

$$v_m(t) = \frac{\omega_2}{2n\omega_1} \sum_{k=1}^{n} \frac{\cos\phi_k \sin 2m\phi_k}{\sqrt{1 + [(\omega_2/2\omega_1)\sin\phi_k]^2}} (\cos\omega_{k1}t - \cos\omega_{k2}t),$$
$$m = 1, 2, \ldots, n$$

[note that careful consideration must be given to the choice of signs in (9–53) and the manner in which they are associated with $\pm\omega_{k1}$ and $\pm\omega_{k2}$].▲

We now discuss the case of a short-circuit termination. Suppose that the input is a unit step $V_0 = 1/s$. It follows from (9–25) that the poles of V_m and I_m are determined by $s = 0$ and by the roots of

$$\sinh n\gamma(s) = 0. \tag{9–54}$$

These roots are designated by s_k. Equation (9–54) requires that $\gamma(s_k)$ be pure imaginary. Thus

$$\gamma(s_k) = \gamma_k = j\beta_k, \tag{9–55}$$

where

$$\sin n\beta_k = 0. \tag{9–56}$$

The roots of this equation are

$$\beta_k = \frac{\pi k}{n}, \qquad k = 1, 2, \ldots, n - 1. \tag{9–57}$$

The poles s_k are determined by (9–30). In the case of V_m, values of k other than those indicated by (9–57) need not be considered, since they do not result in additional poles. The values $k = 0$ and $k = n$ do not result in poles, since the zero of $\sinh n\gamma$ is cancelled by the zero of $\sinh (n - m)\gamma$. The same is true for I_m in the case of π-network sections. This can be seen by substituting (9–21b) into (9–25b).

To determine the inverse transform of I_m with the aid of the Heaviside expansion, the function

$$F(s) = \frac{V_0 \cosh (n - m)\gamma}{Z_0(d/ds)(\sinh n\gamma)}$$

must be evaluated at the poles s_k ($k = 1, 2, \ldots, n - 1$). In the case of lattice or T-network sections, the value $k = n$ results in a pole s_n and $\gamma_n = j\pi$. In this case, $\sinh \gamma_n = 0$. However, it follows from (9–22b) and (9–23b) that $\sinh \gamma/Z_0$ is finite for $s = s_n$. Thus (9–25b) can be written in the form

$$I_m = V_0 \frac{\sinh \gamma}{Z_0} \frac{\cosh (n - m)\gamma}{\sinh \gamma \sinh n\gamma}.$$

To determine the contribution of the pole s_n to the response, the function

$$G(s) = V_0 \frac{\sinh \gamma}{Z_0} \frac{\cosh (n - m)\gamma}{(d/ds)(\sinh \gamma \sinh n\gamma)}$$

must be evaluated at $s = s_n$. It is easily seen that

$$G(s_n) = \tfrac{1}{2}F(s_n).$$

A general formula for the current response can be obtained if we set $F_k = 1$ ($k = 1, 2, \ldots, n - 1$), and set $F_n = 0$ for a π-section and $F_n = \frac{1}{2}$ for a lattice or T-section. Using contour integration to evaluate the inverse transform of (9–25b) yields

$$i_m(t) = \frac{1}{2\pi j} \oint_{s=0} \frac{\cosh (n - m)\gamma}{sZ_0 \sinh n\gamma} e^{st}\, ds$$

$$+ \sum_{k=1}^{n} F_k \frac{\cosh (n - m)\gamma_k}{s_k Z_0(s_k)\left[\dfrac{d \sinh n\gamma}{ds}\right]_{s=s_k}} e^{s_k t}. \qquad (9\text{–}58)$$

This can be simplified by means of (9–55) and (9–56). Thus

$$\cosh (n - m)\gamma_k = \cos m\beta_k \cos n\beta_k$$

$$\left[\frac{d \sinh n\gamma}{ds}\right]_{s=s_k} = \frac{n \cos n\beta_k}{j \sin \beta_k}\left[\frac{d \cosh \gamma}{ds}\right]_{s=s_k}.$$

Substituting these results into (9–58) yields

$$i_m(t) = \frac{1}{2\pi j} \oint_{s=0} \frac{\cosh (n-m)\gamma}{sZ_0 \sinh n\gamma} e^{st}\, ds$$

$$+ \frac{1}{n} \sum_{k=1}^{n} F_k \frac{j \sin \beta_k \cos m\beta_k}{Z_0(s_k)\left[s \dfrac{d \cosh \gamma}{ds}\right]_{s=s_k}} e^{s_k t}. \qquad (9\text{–}59)$$

EXAMPLE 4. Equation (9–59) will now be applied to a filter composed of low-pass π-network sections (Fig. 9–8). The terms in the sum can be evaluated with the aid of (9–39) and (9–41), which apply for this type of section. To evaluate the integral, consider the integrand

$$I(s)e^{st} = \frac{\cosh (n-m)\gamma \sinh \gamma}{Ls^2 \sinh n\gamma} e^{st},$$

where Z_0 has been eliminated with the aid of (9–35). It follows from (9–34) that $\gamma \cong LCs^2$ as $s \to 0$. Thus $I(s)$ has a second-order pole at $s = 0$. The pole coefficient is

$$F(s) = \frac{\cosh (n-m)\gamma \sinh \gamma}{L \sinh n\gamma} e^{st} = \frac{1}{nL} (1 + st + \cdots),$$

where a Taylor series expansion at $s = 0$ has been used. Thus

$$F^{(1)}(0) = \frac{t}{nL}.$$

Substituting these results into (9–59) yields

$$i_m(t) = \frac{t}{nL} + \frac{1}{n}\sqrt{\frac{C}{L}} \sum_{k=1}^{n-1} \frac{\cos^2 \phi_k \cos 2m\phi_k \sin \omega_k t}{\sin \phi_k}.$$

The fact that $i_m(t) \to \infty$ as $t \to \infty$ is a result of the assumption that the network elements are lossless. In any actual network, the current would be limited by the fact that there is always some loss in the elements. ▲

EXAMPLE 5. Consider a network composed of T-sections, as shown in Fig. 9–13, with a short-circuit termination. We have $Z_1 = R$ and $Z_2 = 1/Cs$. Thus

$$A = \cosh \gamma = 1 + \frac{RC}{2} s. \qquad (9\text{–}60)$$

For the short-circuit termination, the results given by (9–55) and (9–57) can be used. If we substitute $\gamma = j\beta_k = j2\phi_k$ into (9–60) and solve for

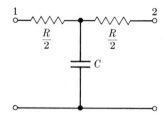

FIG. 9–13. RC T-section.

the roots s_k, we obtain

$$s_k = -\frac{4}{RC}\sin^2\phi_k, \qquad k = 1, 2, \ldots, n.$$

We have

$$\left[s\,\frac{d\cosh\gamma}{ds}\right]_{s=s_k} = \frac{RC}{2}\,s_k = -2\sin^2\phi_k.$$

It follows from (9–22b) that

$$Z_0(s_k) = \frac{1}{Cs_k}\sinh\gamma_k = \frac{j\sin 2\phi_k}{Cs_k},$$

and that the integrand of the integral in (9–59) is, for $s \cong 0$,

$$C\,\frac{\cosh(n-m)\gamma e^{st}}{\sinh\gamma\sinh n\gamma} \cong \frac{C}{n\gamma^2} \cong \frac{1}{nRs}.$$

The fact that $\gamma^2 \cong RCs$ for $s \cong 0$ follows from (9–60). There is thus a simple pole at $s = 0$ and the residue is $1/nR$. Substituting these results into (9–59) yields

$$i_m(t) = \frac{1}{nR}\left[1 + (-1)^m e^{s_n t} + 2\sum_{k=1}^{n-1}\cos 2m\phi_k e^{s_k t}\right].\ \blacktriangle$$

9–5 The infinite filter. Consider a filter composed of n identical symmetrical ($a = 1$) sections. If the output is terminated in the characteristic impedance Z_0, (9–17) and (9–18) apply and yield

$$\frac{V_n}{V_0} = \frac{I_n}{I_0} = e^{-n\gamma} \tag{9–61}$$

Since the input impedance is Z_0, we obtain

$$V_n = V_0 e^{-n\gamma},$$

$$I_n = \frac{V_0}{Z_0}e^{-n\gamma}. \tag{9–62}$$

In general the impedance Z_0 is not physically realizable. It is, however, possible to approximate Z_0 over a specified frequency range by means of physically realizable elements. In a mathematical sense, Z_0 can be realized by considering the filter to be composed of an infinite number of sections. In this case the condition $V_n/I_n = V_0/I_0$ applies for any n, and this again results in (9–61) and (9–62).

The importance of the infinite filter lies not only in the considerable mathematical simplicity of (9–62) over (9–20), but also in the insight that it yields concerning filter behavior. If, for example, a low-pass filter is excited by a voltage source, it is permissible to approximate the voltage response by means of a voltage wave propagating with a finite velocity through the various sections. The propagation characteristics of this wave are governed by the factor $e^{-n\gamma}$. When this voltage wave reaches the termination, it gives rise to a reflected wave, which is governed by the factor $e^{n\gamma}$. (It is for this reason that γ is called the propagation function.) The resultant waveform then consists of linear combinations of these exponentials, which results in (9–20) with $m = 0$. If the load termination is the characteristic impedance, or if the filter is infinitely long, there is no reflected wave. Thus the term $e^{n\gamma}$ does not occur in (9–62). Actually, since the filter is composed of lumped-parameter elements, the representation of the response in terms of waves is only approximate. However, in the discussion of Example 1, we have seen that the approximation is a useful one (see Fig. 9–10). For distributed-parameter systems, an exact formulation in terms of incident and reflected waves is possible. This will be discussed in subsequent chapters. Here, however, it is sufficient to note the following. For a low-pass filter we have obtained the result [see the discussion of Eq. (9–45)] that $\gamma^2 \cong LCs^2$ for $s \cong 0$. Substituting this into (9–61) yields $V_n \cong V_0 e^{-n\sqrt{LC}s} = V_0 e^{-Ts}$. The filter, for small s, thus approximates the properties of a delay line having a time delay $T = n\sqrt{LC}$ [see Eq. (9–46)].

EXAMPLE 6. Consider an infinite filter composed of symmetrical lattice sections of the type shown in Fig. 9–14. We have $Z_1 = Ls$ and $Z_2 = 1/Cs$. Equations (9–23) yield

$$\cosh \gamma = \frac{1 + p^2}{1 - p^2}, \quad \text{and} \quad Z_0 = \sqrt{L/C}, \qquad (9\text{–}63)$$

where $s = \omega_c p$ and $\omega_c = 1/\sqrt{LC}$. The propagation function can be found from

$$e^\gamma = \cosh \gamma + \sinh \gamma \qquad (9\text{–}64\text{a})$$

$$= \frac{1 + p}{1 - p}. \qquad (9\text{–}64\text{b})$$

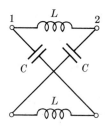

FIG. 9–14. LC lattice section.

Substituting this into (9–61) yields

$$V_n(s) = V_0(s) \left(\frac{1 - p}{1 + p} \right)^n . \tag{9–65}$$

If the input is a unit step, (9–65) takes the form

$$\omega_c V_n(s) = \omega_c V_n[p] = (-1)^n \frac{p + 1}{p} \frac{(p - 1)^n}{(p + 1)^{n+1}} .$$

The inverse transform of this expression can be found with the aid of Appendix (B–8). Note that $1/p$ represents integration with respect to τ in the time domain. Applying the scaling theorem, we obtain

$$v_n(t) = \omega_c v_n[\tau] = (-1)^n \left[e^{-\tau} L_n(2\tau) + \int_0^\tau e^{-u} L_n(2u) \cdot du \right], \tag{9–66}$$

where $\tau = \omega_c t$ and $L_n(x)$ is the *Laguerre polynomial of order n*. Equation (9–66) can be expressed explicitly in terms of τ and $e^{-\tau}$ [see Appendix (B–9) and (B–11)]. For this particular filter, a resistive termination, $Z_0 = \sqrt{L/C}$, can be used. ▲

EXAMPLE 7. An infinite filter composed of low-pass T-sections will now be considered (Fig. 9–6). We have $Z_1 = Ls$ and $Z_2 = 1/Cs$. It follows from (9–22a) that

$$\cosh \gamma = 1 + 2p^2, \tag{9–67}$$

where $s = \omega_c p$ and $\omega_c = 2/\sqrt{LC}$.

To determine γ, $\sinh \gamma$ is first found by means of

$$\sinh \gamma = \sqrt{(\cosh \gamma - 1)(\cosh \gamma + 1)} \tag{9–68a}$$

$$= 2p\sqrt{1 + p^2}. \tag{9–68b}$$

Substituting (9–67) and (9–68b) into (9–64a) yields

$$e^\gamma = 1 + 2p^2 + 2p\sqrt{1 + p^2} = (p + \sqrt{1 + p^2})^2. \tag{9–69}$$

The characteristic impedance is determined from (9–22b). Thus

$$Z_0 = \frac{2}{\omega_c C}\sqrt{1+p^2} = \sqrt{\frac{L}{C}}\sqrt{1+p^2}. \tag{9–70}$$

Substituting (9–69) and (9–70) into (9–62) and taking $V_0 = 1/s$ yields

$$\omega_c I_n(s) = \omega_c I_n[p] = \sqrt{\frac{C}{L}}\frac{1}{p}\frac{(p+\sqrt{1+p^2})^{-2n}}{\sqrt{1+p^2}}. \tag{9–71}$$

This transform is an irrational function of p, and its singularities are no longer just poles. Thus the method of determining the inverse transform based on pole coefficients and Cauchy's integral formula is no longer applicable. This is a consequence of the fact that the network now contains an infinite number of elements. The methods to be used to determine the inverse transforms of expressions of the type (9–71) consist of algebraic manipulations to reduce them to standard tabulated transforms. The required transform is [see Appendix (D–11a)]

$$\mathcal{L}[J_n(\tau)] = \frac{(p+\sqrt{1+p^2})^{-n}}{\sqrt{1+p^2}}, \tag{9–72}$$

where $J_n(t)$ is the Bessel function of the first kind of order n.

The factor $1/p$ in (9–71) represents integration with respect to τ in the time domain. Thus, with the aid of (9–72), we obtain

$$i_n(t) = \omega_c i_n[\tau] = \sqrt{\frac{C}{L}}\int_0^\tau J_{2n}(u)\,du, \tag{9–73}$$

where $\tau = \omega_c t = 2t/\sqrt{LC}$. ▲

EXAMPLE 8. This example differs from the previous one in that the sections are of the high-pass type (Fig. 9–15). Thus $Z_1 = 1/Cs$ and $Z_2 = Ls$. Substituting into (9–22a) yields

$$\cosh\gamma = 1 + \frac{2}{p^2},$$

where $s = \omega_c p$ and $\omega_c = 1/2\sqrt{LC}$.

The propagation function is determined from (9–64a). Thus

$$e^\gamma = \left[\frac{1}{p}+\sqrt{1+\frac{1}{p^2}}\right]^2; \tag{9–74}$$

Z_0 is determined from (9–22b):

$$Z_0 = \sqrt{\frac{L}{C}}\sqrt{1+\frac{1}{p^2}}. \tag{9–75}$$

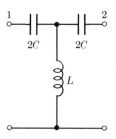

FIG. 9–15. High-pass T-section.

Substituting (9–74) and (9–75) into (9–62) and taking $V_0 = 1/s$ yields

$$\omega_c I_n(s) = \omega_c I_n[p] = \sqrt{\frac{C}{L}} \frac{1}{p} \frac{1}{\sqrt{1 + 1/p^2}} \left[\frac{1}{p} + \sqrt{1 + \frac{1}{p^2}} \right]^{-2n}. \qquad (9\text{–}76)$$

The similarity of (9–76) with the low-pass case (9–71) should be noted. If the right-hand sides of Eqs. (9–71) and (9–76) are denoted by $G(p)$ and $H(p)$, respectively, it is seen that

$$H\left(\frac{1}{p}\right) = p^2 G(p). \qquad (9\text{–}77)$$

A transformation of the type $p \leftrightarrow 1/p$ is known as a low-pass to high-pass transformation and is used extensively in network theory to derive high-pass filters from low-pass prototypes. It is of interest to inquire if there is then any relationship between the transient responses. Stated in mathematical terms, we inquire into the possibility of determining $h(\tau) = \mathcal{L}^{-1}[H(p)]$ if $g(\tau) = \mathcal{L}^{-1}[G(p)]$ is known. The required relationship is [see Appendix (D–33)]

$$h(\tau) = \int_0^\infty J_0(2\sqrt{u\tau}) \frac{dg(u)}{du} du. \qquad (9\text{–}78)$$

Applying this to (9–76) and noting that $g(u)$ is the right-hand side of (9–73), we obtain

$$i_n(t) = \omega_c i_n[\tau] = \sqrt{\frac{C}{L}} \int_0^\infty J_0(2\sqrt{\omega_c tu}) J_{2n}(u)\, du. \; \blacktriangle$$

EXAMPLE 9. Figure 9–16 shows a T-section, where the inductance L has a series loss represented by the resistance R and the capacitance has a shunt loss represented by the conductance G. Thus $Z_1 = R + Ls$ and $1/Z_2 = G + Cs$. Substituting into (9–22a) yields

$$\cosh \gamma = 1 + \frac{2}{\omega_c^2} [(s + b)^2 - a^2], \qquad (9\text{–}79)$$

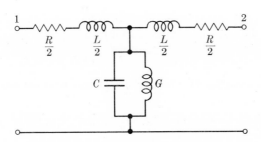

Fig. 9–16. T-section having losses.

where

$$b = \frac{1}{2}\left(\frac{R}{L} + \frac{G}{C}\right), \qquad a = \frac{1}{2}\left(\frac{R}{L} - \frac{G}{C}\right), \qquad \text{and} \qquad \omega_c = \frac{2}{\sqrt{LC}}.$$

From (9–68a), we obtain

$$\sinh \gamma = \frac{2}{\omega_c} \sqrt{(s+b)^2 - a^2} \sqrt{1 + \frac{(s+b)^2 - a^2}{\omega_c^2}}. \qquad (9\text{–}80)$$

Substituting (9–79) and (9–80) into (9–64a) yields

$$e^\gamma = \left[\frac{1}{\omega_c} \sqrt{(s+b)^2 - a^2} + \sqrt{1 + \frac{(s+b)^2 - a^2}{\omega_c^2}}\right]^2.$$

The characteristic impedance is determined by (9–22b). Thus

$$\frac{1}{Z_0} = \frac{G + Cs}{\sinh \gamma} = C \frac{s + b - a}{\sinh \gamma}.$$

Substituting these results into (9–62) and taking $V_0 = 1/s$ yields

$$I_n(s) = \sqrt{\frac{C}{L}} \frac{s + b - a}{s}$$
$$\times \frac{\{(1/\omega_c)\sqrt{(s+b)^2 - a^2} + \sqrt{1 + [(s+b)^2 - a^2]/\omega_c^2}\}^{-2n}}{\sqrt{(s+b)^2 - a^2} \cdot \sqrt{1 + [(s+b)^2 - a^2]/\omega_c^2}}.$$

The first factor in this expression can be written as $1 + (b - a)/s$, and $1/s$ interpreted as representing integration with respect to t in the time domain. The remaining factors can be simplified by application of the s-translation theorem. Thus

$$i_n(t) = e^{-bt} h(t) + (b - a)\int_0^t e^{-b\tau} h(\tau)\, d\tau, \qquad (9\text{–}81)$$

where

$$H(s) = \sqrt{\frac{C}{L}} \frac{[(1/\omega_c)\sqrt{s^2 - a^2} + \sqrt{1 + (s^2 - a^2)/\omega_c^2}]^{-2n}}{\sqrt{s^2 - a^2} \cdot \sqrt{1 + (s^2 - a^2)/\omega_c^2}}.$$

The similarity of this expression with (9–71) should be noted. If we let $\omega_c G(s)$ denote the right-hand side of (9–71), where $s = \omega_c p$, it follows that

$$H(\sqrt{s^2 + a^2}) = G(s). \tag{9–82}$$

It is shown in Appendix (D–43) that, if $H(s)$ and $G(s)$ are related by (9–82),

$$h(t) = \mathcal{L}^{-1}[H(s)] = \int_0^t I_0(a\sqrt{t^2 - u^2})\, \frac{dg(u)}{du}\, du,$$

where $I_0(t)$ is the *modified Bessel function of order zero* and $g(t) = \mathcal{L}^{-1}[G(s)]$. Noting that $g(t)$ is given by the right-hand side of (9–73) and using the substitution $x = \omega_c u$, we obtain

$$h(t) = \sqrt{\frac{C}{L}} \int_0^{\omega_c t} I_0\left(\frac{a}{\omega_c}\sqrt{(\omega_c t)^2 - x^2}\right) J_{2n}(x)\, dx. \tag{9–83}$$

Consider now the case where $a = 0$ ($R/L = G/C$). It follows from (9–81), by means of integration by parts, that

$$i_n(t) = e^{-bt} h(t) + b \int_0^t e^{-b\tau} h(\tau)\, d\tau$$

$$= e^{-bt} h(t) - e^{-b\tau} h(\tau)]_0^t + \int_0^t e^{-b\tau}\, \frac{dh(\tau)}{d\tau}\, d\tau$$

$$= \sqrt{\frac{C}{L}} \int_0^{\omega_c t} e^{-bx/\omega_c} J_{2n}(x)\, dx. \tag{9–84}$$

The final result is obtained with the aid of (9–83), where $I_0(0) = 1$. ▲

For a distributed-parameter transmission line (see Section 11–2), the condition $a = 0$ results in a distortionless response to the input. The expression (9–84) only approximates a distortionless response, and hence this case is designated as being quasi-distortionless.

9–6 Response of filters to sinusoidal inputs. Sinusoidal inputs arise, for example, in systems where the networks are of the bandpass type. Examples of the response of bandpass networks have been given in Section 4–7. It was shown that, for the narrow-band case, the response could be found by means of a bandpass to low-pass transformation.

EXAMPLE 10. Consider now an infinite filter composed of bandpass sections of the type shown in Fig. 9–12. Let ω_0 be the carrier angular frequency. Substituting $s = \omega_0 p$ into (9–50) yields

$$\cosh \gamma = 1 + 2a^2 \left(p + \frac{1}{p}\right)^2,$$

where $a = \omega_1/\omega_2$ and $\omega_0 = \omega_1$. The propagation function is determined from (9–64a). Thus

$$e^\gamma = \left[a\left(p + \frac{1}{p}\right) + \sqrt{1 + a^2\left(p + \frac{1}{p}\right)^2} \right]^2. \tag{9–85}$$

The voltage transfer function is $V_n/V_0 = e^{-n\gamma}$. However, for the narrow-band case, it is preferable to deal with the envelope transfer function V_n'/V_0', where $v_n(t) = v_n'(t) \sin \omega_0 t$ and $v_0(t) = v_0'(t) \sin \omega_0 t$. Let

$$p = j + p',$$

where $p = s/\omega_0$ is the normalized complex frequency for the spectral terms of the carrier signal and $p' = s'/\omega_0$ is the normalized complex frequency for the spectral terms of the envelope. The condition for a narrow-band system is that $|p'| \ll 1$. Consider now

$$p + \frac{1}{p} = \frac{(p + j)(p - j)}{p} \cong 2p'.$$

Substituting this into (9–85) yields

$$\frac{V_n[p]}{V_0[p]} \cong \frac{V_n'[p']}{V_0'[p']} = [2ap' + \sqrt{1 + (2ap')^2}]^{-2n}. \tag{9–86}$$

Since this is a function of p' alone, it is the desired envelope transfer function, which we will designate by $H_n(p')$. If we compare this with (9–69) and (9–67), we see that

$$H_n(p') = e^{-n\gamma}, \tag{9–87}$$

where

$$\cosh \gamma = 1 + 2(2ap')^2. \tag{9–88}$$

The envelope transfer function $H_n(p')$ is thus the same as that obtained from an infinite low-pass LC-filter. The cut off frequency is determined by $p' = j\omega_c' = j(1/2a)$, and the frequency response characteristics are found by substituting $p' = ju\omega_c'$ into (9–88). These are shown in Fig. 9–17 for the case where $n = 5$. The time delay T is obtained from (9–87) and (9–88) by considering p' to be small. We then have $\gamma \cong 4ap'$ and $e^{-n\gamma} \cong e^{-4anp'}$. Thus $T/2a = 2n$.

For a unit-step carrier input, $V'(s') = 1/s'$. Thus $V'[p'] = 1/\omega_0 p'$ and

$$\omega_0 V_n'(s') = \omega_0 V_n'[p'] = \frac{1}{p'} [2ap' + \sqrt{1 + (2ap')^2}]^{-2n}. \tag{9–89}$$

The inverse transform of this expression can be obtained from Appendix (D–10), which yields, after substituting $s = 2ap'$ and applying the scaling

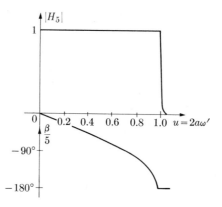

FIG. 9-17. Magnitude and phase characteristics for the function $|H_5| = e^{-5\gamma}$.

theorem,

$$\mathcal{L}\left[\frac{2n}{\tau} J_{2n}\left(\frac{\tau}{2a}\right)\right] = [2ap' + \sqrt{1 + (2ap')^2}]^{-2n}.$$

The inverse transform of (9–89) is thus

$$v'_n(t) = \omega_0 v'_n[\tau] = 2n \int_0^{\tau/2a} \frac{J_{2n}(u)}{u}\, du,$$

where $\tau = \omega_0 t$. This integral can be evaluated by means of the recurrence formulas, Appendix (D–4c) and (D–4e). These yield

$$2n \int_0^z \frac{J_{2n}(u)}{u}\, du = J_{2n} + F_{2n+1} = -J_{2n} + F_{2n-1}, \qquad (9\text{–}90)$$

where

$$F_k = \int_0^z J_k(u)\, du \qquad \text{and} \qquad J_k = J_k(z).$$

The function F_k can be evaluated by recursive application of (9–90). This yields

$$\begin{aligned}
F_{2n-1} &= F_{2n-3} - 2J_{2(n-1)} \\
&= F_{2n-5} - 2[J_{2(n-1)} + J_{2(n-2)}] \\
&\ \vdots \\
&= F_1 - 2[J_{2(n-1)} + \cdots + J_2].
\end{aligned}$$

The function F_1 can be found with the aid of Appendix (D–4c). Thus

$$F_1 = \int_0^z J_1(u)\, du = -J_0 + 1.$$

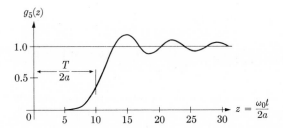

FIG. 9–18. Unit-step voltage response for the 5th section of an infinite low-pass LC-filter.

Substituting these results into (9–90) yields

$$g_n(z) = 1 - J_0(z) - J_{2n}(z) - 2 \sum_{k=1}^{n-1} J_{2k}(z),$$

where g_n represents the integral on the left-hand side of (9–90). This can be readily evaluated [1] and the case where $n = 5$ is shown in Fig. 9–18.

It is possible to derive an asymptotic expansion for g_n from (9–89) by considering the complex integral representation of the inverse transform. The result is [see Appendix (D–58)]

$$g_n \sim 1 + (-1)^n \sqrt{\frac{2}{\pi z}} \left\{ \frac{2n^2}{z} \cos\left(z - \frac{\pi}{4}\right) + \left(1 - \frac{2n^4}{z^2}\right) \sin\left(z - \frac{\pi}{4}\right) \right\},$$

which is valid for sufficiently large z. ▲

EXAMPLE 11. Consider now the excitation of an infinite low-pass filter with a sinusoidal input. The current response to a unit-step input voltage has been determined in Example 7, and is given by (9–73). The right-hand side of this equation will now be denoted by $g_n(t)$. Thus

$$g_n(t) = \sqrt{\frac{C}{L}} \int_0^\tau J_{2n}(u) \, du,$$

where $\tau = \omega_c t$. If the input voltage is $v_0(t) = \sin \omega_0 t = \sin a\tau$, where $a = \omega_0/\omega_c$, the current response can be obtained by means of the convolution theorem, which yields

$$i_n(t) = \sqrt{\frac{C}{L}} \int_0^\tau \sin a(\tau - u) J_{2n}(u) \, du. \tag{9–91}$$

An alternative possibility is to consider the input voltage transform

$$V_0(s) = \frac{\omega_0}{s^2 + \omega_0^2} = \frac{1}{\omega_c} \frac{a}{p^2 + a^2},$$

where $s = \omega_c p$. Thus $a/(p^2 + a^2)$ is to replace $1/p$ in (9–71), and we obtain

$$\omega_c I_n(s) = \omega_c I_n[p] = \sqrt{\frac{C}{L}} \frac{a}{p^2 + a^2} \frac{(p + \sqrt{1 + p^2})^{-2n}}{\sqrt{1 + p^2}}. \qquad (9\text{–}92)$$

A method of obtaining an asymptotic expansion from (9–92), which is valid for large t, is discussed in Appendix D [see (D–60) and (D–64)]. Here, however, we will discuss means of evaluating (9–92) directly. Consider the integrals

$$S_n(t) = S_n = \int_0^t J_n(u) \sin a(t - u) \, du,$$
$$\qquad (9\text{–}93)$$
$$C_n(t) = C_n = \int_0^t J_n(u) \cos a(t - u) \, du.$$

Integrating these integrals by parts and using the recurrence relations in Appendix (D–4) yields

$$C_{n+1} = 2aS_n - 2J_n + C_{n-1}, \qquad S_{n+1} = S_{n-1} - 2aC_n. \qquad (9\text{–}94)$$

It follows from (9–93) that

$$S_n = a \int_0^t C_n(u) \, du. \qquad (9\text{–}95)$$

By means of numerical integration S_0, C_0, S_1, and C_1 can be determined from (9–93) and (9–95). The remaining S_n and C_n can then be computed recursively from (9–94).

It is possible to derive an asymptotic expansion from (9–91) which is valid for large t. Equation (9–91) is first written in the form

$$i_n(t) = \sqrt{C/L} \left[\int_0^\infty J_{2n}(u) \sin a(\tau - u) \, du - \int_\tau^\infty J_{2n}(u) \sin a(\tau - u) \, du \right].$$
$$\qquad (9\text{–}96)$$

It is shown in Appendix (D–18) and (D–19) that

$$\int_0^\infty J_n(u) \sin au \, du = \begin{cases} \dfrac{\sin n\theta}{\sqrt{1 - a^2}}, & a < 1, \\[3mm] \dfrac{\cos \pi n/2}{\sqrt{a^2 - 1} \, (a + \sqrt{a^2 - 1})^n}, & a > 1, \end{cases}$$

$$\int_0^\infty J_n(u) \cos au \, du = \begin{cases} \dfrac{\cos n\theta}{\sqrt{1 - a^2}}, & a < 1, \\[3mm] \dfrac{-\sin \pi n/2}{\sqrt{a^2 - 1} \, (a + \sqrt{a^2 - 1})^n}, & a > 1, \end{cases}$$
$$\qquad (9\text{–}97)$$

where $\theta = \text{arc sin } a$.

By means of these expressions the first integral in (9–96) is easily evaluated. The remaining integral can be evaluated by means of integration by parts [note that $J_n(\infty) = 0$]:

$$\int_\tau^\infty \sin a(\tau - u)J_n(u)\,du = -\frac{1}{a}J_n(\tau) - \frac{1}{a}\int_\tau^\infty \frac{dJ_n(u)}{du}\cos a(\tau - u)\,du$$

$$= -\frac{1}{a}J_n(\tau) - \frac{1}{a^2}\int_\tau^\infty \frac{d^2J_n(u)}{du^2}\sin a(\tau - u)\,du.$$
$$(9\text{–}98)$$

From Appendix (D–1) we obtain

$$\frac{d^2J_n}{du^2} = -\frac{1}{u}\frac{dJ_n}{du} - \left(1 - \frac{n^2}{u^2}\right)J_n \cong -J_n, \qquad u \gg n.$$

Substituting this into (9–98) yields

$$\int_\tau^\infty \sin a(\tau - u)J_n(u)\,du \cong \frac{-a}{a^2 - 1}J_n(\tau). \qquad (9\text{–}99)$$

With the aid of (9–97) and (9–99) we can write (9–91) in the form

$$i_n(t) \cong \sqrt{\frac{C}{L}}\left\{\frac{\sin(a\tau - 2n\theta)}{\sqrt{1 - a^2}} + \frac{a}{a^2 - 1}J_{2n}(\tau)\right\}, \qquad (9\text{–}100a)$$

which is valid for $a < 1$, and

$$i_n(t) \cong \sqrt{\frac{C}{L}}\left\{\frac{(-1)^{n+1}\cos a\tau}{\sqrt{a^2 - 1}\,(a + \sqrt{a^2 - 1})^{2n}} + \frac{a}{a^2 - 1}J_{2n}(\tau)\right\}, \qquad (9\text{–}100b)$$

which is valid for $a > 1$.

It is thus seen that when ω_0 is outside the pass-band of the filter ($a > 1$), the sections near the input respond with a finite amplitude in the steady state. This results from the fact that the input contains spectral terms within the pass band and that a finite energy is associated with these terms. Since the filter is considered to be lossless, the oscillations excited by these spectral terms do not damp out.

The energy input to the filter in the steady state can be discussed with the aid of (9–70) which, substituting $p = ja$ yields

$$Z_0 = \sqrt{\frac{L}{C}}\sqrt{1 - a^2},$$

where Z_0 is real for $a < 1$ and pure imaginary for $a > 1$. In the steady state there is thus, for $a > 1$, no average energy flow into the filter. The finite solution (9–100b) arises from the fact that there is a flow of energy into the filter during the transient condition.

For $a = 1$, (9–100) yields an infinite current response. This special case can be treated by considering (9–91). This integral is evaluated in the Appendix [see Appendix (D–28)]. The result is

$$i_n(t) = \sqrt{\frac{C}{L}} \{\tau J_{2n+1} + (-1)^n$$
$$\times 2n[\cos \tau - J_0 + 2J_1 - \cdots + (-1)^{n+1}2J_{2n}]\},$$

where $J_k = J_k(\tau)$ and $\tau = \omega_c t$.

For large τ we can use the asymptotic formula [see Appendix (D–53)]

$$J_n(\tau) \sim \sqrt{\frac{2}{\pi\tau}} \cos\left(\tau - \frac{2n+1}{4}\pi\right),$$

and obtain

$$i_n(t) \sim \sqrt{\frac{C}{L}} (-1)^{n+1} \left\{\sqrt{\frac{2\tau}{\pi}} \cos\left(\tau + \frac{\pi}{4}\right) - 2n \cos \tau\right\}. \; \blacktriangle$$

9–7 The finite filter with source and load impedances. In all the previous examples the source impedance was zero and the load impedance was taken to be either Z_0, a short circuit, or an open circuit. Consider now a filter of n sections terminated in a load impedance Z_l and driven from a voltage source having an internal impedance Z_g (see Fig. 9–19). We have

$$V_g = V_0 + Z_g I_0, \qquad V_n = Z_l I_n.$$

With the aid of (9–20) we obtain, for $m = 0$,

$$V_g = I_n \left[(Z_l + Z_g) \cosh n\gamma + \left(\frac{Z_l Z_g}{Z_0} + Z_0\right) \sinh n\gamma\right]. \qquad (9\text{--}101)$$

Thus the current and voltage transforms for the load are

$$I_n = \frac{V_g}{D}, \qquad V_n = \frac{Z_l V_g}{D}, \qquad (9\text{--}102)$$

where

$$D = D(s) = (Z_l + Z_g) \cosh n\gamma + \left(\frac{Z_l Z_g}{Z_0} + Z_0\right) \sinh n\gamma.$$

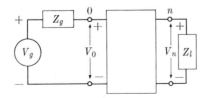

FIG. 9–19. Finite filter with source and load impedances.

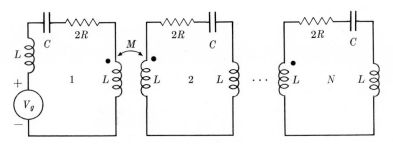

FIG. 9–20. Transformer-coupled network.

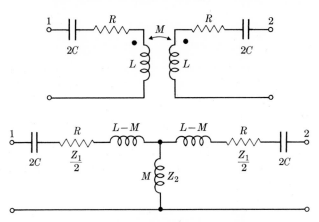

FIG. 9–21. Equivalent T-section.

The solution of the equation $D(s) = 0$ for the poles and the determination of the inverse transform of (9–102) can, in general, be carried out only with the aid of numerical methods. A case where an analytic solution is possible will now be discussed.

EXAMPLE 12. Fig. 9–20 shows a network consisting of N identical transformer-coupled network sections, where the first section is driven by a voltage source V_g. It is possible to reduce this network to a filter composed of T-sections as shown in Fig. 9–21. The number of such sections is $n = N - 1$. Consideration of the first and last sections indicate that the load impedance is

$$Z_l = R + Ls + \frac{1}{2Cs},$$

and that we must consider this network to be driven through an impedance $Z_g = Z_l$. From (9–22) we obtain

$$\cosh \gamma = 1 + \frac{Z_1}{2Z_2} = \frac{Z_l}{Z_2}, \qquad Z_0 = Z_2 \sinh \gamma.$$

Furthermore

$$\frac{Z_0^2 + Z_l^2}{Z_0} = \frac{Z_2 \cosh 2\gamma}{\sinh \gamma}.$$

Substituting these results into (9–101) yields

$$I_n = \frac{V_g}{Z_2} \frac{\sinh \gamma}{\sinh (N + 1)\gamma}. \tag{9–103}$$

The poles of I_n are determined by the poles of V_g and the roots of the equation $\sinh (N + 1)\gamma = 0$. This yields $\gamma_k = j\beta_k$, where

$$\beta_k = \frac{\pi k}{N + 1}, \qquad k = 1, 2, \ldots, N.$$

Consider now a unit-step input $V_g = 1/s$. The apparent pole at $s = 0$ is cancelled by the numerator term. This can be seen from

$$\cosh \gamma = 1 + \frac{1}{2MCs^2} + \frac{R}{Ms} + \frac{L}{M}, \tag{9–104}$$

which yields $e^\gamma \cong 1/MCs^2$, for $s \cong 0$. Thus $I_n \cong (1/Ms^2)e^{-N\gamma} \cong 0$.

The inverse transform of (9–103) can be obtained by means of the Heaviside expansion

$$i_n(t) = \sum_{k=1}^{N} \frac{\sinh \gamma_k}{Ms_k^2[(d/ds) \sinh (N + 1)\gamma]_{s=s_k}} e^{s_k t}. \tag{9–105}$$

This can be simplified by noting that

$$\left[\frac{d}{ds} \sinh (N + 1)\gamma\right]_{s=s_k} = \frac{(N + 1) \cos (N + 1)\beta_k}{j \sin \beta_k} \left[\frac{d \cosh \gamma}{ds}\right]_{s=s_k}. \tag{9–106}$$

Furthermore, it follows from (9–104) that

$$M\left[s^2 \frac{d \cosh \gamma}{ds}\right]_{s=s_k} = -\left(\frac{1}{Cs_k} + R\right). \tag{9–107}$$

The poles s_k are determined from (9–104) by substituting $\gamma = j\beta_k$ and solving for s_k. This yields

$$s_k = -\sigma_k \pm j\omega_k,$$

where $\sigma_k = R/2L_k$,

$$\omega_k = \sqrt{\frac{1}{2L_kC} - \left(\frac{R}{2L_k}\right)^2},$$

and $L_k = L - M \cos \beta_k$. (It follows from the formula $M = K\sqrt{L_1L_2}$, where $K < 1$, that $L/M \geq 1$. Thus $L_k > 0$.)

It is possible to simplify (9–107) by noting that

$$|s_k|^2 = \frac{1}{2L_kC}, \qquad s_k + s_k^* = -\frac{R}{L_k}$$

and considering

$$\frac{Cs_k}{1 + RCs_k} \frac{1 + RCs_k^*}{1 + RCs_k^*} = \frac{C(\pm j\omega_k)}{1 - RC\sigma_k}. \qquad (9\text{–}108)$$

Substituting (9–106), (9–107), and (9–108) into (9–105) yields

$$i_n(t) = \frac{2C}{N+1} \sum_{k=1}^{N} (-1)^{k+1} \frac{\omega_k e^{-\sigma_k t} \sin^2 \beta_k \sin \omega_k t}{1 - RC\sigma_k}. \; \blacktriangle$$

9–8 Mechanical filters [2]. All the results of this chapter apply to any physical system which can be represented by an analogous mathematical model. Let us consider, for example, a mechanical filter composed of lumped-inertia elements each having a moment of inertia J. Let K be the torsion constant, so that the transform of the torque acting on the output of the mth section is $T_{m+1} = K(\Theta_{m+1} - \Theta_m)$, where Θ_m is the transform of the shaft rotation (Fig. 9–22). The equation of rotary motion for the mth inertia element is, in transform notation,

$$Js^2\Theta_m = T_{m+1} - T_m. \qquad (9\text{–}109)$$

In order to determine a suitable network analog, we substitute $s\Theta_m = I_m$ and $V_m = -T_m$ into (9–109), which yields

$$JsI_m = V_m - V_{m+1}.$$

Since

$$V_m = -T_m = \frac{K}{s}(I_{m-1} - I_m),$$

it is seen that the LC-network shown in Fig. 9–23 is a suitable network analog if we choose $C = K^{-1}$ and $J = L$. Note that $i_m(t)$ is taken to represent the current in the series branch, and that this current is analogous

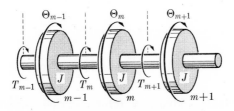

Fig. 9–22. Mechanical filter.

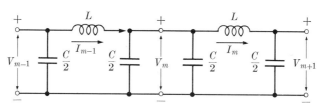

FIG. 9–23. Network analog of mechanical filter.

to the angular velocity. The voltage $v_m(t)$ is analogous to the torque acting on the input to the mth section. Note that dynamic equilibrium requires this torque to be equal and opposite to the torque T_m acting on the output of the $(m - 1)$th section.

If the mechanical filter has a free end, this means that $T_n = 0$. Thus $V_n = 0$, and the network is terminated in a short circuit. If the mechanical filter has a clamped end, $\Theta_n = 0 = I_n$, and the network is terminated in an open circuit.

9–9 Filter networks for obtaining orthogonal functions. An important problem occurring in the study of communication and control systems is the representation of a signal or impulse response, $h'(t)$, in terms of a fundamental set of functions [3, 4]. Let these be designated by $h_k(t)$ and let

$$h(t) = \sum_{k=0}^{n} c_k h_k(t), \qquad (9\text{–}110)$$

where the coefficients c_k are chosen to minimize, in some sense, the error $\epsilon = h' - h$. It is convenient to introduce the notation

$$(g, h) = \int_0^\infty g(t)h(t)\, dt$$

and to define this as the scalar product of g and h. The functions are taken to be *orthonormal*, i.e.,

$$(h_k, h_m) = \begin{cases} 0, & k \neq m, \\ 1, & k = m. \end{cases} \qquad (9\text{–}111)$$

Equation (9–110) is a representation of $h(t)$ in terms of an orthonormal set of functions $h_k(t)$. The coefficient c_m is obtained by scalar multiplication of h with h_m. Thus, with the aid of (9–111)

$$(h, h_m) = \sum_{k=0}^{n} c_k(h_k, h_m) = c_m. \qquad (9\text{–}112)$$

The most convenient choice of error criterion is to minimize $f(\epsilon) = (\epsilon, \epsilon)$ by choice of c_k, which yields the least mean-square error. This requires that

$$\frac{\partial f}{\partial c_k} = \left(\epsilon, \frac{\partial \epsilon}{\partial c_k} \right) + \left(\frac{\partial \epsilon}{\partial c_k}, \epsilon \right) = 2 \left(\epsilon, \frac{\partial \epsilon}{\partial c_k} \right) = 0, \qquad k = 0, 1, \ldots, n.$$
(9-113)

From the definition of the error and (9-110) it follows that $\partial \epsilon / \partial c_k = -h_k$. Substituting this into (9-113) yields $(\epsilon, h_k) = 0$. Thus $(h', h_k) = c_k = (h, h_k)$. With this choice of c_k, the function $h(t)$ represents the best approximation to $h'(t)$ in the sense that $f(\epsilon)$ is a minimum.

We now discuss means of realizing the condition (9-112) by means of filters. This is based on *Parseval's identity*

$$\int_0^\infty f(t)g(t)\, dt = \frac{1}{2\pi j} \int_{-j\infty}^{+j\infty} F(s)G(-s)\, ds, \qquad (9\text{-}114)$$

which can be proved by substituting $f(t) = \mathcal{L}^{-1}[F(s)]$ into the left-hand integral and interchanging the order of integration. Thus

$$\frac{1}{2\pi j} \int_{-j\infty}^{+j\infty} F(s) \left\{ \int_0^\infty g(t)e^{st}\, dt \right\} ds = \frac{1}{2\pi j} \int_{-j\infty}^{+j\infty} F(s)G(-s)\, ds. \qquad (9\text{-}115)$$

All poles of $F(s)$ and $G(s)$ must be located to the left of the path of integration. Due to the substitution of $-s$ for s used in (9-115), this requires that all poles of $G(-s)$ be located to the right. Thus the path of integration has the poles of $F(s)$ to the left and those of $G(-s)$ to the right.

Consider now the transfer function

$$H_n(s) = \frac{\sqrt{2a_n}}{s + a_n} G_n(s),$$

where

$$G_n(s) = \left(\frac{a_{n-1} - s}{a_{n+1} + s} \right) \cdots \left(\frac{a_0 - s}{a_0 + s} \right),$$

and $a_k > 0$ is real, $(k = 0, 1, \ldots, n)$. It follows that

$$H_n(s)H_n(-s) = \frac{-2a_n}{(s + a_n)(s - a_n)}.$$

The path of integration can be completed in either the left half or right half of the s-plane and encloses the pole $s = -a_n$ or $s = a_n$, respectively. The result, for either case, is the same

$$\frac{1}{2\pi j} \int_{-j\infty}^{+j\infty} H_n(s)H_n(-s)\, ds = 1 = \int_0^\infty h_n^2(t)\, dt.$$

Parseval's identity has been used here to show that $h_n(t)$ satisfies one of the conditions (9–111). The fact that the other condition is satisfied can be seen by noting that for $n > k$,

$$H_n(s)H_k(-s) = \frac{2\sqrt{a_n a_k}}{(s + a_n)(s + a_k)}\left(\frac{a_{n-1} - s}{a_{n-1} + s}\right)\cdots\left(\frac{a_{k+1} - s}{a_{k+1} + s}\right) \quad (9\text{–}116)$$

does not contain any poles in the right half of the s-plane. The path of integration can then be completed to the right and, since no poles are enclosed, it follows from Cauchy's theorem that

$$\frac{1}{2\pi j}\int_{-j\infty}^{+j\infty} H_n(s)H_k(-s)\,ds = 0 = \int_0^\infty h_n(t)h_k(t)\,dt. \quad (9\text{–}117)$$

The same result is obtained if the path of integration is completed to the left. In this case the poles $s = -a_k, \ldots, -a_n$ are enclosed. The simplest way of showing that the result is zero is to let $V(s)$ represent the function given by (9–116) and note that the left-hand integral in (9–117) represents the initial value of $v(t) = \mathcal{L}^{-1}[V(s)]$. Using the initial value theorem we obtain

$$v(0) = \lim_{s\to\infty} sV(s) = 0.$$

The term $G_n(s)$ can be realized as the voltage transfer function of a network composed of lattice sections. It follows from (9–63) and (9–64b) that by choosing

$$Z_0 = \sqrt{L_k/C_k}$$

$$\frac{V_{k+1}}{V_k} = \frac{a_k - s}{a_k + s},$$

where $a_k = 1/\sqrt{L_k C_k}$ for the kth section, the voltage transfer function

$$G_n(s) = \frac{V_n}{V_o} = \left(\frac{V_n}{V_{n-1}}\right)\cdots\left(\frac{V_1}{V_o}\right)$$

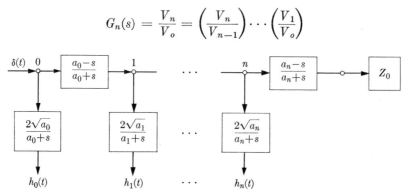

FIG. 9–24. Generation of orthogonal functions.

is obtained. This results from the fact that each section is terminated in the characteristic impedance.

If a unit-impulse voltage is applied at the input, the signals $h_k(t)$ can be obtained as shown in Fig. 9–24. The case where $a_0 = a_1 = \cdots = a_n = a$ leads to

$$H_n(s) = \sqrt{2a}\ \frac{(a - s)^n}{(a + s)^{n+1}}.$$

Thus [see Appendix (B–8)]

$$h_n(t) = (-1)^n\sqrt{2a}\ e^{-at}L_n(2at),$$

and the network generates the Laguerre polynomials with a *weighting factor* of $(-1)^n\sqrt{2a}\ e^{-at}$.

PROBLEMS

9–1. Consider a filter composed of $n\,\pi$-sections of the high-pass type (Fig. 9–25). The filter is driven by a unit-step voltage and is terminated in an open circuit. Determine the voltage response of the mth section.

9–2. Solve Example 5 of this chapter if the termination is changed to an open circuit.

9–3. A filter is composed of n sections of the π-type shown in Fig. 9–26. The termination is a short circuit. Determine the current response to a unit-step voltage input.

FIGURE 9–25

FIGURE 9–26

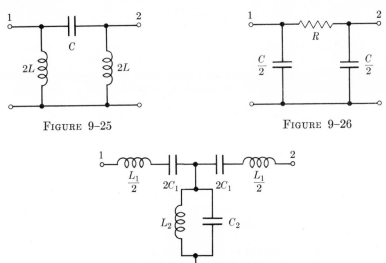

FIGURE 9–27

9-4. Determine the current response of the bandpass filter considered in Example 3 of this chapter.

9-5. A bandpass filter is composed of n sections of the T-type shown in Fig. 9-27. The termination is a short circuit. Determine the current response to a unit-step input voltage.

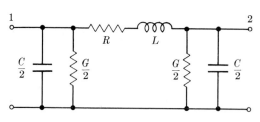

FIGURE 9-28

9-6. An infinite filter is composed of π-type sections as shown in Fig. 9-28. Determine expressions for the voltage and current response to a unit-step input voltage.

9-7. A bandpass filter is composed of an infinite number of T-sections as shown in Fig. 9-27. Let $\omega_1 = 1/\sqrt{L_1 C_1} = 1/\sqrt{L_2 C_2} = \omega_0$ be the angular frequency of a carrier signal. Determine the envelope response of the current $i'_n(t)$ for a unit-step carrier input voltage.

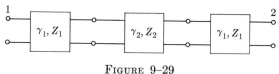

FIGURE 9-29

9-8. Three symmetrical two-terminal-pair network sections are connected in cascade as shown in Fig. 9-29. Using matrix methods determine the A, B, C parameters of the combined network. From these show that the propagation function γ and the characteristic impedance Z_0 of this network are determined by

$$\cosh \gamma = \cosh 2\gamma_1 \cosh \gamma_2 + \frac{1}{2}\left(\frac{Z_2}{Z_1} + \frac{Z_1}{Z_2}\right) \sinh 2\gamma_1 \sinh \gamma_2,$$

$$\left(\frac{Z_0}{Z_1}\frac{Z_2}{Z_1}\right)^2 = \frac{\tanh^2 \gamma_1 + 2(Z_2/Z_1)\tanh \gamma_1 \cotanh \gamma_2 + (Z_2/Z_1)^2}{\tanh^2 \gamma_1 + 2(Z_1/Z_2)\tanh \gamma_1 \cotanh \gamma_2 + (Z_1/Z_2)^2}.$$

9-9. Consider the Laplace transform [see Appendix (D-32)]

$$\mathcal{L}[J_0(2\sqrt{a\tau t})] = \frac{1}{s}e^{-a\tau/s}.$$

Use the t-translation theorem [see (11-17)] and prove that

$$\mathcal{L}[u(t - b)J_0(2\sqrt{a\tau(t - b\tau)})] = \frac{1}{s}e^{-(a/s + bs)\tau},$$

where

$$u(t - b\tau) = \begin{cases} 1, & t > b\tau, \\ 0, & t < b\tau. \end{cases}$$

Use this result to prove that if $g(0) = 0$ and if

$$H(s) = \frac{1}{s}\left(\frac{a}{s} + bs\right) G\left(\frac{a}{s} + bs\right),$$

then

$$h(t) = \int_0^{t/b} J_0(2\sqrt{a\tau(t - b\tau)})\, \frac{dg(\tau)}{d\tau}\, d\tau.$$

9–10. Use the transform given in Problem 9–9 to prove that if

$$\int_0^t h(t)\, dt = \int_0^\infty u(t - b\tau) J_0[2\sqrt{a\tau(t - b\tau)}] g(\tau)\, d\tau,$$

then $H(s) = G(a/s + bs)$ and that $h(t)$ can be found from

$$h(t) = \frac{1}{b}\, g\left(\frac{t}{b}\right) - 2a \int_0^{t/b} \frac{J_1(z)}{z}\, \tau g(\tau)\, d\tau,$$

where $z = 2\sqrt{a\tau(t - b\tau)}$. The results given in Problems 9–9 and 9–10 permit the transient response of a bandpass filter to be determined from the low-pass filter which results from the transformation $s \leftrightarrow a/s + bs$.

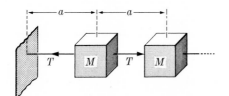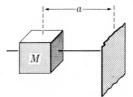

FIGURE 9–30

9–11. Consider n uniform masses M coupled together by strings having a uniform length a and tension T (see Fig. 9–30). Determine an electrical network analog for the small-amplitude lateral oscillations of this system.

9–12. Legendre functions can be defined for $|z| \leq 1$ by the equation [5]

$$P_n(z) = \frac{1}{2^n n!}\, \frac{d^n}{dz^n}\, (z^2 - 1)^n.$$

These functions satisfy the condition $P_n(1) = 1$ and the recurrence formulas

$$\frac{dP_n}{dz} = z\frac{dP_{n-1}}{dz} + nP_{n-1}, \qquad z\frac{dP_n}{dz} - nP_n = \frac{dP_{n-1}}{dz}.$$

If the substitution $z = 2e^{-at} - 1$ is used and if $Q(s) = \mathcal{L}[P_n(z)]$ denotes the Laplace transform, show that

$$(s + na)Q_n(s) = (s - na)Q_{n-1}(s).$$

Since $\mathcal{L}[P_0(z)] = 1/s$, explain why the $Q_n(s)$ cannot be used to generate orthogonal functions but that the difficulty can be overcome by using $Q_n(s + a/2)$. Show how this transfer function can be realized by a lattice network. Determine the response $h_n(t)$ to a unit-impulse input voltage.

References

1. E. JAHNKE, F. EMDE, and F. LOESCH, *Tables of Higher Functions*, 6th ed., McGraw-Hill, New York, 1960.

2. W. P. MASON, *Electrodynamical Transducers and Wave Filters*, D. Van Nostrand, New York, 1942.

3. Y. W. LEE, *Statistical Theory of Communication*, Wiley and Sons, New York. 1960.

4. W. H. KAUTZ, "Transient synthesis in the time domain," *Trans. IRE, PGCT*, CT–1, 29–39 (1954).

5. E. T. WHITAKER and G. N. WATSON, *A Course of Modern Analysis*, Cambridge University Press, 1952.

CHAPTER 10

DISTRIBUTED-PARAMETER MECHANICAL SYSTEMS

10–1 Introduction. Electromechanical transducers having distributed parameters are of considerable importance. They find applications in filters, delay lines, loudspeakers, microphones, and oscillators. The interested reader is referred to the references at the end of the chapter for further details concerning these applications. We shall concern ourselves exclusively with the mathematical and physical principles involved in determining the response of systems of this type.

10–2 The transverse vibrations of a uniform string. The terminology and mathematical methods to be used can best be illustrated by means of an example. Consider a uniform string of length l fixed at both ends under a constant tension T (mks units will be used, where length is expressed in meters and force in newtons). Let

$f(x, t) = $ the externally applied transverse force per unit length,

$\rho = $ the mass per unit length.

Newton's law of motion is

$$\text{mass} \times \text{acceleration} = \text{force} = F.$$

Let us consider the motion of an element dx of the string (Fig. 10–1). For this element, Newton's law of motion is

$$\rho \, dx \, \frac{\partial^2 u}{\partial t^2} = T \sin (\theta + d\theta) - T \sin \theta + f(x, t) \, dx, \qquad (10\text{–}1)$$

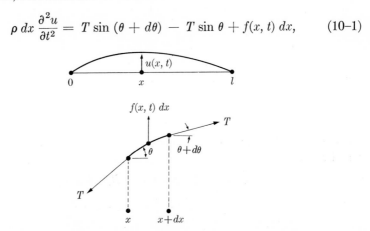

FIG. 10–1. The transverse vibrations of a uniform string.

209

where $u(x, t)$ is the transverse displacement. If the displacement is small, θ is small and

$$\frac{\partial u}{\partial x} = \tan \theta \cong \sin \theta. \tag{10-2}$$

Dividing (10–1) by dx and using (10–2), we obtain the equation of motion

$$\frac{\partial^2 u}{\partial t^2} = a^2 \frac{\partial^2 u}{\partial x^2} + \frac{1}{\rho} f(x, t), \tag{10-3}$$

where $a^2 = T/\rho$. The boundary conditions at $x = 0$ and $x = l$ require that

$$u(0, t) = u(l, t) = 0. \tag{10-4}$$

The force density $f(x, t)$ is applied externally and is considered known. The problem is to find the displacement $u(x, t)$ so that (10–3) and (10–4) are satisfied. The method to be used is, in principle, the same as that used in the previous chapters, where the system response was represented as a linear combination of the characteristic exponentials. With this in mind we now choose a representation of the response $u(x, t)$ in the form

$$u(x, t) = \sum_{n=1}^{\infty} u_n(t) y_n(x), \tag{10-5}$$

where the product $u_n(t)y_n(x)$ represents a suitable *characteristic response* of the system. The function $y_n(x)$ determines the spatial form of the response and will be called the nth *mode*, while $u_n(t)$ determines the *instantaneous amplitude* or *component* of this mode.

The functions $y_n(x)$ are defined as the *natural* or *free modes of oscillation*. Thus $u_n(t)y_n(x)$ must be a solution of

$$\frac{\partial^2 u}{\partial t^2} = a^2 \frac{\partial^2 u}{\partial x^2}.$$

Separation of variables yields

$$\frac{1}{u_n} \frac{d^2 u_n}{dt^2} = \frac{a^2}{y_n} \frac{d^2 y_n}{dx^2} = -\omega_n^2, \tag{10-6}$$

where ω_n^2 is the separation constant. The solutions of the two differential equations (10–6) are

$$u_n(t) = A_n \cos \omega_n t + B_n \sin \omega_n t,$$

$$y_n(x) = C_n \cos \frac{\omega_n x}{a} + D_n \sin \frac{\omega_n x}{a}.$$

It is thus evident that the constant ω_n represents the angular frequency for the component of the nth mode. Its value is determined from the boundary conditions (10–4) which require that

$$y_n(0) = 0 = C_n, \qquad y_n(l) = 0 = D_n \sin \frac{\omega_n l}{a}.$$

Thus

$$\omega_n = \frac{\pi a n}{l}, \qquad n = 1, 2, \ldots.$$

The constant D_n is arbitrary and we can choose it equal to one. Thus

$$y_n(x) = \sin \frac{\pi n x}{l}. \tag{10–7}$$

10–3 A geometric representation. Before discussing the case of forced oscillation [where $f(x, t) \neq 0$], we shall discuss a very useful geometric terminology applicable to expansions of the form (10–5). Let us consider Fig. 10–2, where a vector $\mathbf{U}$ is to be represented by a linear combination of the three orthogonal vectors $\mathbf{Y}_1$, $\mathbf{Y}_2$, and $\mathbf{Y}_3$ in the form

$$\mathbf{U} = \sum_{n=1}^{3} u_n \mathbf{Y}_n. \tag{10–8}$$

The vectors $\mathbf{Y}_n$ can be expressed in terms of the unit vectors $\mathbf{I}$, $\mathbf{J}$, and $\mathbf{K}$ of a rectangular cartesian coordinate system. Thus

$$\mathbf{Y}_n = y_{n1}\mathbf{I} + y_{n2}\mathbf{J} + y_{n3}\mathbf{K}.$$

Since the vectors are orthogonal, the *scalar product* of the vectors $\mathbf{Y}_n$ and $\mathbf{Y}_m$ is

$$(\mathbf{Y}_n \cdot \mathbf{Y}_m) = y_{n1}y_{m1} + y_{n2}y_{m2} + y_{n3}y_{m3}$$

$$= \sum_{k=1}^{3} y_{nk}y_{mk} = 0, \qquad n \neq m. \tag{10–9}$$

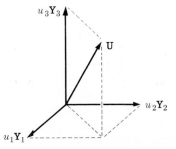

FIG. 10–2. The components of a vector.

The coefficient u_m in the expansion (10–8) can be found by scalar multiplication of this equation with $\mathbf{Y}_m$. Thus

$$(\mathbf{U} \cdot \mathbf{Y}_m) = u_m(\mathbf{Y}_m \cdot \mathbf{Y}_m). \qquad (10\text{–}10)$$

We can consider the $\mathbf{Y}_n$'s to represent the characteristic terms or modes of response for a system. Equation (10–8) then represents a general state of the system (the vector $\mathbf{U}$) in terms of a linear combination of the modes. It is seen that (10–5) has the same general form. The state of the system [the function $u(x, t)$] is represented by a linear combination of the modes. It is actually not possible to visualize this representation in a three-dimensional geometric form. However, there is a correspondence between the geometric vector relations and the analytic relations in an expansion of the form (10–5). This correspondence allows us to interpret the analytic relations in terms of the corresponding geometric ones, which can be visualized. The geometric terminology which can then be used makes it easier to understand and carry out analytic operations with (10–5).

It is now necessary to determine an equation similar to (10–10) so that the coefficient $u_m(t)$ in (10–5) may be found. Let us define a scalar product by means of the integral

$$(y_n, y_m) = \int_0^l y_n(x)y_m(x)\,dx, \qquad (10\text{–}11)$$

which is similar to (10–9) in the sense that it is formed by summing (integrating) the product of the components. It is left as a simple exercise for the reader to show that, if the modes are given by (10–7),

$$(y_n, y_m) = \begin{cases} 0, & n \neq m, \\[2mm] \dfrac{l}{2}, & n = m. \end{cases} \qquad (10\text{–}12)$$

The modes are thus orthogonal. To obtain the component of the mth mode, we scalar multiply (10–5) with y_m and use (10–12), which yields

$$(u, y_m) = u_m(t)(y_m, y_m) = \frac{l}{2}\,u_m(t). \qquad (10\text{–}13)$$

This equation is analogous to (10–10) and allows us to use the same geometric terminology as with actual vectors.

The geometric interpretation of the expansion (10–5) and the use of the scalar product (10–11) are of considerable assistance in understanding problems where the modes are not orthogonal, i.e., where $(y_n, y_m) \neq 0$. The geometric representation then takes the form shown in Fig. 10–3(a), where the vectors $\mathbf{Y}_n$ form an oblique coordinate system which complicates the problem considerably. It then becomes necessary to determine a

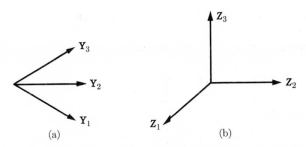

FIG. 10–3. An oblique and an orthogonal coordinate system.

suitable transformation converting the oblique system Y_n to an orthogonal system Z_n, Fig. 10–3(b).

To cope with the possibility of an oblique coordinate system it is convenient to express (10–13) in a different form. We define a transform $\mathfrak{I}$ by means of the operation

$$\mathfrak{I}[u(x, t)] = u_m(t). \qquad (10\text{–}14)$$

In a geometric sense $\mathfrak{I}$ is a *projection operator* which projects $u(x, t)$ onto the mth mode, and thus yields the component of this mode. If the modes are orthogonal, we have

$$\mathfrak{I}[u] = u_m(t) = \frac{(u, y_m)}{(y_m, y_m)} = \frac{\displaystyle\int_0^l u(x, t) y_m(x)\, dx}{\displaystyle\int_0^l y_m^2(x)\, dx}, \qquad (10\text{–}15)$$

which can then be taken as the definition of the $\mathfrak{I}$-transform in analytic form.

10–4 The forced vibrations of a string. Equation (10–3) will now be solved, where the force density $f(x, t)$ and the initial conditions are known functions. These quantities excite the various modes, and the response has the form (10–5), where the modes y_n are known and are given by (10–7). The problem is to determine the components $u_n(t)$ of these modes. It is seen from (10–14) that the $\mathfrak{I}$-transform yields the component $u_m(t)$. We thus apply $\mathfrak{I}$ to (10–3) and obtain

$$\mathfrak{I}\left[\frac{\partial^2 u}{\partial t^2}\right] = a^2 \mathfrak{I}\left[\frac{\partial^2 u}{\partial x^2}\right] + \frac{1}{\rho}\, \mathfrak{I}[f(x, t)]. \qquad (10\text{–}16)$$

This equation can be easily interpreted in geometric terms. We are equating the components of the mth mode, obtained by means of the $\mathfrak{I}$-transform, of both sides of the equation.

Each of the terms of (10–16) will now be determined. By definition, we have $\Im[f(x, t)] = f_m(t)$.

Differentiating (10–5) twice with respect to t yields

$$\frac{\partial^2 u}{\partial t^2} = \sum_{n=1}^{\infty} \frac{d^2 u_n}{dt^2} y_n.$$

Thus, by definition

$$\Im\left[\frac{\partial^2 u}{\partial t^2}\right] = \frac{d^2 u_m}{dt^2}. \tag{10–17}$$

Differentiating (10–5) twice with respect to x yields

$$\frac{\partial^2 u}{\partial x^2} = \sum_{n=1}^{\infty} u_n \frac{d^2 y_n}{dx^2}.$$

In order to determine $\Im[\partial^2 u/\partial x^2]$ we must first express $d^2 y_n/dx^2$ in terms of y_n. This is given by (10–6). Thus

$$\frac{\partial^2 u}{\partial x^2} = \sum_{n=1}^{\infty} -u_n \left(\frac{\omega_n}{a}\right)^2 y_n,$$

and, by definition

$$\Im\left[\frac{\partial^2 u}{\partial x^2}\right] = -\left(\frac{\omega_m}{a}\right)^2 u_m.$$

Substituting these results into (10–16) yields

$$\frac{d^2 u_m}{dt^2} + \omega_m^2 u_m = \frac{1}{\rho} f_m(t).$$

A particular integral of this equation can be found with the aid of the convolution theorem. Adding the complementary function to this yields the general solution

$$u_m(t) = A_m \cos \omega_m t + B_m \sin \omega_m t + \frac{1}{\rho \omega_m} \int_0^t f_m(\tau) \sin \omega_m(t - \tau) \, d\tau. \tag{10–18}$$

The constants A_m and B_m are determined by the initial conditions. Suppose that $u_m(0)$ and $u_m'(0)$ are known. It follows directly from (10–18) that

$$A_m = u_m(0), \qquad \omega_m B_m = u_m'(0). \tag{10–19}$$

However, what is actually given is the initial displacement function

$$u(x, 0) = F(x),$$

and the initial velocity function

$$\frac{\partial u(x, t)}{\partial t}\bigg]_{t=0} = G(x).$$

The constants A_m and B_m must now be expressed in terms of the given functions $F(x)$ and $G(x)$. This can be done with the aid of the expansion (10–5). At $t = 0$ this yields

$$u(x, 0) = F(x) = \sum_{n=1}^{\infty} u_n(0)y_n(x).$$

Scalar multiplication with $y_m(x)$ yields

$$(F, y_m) = u_m(0)(y_m, y_m). \qquad (10\text{–}20)$$

Similarly, we obtain

$$\frac{\partial u(x, t)}{\partial t}\bigg]_{t=0} = G(x) = \sum_{n=1}^{\infty} u'_n(0)y_n(x),$$

which yields

$$(G, y_m) = u'_m(0)(y_m, y_m). \qquad (10\text{–}21)$$

Equations (10–20) and (10–21) determine $u_m(0)$ and $u'_m(0)$, and these, in turn, determine A_m and B_m by means of (10–19).

The final solution is evidently very complicated, so that it is best to write it in terms of its component parts. These are summarized below.

The response:

$$u(x, t) = \sum_{n=1}^{\infty} u_n(t)y_n(x)$$

The modes:

$$y_n(x) = \sin \frac{\pi n x}{l}.$$

The components:

$$u_n(t) = A_n \cos \omega_n t + B_n \sin \omega_n t + \frac{1}{\rho \omega_n} \int_0^t f_n(\tau) \sin \omega_n(t - \tau)\, d\tau.$$

The angular velocities:

$$\omega_n = \frac{\pi a n}{l}.$$

Initial values:

$$A_n = u_n(0) = \frac{(F, y_n)}{(y_n, y_n)} = \frac{2}{l} \int_0^l F(x) \sin \frac{\pi n x}{l}\, dx,$$

$$\omega_n B_n = u'_n(0) = \frac{(G, y_n)}{(y_n, y_n)} = \frac{2}{l} \int_0^l G(x) \sin \frac{\pi n x}{l}\, dx,$$

where $F(x)$ is the initial displacement function and $G(x)$ the initial velocity function.

10–5 A general class of systems. The systems to be discussed in the following sections all satisfy an equation of the type

$$\frac{\partial^2 u}{\partial t^2} + Du = g(x, t), \tag{10-22}$$

where D is a *differential operator* having one of the following forms:

$$D = -a^2 \frac{\partial^2}{\partial x^2}, \tag{10-23a}$$

$$D = a^4 \frac{\partial^4}{\partial x^4}. \tag{10-23b}$$

In addition to (10–22), the function $u(x, y)$ must satisfy the boundary conditions. These take a wide variety of forms which involve conditions on the functions and its derivatives. The solution is to be represented in the form (10–5). The free modes of oscillation y_n can be considered as corresponding to a geometric coordinate system. Equation (10–22) is solved by applying the $\mathfrak{J}$-transform, which yields the component of the mth mode (coordinate) of both sides of the equation. Thus

$$\mathfrak{J}\left[\frac{\partial^2 u}{\partial t^2}\right] + \mathfrak{J}[Du] = \mathfrak{J}[g(x, t)]. \tag{10-24}$$

By definition, $\mathfrak{J}[g(x, t)] = g_m(t)$, and, from (10–17),

$$\mathfrak{J}\left[\frac{\partial^2 u}{\partial t^2}\right] = \frac{d^2 u_m}{dt^2}.$$

To determine $\mathfrak{J}[Du]$ we consider first Du, which is

$$Du = \sum_{n=1}^{\infty} u_n(t) Dy_n(x); \tag{10-25}$$

$Dy_n(x)$ must now be expressed in terms of $y_n(x)$. We therefore set

$$Dy_n = \omega_n^2 y_n, \tag{10-26}$$

where ω_n is to be determined from the boundary conditions. Equation (10–26), in conjunction with the boundary conditions, determines the particular coordinate system (set of modes) which is best suited for representing $u(x, t)$. From (10–25) and (10–26), we obtain

$$\mathfrak{J}[Du] = \omega_m^2 u_m.$$

Substituting these results into (10–24) yields

$$\frac{d^2 u_m}{dt^2} + \omega_m^2 u_m = g_m(t).$$

The general solution of this equation has been given by (10–18). Thus

$$u_m(t) = A_m \cos \omega_m t + B_m \sin \omega_m t + \frac{1}{\omega_m} \int_0^t g_m(\tau) \sin \omega_m(t - \tau) \, d\tau. \tag{10–27}$$

This equation shows that the constant ω_m represents the angular frequency for the component of the mth mode.

To determine the modes, (10–26) must be solved. Suppose that D is given by (10–23a). Equation (10–26) then has the form

$$Dy_n = -a^2 \frac{d^2 y_n}{dx^2} = \omega_n^2 y_n.$$

The solution is

$$y_n = C_n \cos \frac{\omega_n x}{a} + D_n \sin \frac{\omega_n x}{a}. \tag{10–28}$$

If D is given by (10–23b), we have

$$Dy_n = a^4 \frac{d^4 y_n}{dx^4} = \omega_n^2 y_n. \tag{10–29}$$

This fourth-order differential equation has four linearly independent solutions. These are

$$e^{\pm jk_n x} \qquad e^{\pm k_n x}, \tag{10–30}$$

where

$$k_n = \frac{\sqrt{\omega_n}}{a}.$$

Any linear combination of the functions (10–30) is a solution of (10–29). Suitable combinations are the familiar sin, cos, sinh, and cosh functions. Thus

$$y_n = C_n \cos k_n x + D_n \sin k_n x + E_n \cosh k_n x + F_n \sinh k_n x. \tag{10–31}$$

The value of ω_n, as well as the ratio of the constants in (10–28) and (10–31), is determined from the boundary conditions. Since there is such a variety of possibilities, it is best to discuss them individually as they occur in the following examples.

Since the equation defining y_n [see Eq. (10–26)] does not contain $g_n(t)$, it follows that the y_n represent the modes of free oscillation, where $g(x, t) = 0$.

A general response of the system is due to externally applied forces and initial conditions. These determine the quantities A_m, B_m, and $g_m(t)$ in (10–27). It is therefore necessary to know the analytic form of the з-transform from which these quantities are determined. If the modes are orthogonal, we have seen that the з-transform can be expressed by (10–15). We must therefore investigate the orthogonality of the modes.

Let us consider (10–26), which defines the modes. For the nth and mth modes, we have

$$Dy_n = \omega_n^2 y_n, \qquad Dy_m = \omega_m^2 y_m.$$

The first equation is now scalar multiplied with y_m, the second with y_n. Subtracting these results yields

$$(y_m, Dy_n) - (Dy_m, y_n) = (\omega_n^2 - \omega_m^2)(y_n, y_m). \qquad (10\text{–}32)$$

If the modes are to be orthogonal, i.e., if

$$(y_n, y_m) = 0 \qquad \text{for } n \neq m,$$

we must have

$$(y_m, Dy_n) - (Dy_m, y_n) = 0.$$

Let us consider now the case where D is given by (10–23a). Equation (10–32) is then

$$(\omega_n^2 - \omega_m^2)(y_n, y_m) = -a^2 \left(y_m, \frac{d^2 y_n}{dx^2}\right) + a^2 \left(\frac{d^2 y_m}{dx^2}, y_n\right)$$

$$= a^2 \int_0^l \left[-y_m \frac{d^2 y_n}{dx^2} + \frac{d^2 y_m}{dx^2} y_n\right] dx$$

$$= a^2 \int_0^l \frac{d}{dx}\left[-y_m \frac{dy_n}{dx} + \frac{dy_m}{dx} y_n\right] dx$$

$$= a^2 \left[-y_m \frac{dy_n}{dx} + \frac{dy_m}{dx} y_n\right]_0^l. \qquad (10\text{–}33)$$

Whether this vanishes or not depends on the functions y_n and the boundary conditions at $x = 0$ and $x = l$. For example, the boundary conditions for the vibrating string require that $y_n(0) = 0$ and $y_n(l) = 0$ $(n = 1, 2, \ldots)$. Thus (10–33) vanishes and the modes for the vibrating strings are orthogonal.

Consider now the case where D is given by (10–23b). Equation (10–32) is then

$$(\omega_n^2 - \omega_m^2)(y_n, y_m) = a^4\left(y_m, \frac{d^4 y_n}{dx^4}\right) - a^4\left(\frac{d^4 y_m}{dx^4}, y_n\right)$$

$$= a^4 \int_0^l \left[y_m \frac{d^4 y_n}{dx^4} - \frac{d^4 y_m}{dx^4} y_n\right] dx$$

$$= a^4 \int_0^l \frac{d}{dx}\left[y_m \frac{d^3 y_n}{dx^3} - \frac{d^3 y_m}{dx^3} y_n\right.$$

$$\left. - \frac{dy_m}{dx}\frac{d^2 y_n}{dx^2} + \frac{d^2 y_m}{dx^2}\frac{dy_n}{dx}\right] dx$$

$$= a^4 \left[y_m \frac{d^3 y_n}{dx^3} - \frac{d^3 y_m}{dx^3} y_n - \frac{dy_m}{dx}\frac{d^2 y_n}{dx^2} + \frac{d^2 y_m}{dx^2}\frac{dy_n}{dx}\right]_0^l.$$

$$(10\text{--}34)$$

In Section 10–9 it will be shown that this case occurs for the transverse vibrations of a uniform rod and that (10–34) vanishes for all possible combinations of boundary conditions.

There is a very important point concerning (10–27) which must be discussed. The external and internal damping effects have been neglected so that a single mode may oscillate indefinitely without loss of energy. The component for this free mode of oscillation is given by the first two terms of (10–27). The poles of the transfer function of a system having this type of response are at $s = \pm j\omega_m$ (Fig. 10–4). If damping is taken into account, these poles move out into the left half of the s-plane and

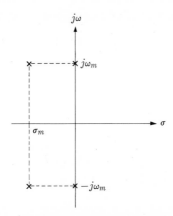

FIG. 10–4. The location of poles in the s-plane.

become $\sigma_m \pm j\omega_m$. However, in general, the modes will no longer be orthogonal. It is also difficult to determine an analytic expression for the damping. This greatly complicates the problem. If the damping is small, (10–27) will be a good approximation for small t. If t is large, the first two terms in (10–27) eventually damp out and the remaining term is

$$u_m(t) = \frac{1}{\omega_m} \int_0^t g_m(\tau) \sin \omega_m(t - \tau)\, d\tau. \qquad (10\text{–}35)$$

Equation (10–27) can be used to determine the initial response for small t and (10–57) the response for large t. In the majority of applications, it is this latter response that is of interest. This can be determined from the general solution by taking $A_m = B_m = 0$, i.e., the initial displacement and velocity are both taken to be identically zero.

10–6 The longitudinal vibrations of a uniform rod. Consider a uniform rod of length l with one end rigidly clamped and the other end free (Fig. 10–5). Let

$$A = \text{the cross-sectional area,}$$
$$E = \text{the modulus of elasticity,}$$
$$\rho = \text{the mass per unit volume,}$$
$$F(x, t) = \text{the internal force at the cross section } x,$$
$$f(x, t) = \text{the externally applied force per unit length,}$$

Hooke's law defines the relation between the stress σ and strain ϵ.

$$\sigma = \frac{F}{A} = E\epsilon = E\frac{\partial u}{\partial x}. \qquad (10\text{–}36)$$

Newton's law of motion, applied to an element dx, yields

$$\rho A\, dx\, (\partial^2 u/\partial t^2) = F(x + dx, t) - F(x, t) + f(x, t)\, dx.$$

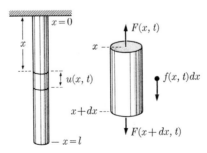

Fig. 10–5. The longitudinal vibrations of a uniform rod with one end clamped and the other end free.

Dividing by dx, we obtain

$$A\rho \frac{\partial^2 u}{\partial t^2} = \frac{\partial F}{\partial x} + f(x, t).$$

The internal force F can be eliminated by using (10–36), and we obtain the equation of motion

$$\frac{\partial^2 u}{\partial t^2} = a^2 \frac{\partial^2 u}{\partial x^2} + \frac{1}{A\rho} f(x, t), \qquad (10\text{–}37)$$

where

$$a^2 = \frac{E}{\rho}. \qquad (10\text{–}38)$$

The boundary conditions require that

$$u(0, t) = 0,$$

$$F(l, t) = AE \left. \frac{\partial u(x, t)}{\partial x} \right]_{x=l} = 0. \qquad (10\text{–}39)$$

The general results obtained in Section 10–5 can now be applied. The modes are determined by [see Eq. (10–28)]

$$y_n = C_n \cos \frac{\omega_n x}{a} + D_n \sin \frac{\omega_n x}{a}$$

and by the boundary conditions (10–39). These conditions yield $C_n = 0$ and

$$\left. \frac{dy_n(x)}{dx} \right]_{x=l} = 0 = D_n \frac{\omega_n}{a} \cos \frac{\omega_n l}{a}. \qquad (10\text{–}40)$$

The solution of (10–40) is

$$\omega_n = \frac{a\pi n}{2l}, \qquad n = 1, 3, 5, \ldots; \qquad (10\text{–}41)$$

D_n is arbitrary and can be taken equal to unity. The modes are then

$$y_n = \sin \frac{\pi n x}{2l}, \qquad n = 1, 3, 5, \ldots. \qquad (10\text{–}42)$$

It follows from (10–33) that the modes are orthogonal, since

$$y_n(0) = 0 \qquad \text{and} \qquad dy_n(x)/dx]_{x=l} = 0.$$

It is a simple matter to show that

$$(y_n, y_n) = \int_0^l \sin^2 \frac{\pi n x}{2l} \, dx = \frac{l}{2}.$$

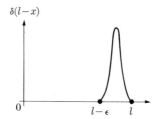

FIG. 10-6. The force density distribution for a concentrated total force at $x = l$.

EXAMPLE 1. Consider the external force density to be concentrated at $x = l$ and to be given by (see Fig. 10–6)

$$f(x, t) = F(t) \delta(l - x), \qquad (10\text{–}43)$$

where $\delta(x)$ is the unit-impulse function. The rod is assumed to be initially at rest in its equilibrium position and the total force $F(t)$ suddenly applied at $t = 0$. The response takes the form

$$u(x, t) = \sum_{n=1,3,5,\ldots}^{\infty} u_n(t) y_n(x),$$

where $y_n(x)$ is given by (10–42) and $u_n(t)$ is determined by the general solution (10–27) with $g(x, t) = (1/A\rho)f(x, t)$. Due to the initial conditions being identically zero, $A_m = B_m = 0$. Thus

$$u_m(t) = \frac{1}{A\rho\omega_m} \int_0^t f_m(\tau) \sin \omega_m(t - \tau) \, d\tau, \qquad (10\text{–}44)$$

where ω_m is given by (10–41).

The problem can be considered solved if $f_m(t)$ can be expressed in terms of the total force $F(t)$. This relation can be found from

$$f(x, t) = \sum_{n=1,3,5,\ldots}^{\infty} f_n(t) y_n(x).$$

Scalar multiplication with $y_m(x)$ yields

$$(f, y_m) = f_m(t)(y_m, y_m)$$

$$= \int_0^l f(x, t) \sin \frac{\pi m x}{2l} \, dx = f_m(t) \frac{l}{2}$$

$$= F(t) \sin \frac{\pi m}{2l} . \qquad (10\text{–}45)$$

In the final step we have used (10–43). Solving for $f_m(t)$, we obtain

$$f_m(t) = \frac{2}{l} (-1)^{(m-1)/2} F(t), \qquad m = 1, 3, 5, \ldots .$$

Substituting this into (10–44) yields

$$u_m(t) = \frac{2(-1)^{(m-1)/2}}{A\rho l \omega_m} \int_0^t F(\tau) \sin \omega_m(t - \tau)\, d\tau. \blacktriangle$$

To summarize these results we note that the first step consists of determining a suitable coordinate system, i.e., the modes are first found. It is then determined whether or not the coordinate system is orthogonal. The application of initial conditions and external forcing terms results in the excitation of these various modes (coordinates). The problem is solved once the component of each coordinate is known. Each of these components has a characteristic angular velocity ω_m, which is found in the process of determining the coordinate system.

Since the modes are orthogonal, the general expression (10–15) for the $\mathfrak{J}$-transform can be used to determine $f_m(t)$. Thus

$$\mathfrak{J}[f] = f_m(t) = \frac{(f, y_m)}{(y_m, y_m)},$$

which is evidently the same as (10–45). Since this formula is so easily derived, it is best not to rely on it but to understand the simple principles involved in obtaining it.

10–7 The longitudinal vibrations of a uniform rod with a load at one end. This problem differs from the preceding one in that a mass M is rigidly attached to the rod at $x = l$ (Fig. 10–7). This alters the boundary condition at $x = l$, since there is now a force F required to accelerate this mass. The boundary conditions are now

$$u(0, t) = 0, \tag{10–46}$$

$$F = -F(l, t) = M \left. \frac{\partial^2 u}{\partial t^2} \right]_{x=l}.$$

The second equation is Newton's law of motion applied to the mass at $x = l$. The internal force $F(x, t)$ is given by (10–36). Thus

$$-AE \left. \frac{\partial u}{\partial x} \right]_{x=l} = M \left. \frac{\partial^2 u}{\partial t^2} \right]_{x=l}. \tag{10–47}$$

Since the boundary conditions are to be satisfied by the modes, which are

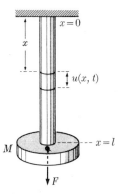

FIG. 10-7. The longitudinal vibrations of a uniform rod with a load at one end.

functions of x alone, (10–47) must be expressed in terms of derivatives with respect to x. If we consider the function $f(x, t)$ to satisfy the condition

$$f(l, t) = 0, \tag{10–48}$$

it is then possible to use (10–37) to eliminate the time derivative, and the second boundary condition becomes

$$-AE \left. \frac{\partial u}{\partial x} \right]_{x=l} = Ma^2 \left. \frac{\partial^2 u}{\partial x^2} \right]_{x=l}. \tag{10–49}$$

The modes are given by [see Eq. (10–28)]

$$y_n = C_n \cos \frac{\omega_n x}{a} + D_n \sin \frac{\omega_n x}{a}.$$

The condition (10–46) requires that $C_n = 0$. We can choose $D_n = 1$. Substituting y_n into (10–49) yields

$$-\frac{AE\omega_n}{a} \cos \frac{\omega_n l}{a} = -M\omega_n^2 \sin \frac{\omega_n l}{a}. \tag{10–50}$$

To simplify this expression let

$$\beta_n = \frac{\omega_n l}{a}, \tag{10–51}$$

$$\alpha = \frac{AEl}{Ma^2} = \frac{A\rho l}{M}, \tag{}$$

where use has been made of (10–38). The parameter α is the ratio of the masses of the rod and load. Equation (10–50) now has the form

$$\alpha = \beta_n \tan \beta_n. \tag{10–52}$$

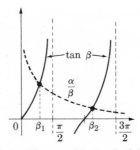

FIG. 10–8. The graphical solution for β_n.

This equation can be solved graphically by plotting the functions α/β and $\tan \beta$ (Fig. 10–8). The points of intersection determine $\beta_1, \beta_2, \ldots$. The angular velocity ω_n can then be found from (10–51) and is

$$\omega_n = \frac{\beta_n a}{l}. \tag{10–53}$$

The mode y_n is then

$$y_n = \sin \frac{\beta_n x}{l}.$$

These modes determine the coordinate system. It is now necessary to discuss the orthogonality of these modes. The test for orthogonality is made with (10–33). Consider the term

$$y_m \frac{dy_n}{dx}\Big]_0^l = \frac{\beta_n}{l} \sin \frac{\beta_m x}{l} \cos \frac{\beta_n x}{l}\Big]_0^l$$

$$= \frac{\beta_n}{l} \sin \beta_m \cos \beta_n.$$

This can be simplified by using (10–52) to eliminate $\cos \beta_n$. Thus

$$y_m \frac{dy_n}{dx}\Big]_0^l = \frac{\beta_n^2}{\alpha l} \sin \beta_m \sin \beta_n.$$

Using this result in (10–33) yields

$$(\omega_n^2 - \omega_m^2)(y_n, y_m) = \frac{a^2}{\alpha l} (-\beta_n^2 + \beta_m^2) \sin \beta_n \sin \beta_m.$$

This can be simplified by using (10–53) to eliminate ω_n and ω_m; thus

$$(y_n, y_m) = -\frac{l}{\alpha} \sin \beta_n \sin \beta_m \neq 0.$$

The modes are not orthogonal. In geometric terminology we have the case of an oblique coordinate system Y_n, Fig. 10–3(a). This must be transformed to a rectangular system Z_n, Fig. 10–3(b), before a vector can be conveniently resolved into its components. Since we are discussing particular examples, we shall not concern ourselves with a general theory of possible transformations. It is desirable that the transformation be as simple and as directly related to the modes as possible. With this in mind, we consider the functions

$$z_n = \cos \frac{\beta_n x}{l}, \qquad n = 1, 2, \dots.$$

These are related to the y_n by differentiation:

$$z_n = \frac{l}{\beta_n} \frac{dy_n}{dx}. \tag{10–54}$$

We now prove that the z_n form an orthogonal system, i.e., $(z_n, z_m) = 0$ if $n \neq m$. The proof is based on (10–33). Consider the term

$$z_m \frac{dz_n}{dx} \bigg]_0^l = - \frac{\beta_n}{l} \cos \frac{\beta_m x}{l} \sin \frac{\beta_n x}{l} \bigg]_0^l$$

$$= - \frac{\beta_n}{l} \cos \beta_m \sin \beta_n.$$

Equation (10–52) can be used to eliminate $\cos \beta_m$, and we obtain

$$z_m \frac{dz_n}{dx} \bigg]_0^l = - \frac{\beta_n \beta_m}{\alpha l} \sin \beta_n \sin \beta_m. \tag{10–55}$$

Substituting (10–55) into (10–33) yields

$$(\omega_n^2 - \omega_m^2)(z_n, z_m) = \frac{a^2 \beta_n \beta_m}{\alpha l} \sin \beta_n \sin \beta_m - \frac{a^2 \beta_m \beta_n}{\alpha l} \sin \beta_m \sin \beta_n = 0.$$

Thus

$$(z_n, z_m) = 0, \qquad n \neq m.$$

The scalar product (z_n, z_n) can be obtained by integration and is

$$(z_n, z_n) = \int_0^l \cos^2 \frac{\beta_n x}{l} \, dx = \frac{l}{2} \left(1 + \frac{\sin 2\beta_n}{2\beta_n} \right). \tag{10–56}$$

EXAMPLE 2. Consider the case where there is an initial deflection due to a static force F applied at $x = l$. At $t = 0$, this force is suddenly removed, and the resultant response $u(x, t)$ is to be determined. The static deflection can be found from (10–36), which yields

$$F = AE \frac{\partial u_s}{\partial x}.$$

We obtain, by integration,

$$u_s = \frac{F}{AE} x = u(x, 0). \qquad (10\text{–}57)$$

Equation (10–57) is the initial condition for $u(x, t)$ which is to have the form (10–5). The general solution for $u_n(t)$ is given by (10–27), with $f_n(t) = 0$, since the rod is free after $t = 0$. Thus

$$u_n(t) = A_n \cos \omega_n t + B_n \sin \omega_n t.$$

The initial value $u_n(0) = A_n$ can now be determined. At $t = 0$, (10–5) yields

$$u(x, 0) = \frac{F}{AE} x = \sum_{n=1}^{\infty} u_n(0) y_n(x). \qquad (10\text{–}58)$$

Before we can scalar multiply, the oblique coordinate system (y_n) must be replaced by the orthogonal coordinate system (z_n). This is done [see Eq. (10–54)] by differentiation. Thus

$$\frac{F}{AE} = \sum_{n=1}^{\infty} u_n(0) \frac{\beta_n}{l} z_n(x).$$

Scalar multiplication with z_m yields

$$\left(\frac{F}{AE}, z_m \right) = \frac{F}{AE} \int_0^l \cos \frac{\beta_m x}{l} \, dx = u_m(0) \frac{\beta_m}{l} (z_m, z_m).$$

Substituting (10–56) and carrying out the integration yields

$$u_m(0) = \frac{4Fl}{AE\beta_m} \frac{\sin \beta_m}{2\beta_m + \sin 2\beta_m}. \qquad (10\text{–}59)$$

Since the initial velocity is identically zero, it seems intuitively obvious that $u'_m(0) = \omega_m B_m = 0$. This can be rigorously proved by starting with

$$\left. \frac{\partial u(x, t)}{\partial t} \right]_{t=0} = 0$$

and carrying out similar steps as in (10–58) and (10–59). The final result for $u_m(t)$ is

$$u_m(t) = \frac{4Fl}{AE\beta_m} \frac{\sin \beta_m \cos \omega_m t}{2\beta_m + \sin 2\beta_m}. \ \blacktriangle$$

EXAMPLE 3. As a further example, which will help explain the necessity for the condition (10–48), consider the rod to be suddenly excited by a concentrated force $F(t)$ applied at $x = l$. The force density will have an impulse-type distribution at $x = l$ given by (Fig. 10–6)

$$f(x, t) = F(t)\, \delta(l - x). \tag{10–60}$$

The general solution for $u_m(t)$ is given by (10–27). The initial conditions are identically zero, thus $A_m = B_m = 0$ and

$$u_m(t) = \frac{1}{A\rho\omega_m} \int_0^t f_m(\tau) \sin \omega_m(t - \tau)\, d\tau. \tag{10–61}$$

To determine $f_m(t)$ in terms of the total force $F(t)$, we start with

$$f(x, t) = \sum_{n=1}^{\infty} f_n(t) y_n(x)$$

and introduce the orthogonal system z_n by differentiation. Thus

$$\frac{\partial f(x, t)}{\partial x} = \sum_{n=1}^{\infty} f_n(t)\, \frac{\beta_n}{l}\, z_n(x).$$

Scalar multiplication with z_m yields

$$\left(\frac{\partial f}{\partial x}, z_m\right) = \frac{\beta_m}{l} f_m(t)(z_m, z_n),$$

$$\int_0^l \frac{\partial f}{\partial x} z_m\, dx = \frac{\beta_m}{2}\left(1 + \frac{\sin 2\beta_m}{2\beta_m}\right) f_m(t). \tag{10–62}$$

The integral can be evaluated by integrating by parts:

$$\int_0^l \frac{\partial f}{\partial x} z_m\, dx = f(x, t) z_m(x)\Big|_0^l + \frac{\beta_m}{l} \int_0^l f(x, t) \sin \frac{\beta_m x}{l}\, dx. \tag{10–63}$$

The first term in (10–63) vanishes due to the condition (10–48) and the fact that $f(0, t) = 0$. The integral on the right-hand side of (10–63) can be evaluated by substituting (10–60). This yields

$$\int_0^l \frac{\partial f}{\partial x} z_m\, dx = \frac{\beta_m}{l} F(t) \sin \beta_m.$$

Substituting this into (10–62) and solving for $f_m(t)$ yields

$$f_m(t) = \frac{2}{l} \frac{\sin \beta_m}{1 + (\sin 2\beta_m)/2\beta_m} F(t).$$

The component of the mth mode, as given by (10–61), is then

$$u_m(t) = \frac{2 \sin \beta_m}{A\rho l \omega_m (1 + \sin 2\beta_m / 2\beta_m)} \int_0^t F(\tau) \sin \omega_m(t - \tau) \, d\tau. \; \blacktriangle$$

10–8 Torsional oscillations of a uniform rod. Let us consider the case of a uniform rod with inertia loading at both ends (Fig. 10–9). From the theory of elasticity we have

$$\text{Torque} = T(x, t) = GI_p \frac{\partial \theta}{\partial x}, \tag{10–64}$$

where

$G =$ the shear modulus,

$I_p =$ the second moment of area of the cross section with respect to the axis of rotation,

$\theta = \theta(x, t) =$ the angular twist of the cross section at x.

If we let ρ equal the mass per unit volume and $f(x, t)$ equal the externally applied moment per unit length, then Newton's equation of angular motion for an element dx is

$$(\rho \, dx I_p) \frac{\partial^2 \theta}{\partial t^2} = T(x + dx, t) - T(x, t) + f(x, t) \, dx.$$

Dividing by dx, we obtain

$$\rho I_p \frac{\partial^2 \theta}{\partial t^2} = \frac{\partial T}{\partial x} + f(x, t).$$

Equation (10–64) can be used to eliminate T. The equation of motion is then

$$\frac{\partial^2 \theta}{\partial t^2} = a^2 \frac{\partial^2 \theta}{\partial x^2} + \frac{1}{\rho I_p} f(x, t), \tag{10–65}$$

where $a^2 = G/\rho$. This equation is of the type (10–22), where

$$g(x, t) = \frac{1}{\rho I_p} f(x, t).$$

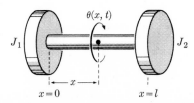

FIG. 10–9. The torsional oscillations of a uniform rod.

The boundary conditions are determined from the equations of motion for the inertia loads. If J_1 and J_2 are the moments of inertia, we have

$$J_1 \frac{\partial^2 \theta}{\partial t^2}\bigg]_{x=0} = T(0, t) = GI_p \frac{\partial \theta}{\partial x}\bigg]_{x=0}, \tag{10-66}$$

$$J_2 \frac{\partial^2 \theta}{\partial t^2}\bigg]_{x=l} = -T(l, t) = -GI_p \frac{\partial \theta}{\partial x}\bigg]_{x=l}. \tag{10-67}$$

As in the previous section we eliminate the time derivative by means of (10-65). For this to be possible it is necessary that

$$f(0, t) = f(l, t) = 0. \tag{10-68}$$

The boundary conditions (10-66) and (10-67) are then

$$J_1 a^2 \frac{\partial^2 \theta}{\partial x^2}\bigg]_{x=0} = GI_p \frac{\partial \theta}{\partial x}\bigg]_{x=0}, \tag{10-69}$$

$$J_2 a^2 \frac{\partial^2 \theta}{\partial x^2}\bigg]_{x=l} = -GI_p \frac{\partial \theta}{\partial x}\bigg]_{x=l}. \tag{10-70}$$

The general form of the mode is given by (10-28), and this must satisfy the boundary conditions. Substituting (10-28) into (10-69) yields

$$J_1 a^2 \left(-\frac{\omega_n^2}{a^2} \right) C_n = GI_p \frac{\omega_n}{a} D_n,$$

which can be simplified:

$$D_n = -\frac{J_1 a \omega_n}{GI_p} C_n = -\alpha_1 \beta_n C_n, \tag{10-71}$$

where we have set

$$\beta_n = \frac{\omega_n l}{a}, \tag{10-72}$$

and

$$\alpha_k = \frac{J_k a^2}{l GI_p} = \frac{J_k}{\rho l I_p} = \frac{J_k}{J_r}, \qquad k = 1, 2. \tag{10-73}$$

The quantities α_1 and α_2 are the ratios of the moments of inertia of the loads and that of the rod.

Substituting (10-28) into the second boundary condition (10-70) yields

$$J_2 a^2 \left(-\frac{\omega_n^2}{a^2} \right) (C_n \cos \beta_n + D_n \sin \beta_n)$$
$$= -GI_p \frac{\omega_n}{a} (-C_n \sin \beta_n + D_n \cos \beta_n),$$

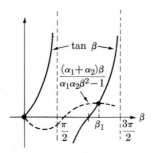

FIG. 10–10. The graphical solution for β_n.

which can be simplified:

$$\frac{J_2 a \omega_n}{GI_p} (C_n \cos \beta_n + D_n \sin \beta_n) = -C_n \sin \beta_n + D_n \cos \beta_n. \qquad (10\text{–}74)$$

Dividing (10–74) by $C_n \cos \beta_n$ and using (10–71), (10–72), and (10–73), we obtain

$$\alpha_2 \beta_n (1 - \alpha_1 \beta_n \tan \beta_n) = -\tan \beta_n - \alpha_1 \beta_n,$$

which can be rearranged into the form

$$\tan \beta_n = \frac{(\alpha_1 + \alpha_2)\beta_n}{\alpha_1 \alpha_2 \beta_n^2 - 1}. \qquad (10\text{–}75)$$

The solutions of this equation can be determined graphically (Fig. 10–10). The points of intersection yield $\beta_1, \beta_2, \ldots$, and the angular frequency of the nth mode is [see Eq. (10–72)]

$$\omega_n = \frac{\beta_n a}{l}. \qquad (10\text{–}76)$$

For the discussion to follow it is convenient to write (10–75) in the alternative form

$$\alpha_2 \beta_n (\cos \beta_n - \alpha_1 \beta_n \sin \beta_n) = -(\sin \beta_n + \alpha_1 \beta_n \cos \beta_n). \qquad (10\text{–}77)$$

With the aid of (10–71) the modes (10–28) can be written as

$$y_n(x) = \cos \frac{\beta_n x}{l} - \alpha_1 \beta_n \sin \frac{\beta_n x}{l}, \qquad (10\text{–}78)$$

where use has been made of (10–72) and C_n has been chosen equal to unity. As was the case with the previous example, the modes are not orthogonal.

To obtain an orthogonal coordinate system, we consider the functions

$$z_n(x) = \sin \frac{\beta_n x}{l} + \alpha_1 \beta_n \cos \frac{\beta_n x}{l}, \qquad n = 1, 2, \ldots,$$

which are related to the y_n by differentiation:

$$z_n = -\frac{l}{\beta_n} \frac{dy_n}{dx}. \tag{10-79}$$

To test for the orthogonality of the z_n's, we use (10–33). We consider the term

$$z_m \frac{dz_n}{dx}\bigg]_0^l = \frac{\beta_n}{l} \left(\sin \frac{\beta_m x}{l} + \alpha_1 \beta_m \cos \frac{\beta_m x}{l} \right) \left(\cos \frac{\beta_n x}{l} - \alpha_1 \beta_n \sin \frac{\beta_n x}{l} \right) \bigg]_0^l$$

$$= \frac{\beta_n}{l} (\sin \beta_m + \alpha_1 \beta_m \cos \beta_m)(\cos \beta_n - \alpha_1 \beta_n \sin \beta_n) - \frac{\alpha_1 \beta_n \beta_m}{l}.$$

This can be simplified with the aid of (10–77). Thus

$$z_m \frac{dz_n}{dx}\bigg]_0^l = -\frac{\alpha_2 \beta_n \beta_m}{l} (\cos \beta_m - \alpha_1 \beta_m \sin \beta_m)$$

$$\times (\cos \beta_n - \alpha_1 \beta_n \sin \beta_n) - \frac{\alpha_1 \beta_n \beta_m}{l}.$$

$$\tag{10-80}$$

Substituting this into (10–33) yields

$$(\omega_n^2 - \omega_m^2)(z_n, z_m) = a^2 \left[-z_m \frac{dz_n}{dx} + \frac{dz_m}{dx} z_n \right]_0^l = 0, \tag{10-81}$$

since (10–80) remains unaffected by interchanging n and m. From (10–81) we obtain

$$(z_n, z_m) = 0, \qquad n \neq m.$$

The scalar product (z_n, z_n) can be found by integration, and is

$$(z_n, z_n) = \frac{l}{2} \left[1 + \alpha_1^2 \beta_n^2 + (\alpha_1^2 \beta_n^2 - 1) \frac{\sin 2\beta_n}{2\beta_n} + 2\alpha_1 \beta_n \frac{1 - \cos 2\beta_n}{2\beta_n} \right].$$

$$\tag{10-82}$$

EXAMPLE 4. Consider the rod to be suddenly excited at $t = 0$ by a concentrated moment $M(t)$ applied at $x = l/2$. The moment per unit length is then

$$f(x, t) = M(t) \delta \left(x - \frac{l}{2} \right). \tag{10-83}$$

The response $u(x, t)$ is to be determined. The modes y_n and the angular frequency ω_n are given by (10–78) and (10–76), respectively. The component of the mth mode is determined from the general formula (10–27), where

$$g_m(t) = \frac{1}{\rho I_p} f_m(t),$$

and $A_m = B_m = 0$ due to the initial conditions. Thus

$$u_m(t) = \frac{1}{\rho I_p \omega_m} \int_0^t f_m(\tau) \sin \omega_m(t - \tau)\, d\tau. \qquad (10\text{–}84)$$

To determine the relation between $f_m(t)$ and the applied moment, we consider

$$f(x, t) = \sum_{n=1}^{\infty} f_n(t) y_n(x)$$

and introduce the orthogonal system z_n by differentiation [see Eq. (10–79)]

$$\frac{\partial f(x, t)}{\partial x} = \sum_{n=1}^{\infty} -\frac{\beta_n}{l} f_n(t) z_n(x).$$

Scalar multiplication with z_m yields

$$\left(\frac{\partial f}{\partial x}, z_m \right) = \int_0^l \frac{\partial f}{\partial x} z_m\, dx = -\frac{\beta_m}{l} f_m(t)(z_m, z_m). \qquad (10\text{–}85)$$

The left-hand integral can be evaluated by integrating by parts:

$$\int_0^l \frac{\partial f}{\partial x} z_m\, dx = f(x, t) z_m \Big]_0^l - \int_0^l f(x, t) \frac{dz}{dx}\, dx.$$

The first term of this expression vanishes due to the conditions (10–68). The remaining integral is easily evaluated by substituting (10–83). Thus

$$\int_0^l \frac{\partial f}{\partial x} z_m\, dx = -\frac{\beta_m}{l} y_m \left(\frac{l}{2} \right) M(t).$$

Substituting this into (10–85) and solving for $f_m(t)$ yields

$$f_m(t) = \frac{y_m(l/2) M(t)}{(z_m, z_m)}.$$

The final result is obtained by substituting this into (10–84). Thus

$$u_m(t) = \frac{y_m(l/2)}{\rho I_p \omega_m (z_m, z_m)} \int_0^t M(\tau) \sin \omega_m(t - \tau)\, d\tau,$$

where the scalar product (z_m, z_m) is given by (10–82). ▲

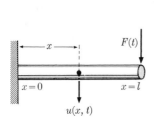

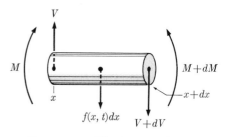

FIG. 10–11. The transverse vibrations of a uniform rod.

FIG. 10–12. The forces and moments on a rod element dx.

10–9 The transverse vibrations of a uniform rod. The transverse vibrations of a uniform rod (Fig. 10–11) will now be considered. From the theory of elasticity we have the relation

$$M(x, t) = -EI \frac{\partial^2 u}{\partial x^2}, \tag{10–86}$$

where

$M(x, t) =$ the internal moment at the cross section x,

$I =$ the second moment of area of the cross section with respect to the axis of zero bending strain.

We let V equal the shear force at the cross section x and consider Newton's equation of motion applied to an element dx (Fig. 10–12). For small displacements the rotary motion of the element may be neglected. The moment of all forces acting on the element is then zero. Neglecting higher-order differentials, we have

$$M(x + dx, t) - M(x, t) = V dx.$$

Thus

$$\frac{\partial M}{\partial x} = V. \tag{10–87}$$

The equation of motion for the lateral displacement $u(x, t)$ is

$$(\rho A \, dx) \frac{\partial^2 u}{\partial t^2} = V(x + dx, t) - V(x, t) + f(x, t) \, dx,$$

where $f(x, t)$ is the externally applied force per unit length. Dividing by dx, we obtain

$$\rho A \frac{\partial^2 u}{\partial t^2} = \frac{\partial V}{\partial x} + f(x, t);$$

V and M can be eliminated by means of (10–86) and (10–87), and we then

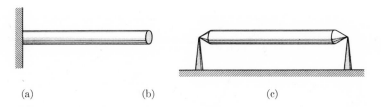

FIG. 10–13. The possible boundary conditions (a) clamped (b) free (c) simply supported.

obtain the equation of motion

$$\frac{\partial^2 u}{\partial t^2} + a^4 \frac{\partial^4 u}{\partial x^4} = \frac{1}{\rho A} f(x, t), \tag{10–88}$$

where $a^4 = EI/\rho A$. Equation (10–88) has been discussed in Section 10–5. The solutions (modes) are given by (10–31). The angular frequency ω_n and the ratio of the constants in (10–31) are determined by the boundary conditions, and the various possibilities are shown in Fig. 10–13. For the clamped end, the displacement and slope are constrained to be zero:

$$y_n = \frac{dy_n}{dx} = 0. \tag{10–89}$$

For the free end, there are no forces or moments acting on the cross section. Thus $M = 0$, $V = 0$. This requires that [see (10–86) and (10–87)]

$$\frac{d^2 y_n}{dx^2} = \frac{d^3 y_n}{dx^3} = 0. \tag{10–90}$$

For the simply supported end, the displacement is constrained to be zero, and there is no moment acting on the cross section. Thus

$$y_n = \frac{d^2 y_n}{dx^2} = 0.$$

EXAMPLE 5. Consider the case where one end is clamped and the other end free (Fig. 10–11). A concentrated force is to be suddenly applied at $x = l$. The boundary conditions are given by (10–89) at $x = 0$ and by (10–90) at $x = l$. Substituting (10–31) into (10–89), we obtain

$$F_n = -D_n \quad \text{and} \quad E_n = -C_n.$$

Thus

$$y_n(x) = C_n(\cos k_n x - \cosh k_n x) + D_n(\sin k_n x - \sinh k_n x).$$

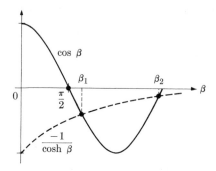

FIG. 10–14. The graphical solution for β_n.

From the boundary conditions (10–90), we obtain the two equations

$$C_n(\cos \beta_n + \cosh \beta_n) + D_n(\sin \beta_n + \sinh \beta_n) = 0, \qquad (10\text{--}91)$$

$$C_n(\sin \beta_n - \sinh \beta_n) - D_n(\cos \beta_n + \cosh \beta_n) = 0, \qquad (10\text{--}92)$$

where

$$\beta_n = k_n l = \frac{l}{a} \sqrt{\omega_n}. \qquad (10\text{--}93)$$

The system of linear equations (10–91) and (10–92) has nonzero solutions for C_n and D_n if

$$\begin{vmatrix} \cos \beta_n + \cosh \beta_n & \sin \beta_n + \sinh \beta_n \\ \sin \beta_n - \sinh \beta_n & -\cos \beta_n - \cosh \beta_n \end{vmatrix} = 0,$$

which leads to $\cos \beta_n \cosh \beta_n = -1$. The roots of this equation can be obtained graphically (Fig. 10–14). The angular frequency ω_n is then obtained from (10–93)

$$\omega_n = \left(\frac{a\beta_n}{l}\right)^2 = \left(\frac{\beta_n}{l}\right)^2 \sqrt{\frac{EI}{\rho A}}.$$

The constant C_n and D_n can be obtained from (10–92). If we choose

$$C_n = \sin \beta_n + \sinh \beta_n,$$

we must have

$$D_n = -(\cos \beta_n + \cosh \beta_n).$$

The modes y_n have been shown to be orthogonal [see (10–34)] and the scalar product (y_n, y_n) can be found by direct integration. Thus the response $u(x, t)$ is completely known once the component $u_m(t)$ is found. This is determined from the general expression (10–27), where

$$g_m(t) = \frac{1}{\rho A} f_m(t).$$

Thus, for zero initial conditions

$$u_m(t) = \frac{1}{\rho A \omega_m} \int_0^t f_m(\tau) \sin \omega_m(t - \tau) \, d\tau. \qquad (10\text{-}94)$$

The force density $f(x, t)$ can be expressed in terms of the total force $F(t)$ by

$$f(x, t) = F(t) \, \delta(l - x). \qquad (10\text{-}95)$$

To determine $f_m(t)$, we use the expansion

$$f(x, t) = \sum_{n=1}^{\infty} f_n(t) y_n(x).$$

Scalar multiplication with y_m yields

$$(f, y_m) = \int_0^l f(x, t) y_m(x) \, dx = f_m(t)(y_m, y_m)$$
$$= F(t) y_m(l), \qquad (10\text{-}96)$$

where (10-95) has been used to evaluate the integral on the left-hand side. Substituting (10-96) into (10-94) yields

$$u_m(t) = \frac{y_m(l)}{\rho A \omega_m (y_m, y_m)} \int_0^l F(\tau) \sin \omega_m(t - \tau) \, d\tau. \; \blacktriangle$$

10-10 The vibration of membranes. Loudspeakers and microphones are composed of plates and shells having some degree of rigidity. This requires using equations from the theory of elasticity, and, due to the boundary conditions and shape of the structures, leads to very unwieldy mathematical expressions. The discussion, therefore, will be restricted to the simplest structure of this type, which is that of a uniform plane membrane under a constant tension T. The same mathematical methods are applicable to the more complicated elastic structures. Let

$T =$ the tension per unit length,

$\rho =$ the mass per unit area,

$f(x, y, t) =$ the externally applied normal force per unit area.

Newton's equation of motion applied to an element $dx \, dy$ is (Fig. 10-15)

$$(\rho \, dx \, dy) \frac{\partial^2 u}{\partial t^2} = T \, dy[\sin (\theta_x + d\theta_x) - \sin \theta_x]$$
$$+ T \, dx[\sin (\theta_y + d\theta_y) - \sin \theta_y] + f(x, y, t) \, dx \, dy. \qquad (10\text{-}97)$$

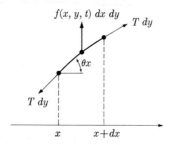

FIG. 10–15. A rectangular membrane element $dx\, dy$.

If the displacement is small, we have

$$\frac{\partial u}{\partial x} = \tan \theta_x \cong \sin \theta_x,$$

$$\frac{\partial u}{\partial y} = \tan \theta_y \cong \sin \theta_y. \tag{10–98}$$

Dividing (10–97) by $dx\, dy$ and using (10–98), we obtain the equation of motion

$$\frac{\partial^2 u}{\partial t^2} = c^2 \left(\frac{\partial^2 u}{\partial x^2} + \frac{\partial^2 u}{\partial y^2} \right) + \frac{1}{\rho} f(x, y, t),$$

where

$$c^2 = \frac{T}{\rho}.$$

This equation is of the type discussed in Section 10–5 [see (10–22)], where

$$D = -c^2 \nabla^2 = -c^2 \left(\frac{\partial^2}{\partial x^2} + \frac{\partial^2}{\partial y^2} \right),$$

and

$$g(x, t) = \frac{1}{\rho} f(x, y, t). \tag{10–99}$$

The response $u(x, y, t)$ can be written as

$$u(x, y, t) = \sum_{n=1}^{\infty} \sum_{m=1}^{\infty} u_{nm}(t) z_{nm}(x, y).$$

The modes z_{nm} are determined from the solutions of (10–26), which yields

$$D z_{nm} = \omega_{nm}^2 z_{nm}, \qquad n, m, = 1, 2, \ldots . \tag{10–100}$$

Rearranging this equation yields

$$\nabla^2 z_{nm} + \left(\frac{\omega_{nm}}{c} \right)^2 z_{nm} = 0. \tag{10–101}$$

A suitable definition for the scalar product of two modes is

$$(z_{nm}, z_{kl}) = \iint_R z_{nm}(x, y) z_{kl}(x, y)\, dx\, dy,$$

where the range R of integration extends over the area of the membrane.

The boundary condition for the membrane is due to the clamping of the edge which supplies the uniform tension. Therefore we must have

$$z_{nm} = 0 \qquad (10\text{–}102)$$

on the boundary.

We now prove that these modes are orthogonal. Consider (10–100) for the modes z_{nm} and z_{kl}. We have

$$Dz_{nm} = \omega_{nm}^2 z_{nm}, \qquad Dz_{kl} = \omega_{kl}^2 z_{kl}.$$

Scalar multiplication of the first equation with z_{kl} and the second with z_{nm} and subtracting yields

$$(\omega_{nm}^2 - \omega_{kl}^2)(z_{nm}, z_{kl})$$

$$= (z_{kl}, Dz_{nm}) - (Dz_{kl}, z_{nm})$$

$$= c^2 \iint_R [-z_{kl}\nabla^2 z_{nm} + z_{nm}\nabla^2 z_{kl}]\, dx\, dy$$

$$= c^2 \iint_R [-\text{div }(z_{kl}\,\text{grad }z_{nm}) + \text{div }(z_{nm}\,\text{grad }z_{kl})]\, dx\, dy$$

$$= c^2 \oint \left[-z_{kl}\frac{\partial z_{nm}}{\partial h} + z_{nm}\frac{\partial z_{kl}}{\partial h} \right] ds. \qquad (10\text{–}103)$$

In the final step use has been made of Green's theorem. This permits the integral over the region R to be transformed into a contour integral along a curve which bounds R. The outward normal of this curve is represented by h and the differential element along the curve by ds. Due to the boundary condition (10–102), the integral (10–103) is identically zero. Thus, if $\omega_{nm} \neq \omega_{kl}$,

$$(z_{nm}, z_{kl}) = 0.$$

EXAMPLE 6.   Consider a rectangular membrane of dimensions a and b (Fig. 10–16). The solution of (10–101) will then have the form

$$z_{nm}(x, y) = \sin \alpha_n x \cdot \sin \beta_m y, \qquad (10\text{–}104)$$

which meets the conditions (10–102) along the edges $x = 0$ and $y = 0$.

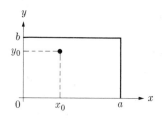

FIG. 10–16. A rectangular membrane.

The condition $z_{nm} = 0$ on the remaining two edges, $x = a$ and $y = b$, requires that

$$\alpha_n a = \pi n \quad \text{and} \quad \beta_m b = \pi m.$$

Thus

$$\alpha_n = \frac{\pi n}{a}, \qquad n = 1, 2, \ldots,$$

$$\beta_m = \frac{\pi m}{b}, \qquad m = 1, 2, \ldots.$$

Substituting (10–104) into (10–101) yields

$$\left(\frac{\omega_{nm}}{c}\right)^2 = \left(\frac{\pi n}{a}\right)^2 + \left(\frac{\pi m}{b}\right)^2,$$

which determines the angular frequency for the component of the nmth mode.

Suppose the membrane is suddenly excited at $t = 0$ by a concentrated force applied at $x = x_0$ and $y = y_0$. The force density is then

$$f(x, y, t) = F(t)\, \delta(x - x_0)\, \delta(y - y_0). \tag{10–105}$$

The component $u_{kl}(t)$ can be found from the general solution (10–27). Substituting (10–99), we obtain

$$u_{kl}(t) = \frac{1}{\rho \omega_{kl}} \int_0^t f_{kl}(\tau) \sin \omega_{kl}(t - \tau)\, d\tau. \tag{10–106}$$

To determine $f_{kl}(t)$ in terms of the concentrated force $F(t)$, we consider

$$f(x, y, t) = \sum_{n=1}^{\infty} \sum_{m=1}^{\infty} f_{nm}(t) z_{nm}(x, y).$$

Scalar multiplication with z_{kl} yields

$$(f, z_{kl}) = f_{kl}(t)(z_{kl}, z_{kl}). \tag{10–107}$$

The scalar product (z_{kl}, z_{kl}) can be found by integration and is

$$(z_{kl}, z_{kl}) = \int_0^a \int_0^b \sin^2 \frac{\pi kx}{a} \sin^2 \frac{\pi ly}{b} \, dx \, dy = \frac{ab}{4}. \qquad (10\text{--}108)$$

The remaining scalar product in (10–107) can be evaluated by using (10–105). This yields

$$(f, z_{kl}) = \int_0^a \int_0^b f(x, y, t) z_{kl}(x, y) \, dx \, dy$$

$$= F(t) z_{kl}(x_0, y_0). \qquad (10\text{--}109)$$

With the aid of (10–108) and (10–109) we can solve (10–107) for $f_{kl}(t)$. Substituting this into (10–106) yields

$$u_{kl}(t) = \frac{4}{\rho \omega_{kl}} \sin \frac{\pi k x_0}{a} \sin \frac{\pi l y_0}{b} \int_0^t F(\tau) \sin \omega_{kl}(t - \tau) \, d\tau. \ \blacktriangle$$

PROBLEMS

10–1. A uniform rod of cross-sectional area A and length l has both of its ends clamped (Fig. 10–17). Determine the modes of longitudinal oscillations. Prove that these modes are orthogonal. Determine the response $u(x, t)$ to a concentrated force F suddenly applied at $x = l/2$. The rod is initially at rest.

10–2. Consider the rod shown in Fig. 10–17. A concentrated constant force F is applied at $x = l/2$. This force is suddenly re-moved at $t = 0$. Determine the response in terms of the static deflection u_0 at $x = l/2$. Use the series

$$\frac{\pi^2}{8} = \sum_{n=1,3,5,\ldots}^{\infty} \frac{1}{n^2}$$

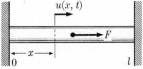

FIGURE 10–17

to determine the response $u(l/2, t)$ at the instants $t = nl/a$, where n is an integer and $a = \sqrt{E/\rho}$. Is the response $u(x, t)$ a periodic function in t for all values of x?

10–3. The characteristic roots for the logitudinal oscillations of a uniform rod with inertia loading are determined by (see Section 10–7) $\alpha = \beta_n \tan \beta_n$. Use the substitution $\beta_n = \pi(n - 1) + x_n$ and derive expressions which are suitable for the iterative computation of x_n. Compute the first three roots for the case where $\alpha = 1$. The quantity $a = \sqrt{E/\rho}$ is the velocity of longitudinal wave propagation [see (12–18)]. For a steel rod, $a = 5.1 \times 10^3$ m/sec. If the length of the rod is $l = 10$ cm, determine the characteristic frequencies of oscillation for the first three modes.

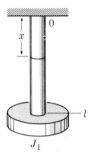

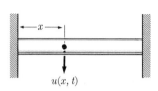

FIGURE 10–18   FIGURE 10–19

10–4. Consider the torsional oscillations of a uniform rod which has one end fixed and has an inertia load J_1 at the other end (Fig. 10–18). Show that the characteristic roots can be determined from (10–52) if α is taken to be $\rho l I_p / J_1$, where I_p is the second moment of area of the cross section with respect to the axis of rotation and ρ is the mass per unit volume.

10–5. The characteristic roots for the torsional oscillations of a uniform rod with inertia loading at both ends are determined by (10–75). Show that this can be written in the form

$$\beta_n = \sqrt{\frac{1}{\alpha_1 \alpha_2} + \left(\frac{1}{\alpha_1} + \frac{1}{\alpha_2}\right) \frac{\beta_n}{\tan \beta_n}}.$$

Use this expression to determine an approximate value for β_1 if $\alpha_1 \gg 1$, $\alpha_2 \gg 1$.

10–6. The characteristic roots for the lateral oscillations of a uniform rod with one end fixed and the other end free are determined by (see Example 5 and Fig. 10–11) $\cos \beta_n \cosh \beta_n = -1$. Use the substitution

$$\beta_n = \frac{\pi}{2}(2n - 1) + x_n$$

and derive an expression suitable for the iterative computation of x_n. Determine the first three characteristic roots. If the rod has a circular cross section of radius r show that the angular frequencies of oscillation are determined by

$$\omega_n = \frac{1}{2}\left(\frac{a}{l}\right)\left(\frac{r}{l}\right)\beta_n^2,$$

where $a = \sqrt{E/\rho}$ is the velocity of longitudinal wave propagation [see (12–18)]. For a steel rod $a = 5.1 \times 10^3$ m/sec. If $l = 10$ cm and $r = 0.1$ cm, determine the frequencies of oscillation for the first three modes.

10–7. (a) Determine the modes of lateral oscillations y_n and the equation for the characteristic roots of a uniform rod with both ends fixed (see Fig. 10–19). Evaluate the scalar product (y_n, y_m). (b) The rod is excited by a concentrated force $F(t)$ applied at $x = l/2$. Determine the response $u(x, t)$ if the rod is initially at rest.

10–8. A uniform plane circular membrane of radius b has its edge clamped and is under a constant tension T. Determine the modes of oscillation and the equation which defines the characteristic roots.

References

MASON, W. P., *Electrodynamical Transducers and Wave Filters*, D. Van Nostrand, New York, 1942.

MOORE, R. K., *Traveling-Wave Engineering*, McGraw-Hill, New York, 1961.

MORSE, P. M., *Vibration and Sound*, McGraw-Hill, New York, 1948.

RAYLEIGH, J. W., *Theory of Sound*, Dover Publications, New York, 1945.

TIMOSHENKO, S., *Vibrations Problems in Engineering*, D. Van Nostrand, New York, 1955.

CHAPTER 11

TRAVELING WAVES ON DISTORTIONLESS TRANSMISSION LINES

11-1 Introduction. The transient and steady-state response of transmission lines are of considerable importance in communication and power distribution systems. A transmission line often takes the form of a uniform two-wire line. However, different forms of waveguides may be used. The wave equation and the relationships between field variables can be derived from Maxwell's equations for the electromagnetic field. If losses as well as boundary conditions are taken into account, the field equations become very complicated. In the case where a *dominant mode* exists and the field variables are functions of the distance x along the line and the time t, it is known that useful approximations can be obtained by introducing field averages and using lumped-parameter circuit concepts [1, 2]. The energy transmission and wave pattern for a dominant mode can then be expressed in terms of a voltage, $v(x, t)$, a current, $i(x, t)$, and the following parameters:

$R =$ the series resistance per unit length,

$L =$ the series inductance per unit length,

$G =$ the shunt conductance per unit length,

$C =$ the shunt capacitance per unit length.

The distance along the transmission line is represented by x. Figure 11–1 shows the equivalent circuit for an element of line having a length dx. The relations for the voltage and current transforms are

$$-\frac{\partial V}{\partial x} = (R + Ls)I, \tag{11-1}$$

where

$$V = V(x, s) = \mathcal{L}[v(x, t)],$$

and

$$-\frac{\partial I}{\partial x} = (G + Cs)V, \tag{11-2}$$

where

$$I = I(x, s) = \mathcal{L}[i(x, t)].$$

By eliminating I from these equations, we obtain

$$\frac{\partial^2 V}{\partial x^2} = \gamma^2 V, \tag{11-3}$$

244

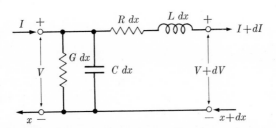

FIG. 11-1. An element dx of a transmission line.

where $\gamma = \sqrt{(R + Ls)(G + Cs)}$ is the *propagation function*. Similarly it can be shown that I satisfies the same differential equation (11–3). This differential equation is the transform of

$$\frac{\partial^2 v}{\partial x^2} = \left(R + L\frac{\partial}{\partial t}\right)\left(G + C\frac{\partial}{\partial t}\right)v$$

$$= RGv + (RC + LG)\frac{\partial v}{\partial t} + LC\frac{\partial^2 v}{\partial t^2}, \tag{11–4}$$

which is known as the *telegraphist's equation*. If there are no losses, $R = G = 0$ and (11–4) reduces to the *wave equation*

$$\frac{\partial^2 v}{\partial x^2} = LC\frac{\partial^2 v}{\partial t^2}.$$

In the derivation of (11–3) from (11–1) and (11–2), the initial conditions were taken to be identically zero. These are then the relations which determine the transfer functions for a transmission line. If initial conditions are present, they can be introduced by means of (11–4) and the corresponding equation for the current.

The solution of (11–3) is

$$V(x, s) = V_+e^{-\gamma x} + V_-e^{\gamma x}, \tag{11–5}$$

and similarly for the current

$$I(x, s) = I_+e^{-\gamma x} + I_-e^{\gamma x}. \tag{11–6}$$

Since V and I are related by (11–1) and (11–2), we must have

$$V_+ = I_+Z_0 \qquad V_- = -I_-Z_0, \tag{11–7}$$

where

$$Z_0 = \sqrt{\frac{R + Ls}{G + Cs}}$$

is the *characteristic impedance* of the transmission line.

FIG. 11–2. Terminal conditions for a transmission line.

Careful consideration must be given to the mathematical model used to represent the transmission line. In electromagnetic theory it is shown that a representation in the form (11–1) and (11–2) is possible, provided that the field energy is transmitted by means of a single dominant mode. Equivalent lumped-parameter networks can be used to account for discontinuities and terminations where higher-order modes are present. These usually are nonpropagating modes which attenuate quickly with distance, so that only the dominant mode remains. The voltage $v(x, t)$ and current $i(x, t)$ represent suitable field averages for the dominant mode.

Consider now the situation shown in Fig. 11–2, where a transmission line of length l is terminated in a load impedance Z_l and is driven by a voltage source $v_g(t)$ with an internal impedance Z_g. The boundary conditions at $x = l$ and $x = 0$ are

$$V(l, s) = Z_l I(l, s), \tag{11–8}$$

and

$$V_g(s) = Z_g I(0, s) + V(0, s),$$

respectively. Substituting (11–5), (11–6), and (11–7) yields

$$V_- = \Gamma_l e^{-2\gamma l} V_+, \quad \text{and} \quad V_+ = \frac{Z_0}{Z_0 + Z_g} \frac{V_g}{1 - \Gamma_0 \Gamma_l e^{-2\gamma l}},$$

where

$$\Gamma_l = \frac{Z_l - Z_0}{Z_l + Z_0} \tag{11–9}$$

and

$$\Gamma_0 = \frac{Z_g - Z_0}{Z_g + Z_0} \tag{11–10}$$

are the *reflection coefficients* at the load and generator ends, respectively. The complete solutions are

$$V(x, s) = \frac{Z_0 V_g(s)}{Z_0 + Z_g} \frac{e^{-\gamma x} + \Gamma_l e^{-\gamma(2l-x)}}{1 - \Gamma_0 \Gamma_l e^{-2\gamma l}} \tag{11–11}$$

and

$$I(x, s) = \frac{V_g(s)}{Z_0 + Z_g} \frac{e^{-\gamma x} - \Gamma_l e^{-\gamma(2l-x)}}{1 - \Gamma_0 \Gamma_l e^{-2\gamma l}}. \tag{11–12}$$

If the numerator and denominator of (11–11) and (11–12) are multiplied with $e^{\gamma l}$ and hyperbolic functions introduced, we obtain

$$V(x, s) = \frac{Z_0 V_g(s)}{Z_0 + Z_g} \frac{(1 + \Gamma_l) \cosh \gamma(l - x) + (1 - \Gamma_l) \sinh \gamma(l - x)}{(1 - \Gamma_0\Gamma_l) \cosh \gamma l + (1 + \Gamma_0\Gamma_l) \sinh \gamma l}$$

$$(11\text{–}13)$$

and

$$I(x, s) = \frac{V_g(s)}{Z_0 + Z_g} \frac{(1 - \Gamma_l) \cosh \gamma(l - x) + (1 + \Gamma_l) \sinh \gamma(l - x)}{(1 - \Gamma_0\Gamma_l) \cosh \gamma l + (1 + \Gamma_0\Gamma_l) \sinh \gamma l}.$$

$$(11\text{–}14)$$

11–2 The distortionless transmission line. If

$$\frac{R}{L} = \frac{G}{C} = \alpha c,$$

where $c = 1/\sqrt{LC}$ and $\alpha = R\sqrt{C/L}$, the line is said to be *distortionless*. In this case we have

$$\gamma = \frac{s}{c} + \alpha \qquad (11\text{–}15)$$

and $Z_0 = \sqrt{L/C}$. It will be shown that c is the *velocity of wave propagation;* α is the attenuation constant. If $\alpha = 0$, the line is *lossless.*

If the losses of a line are small so that

$$\left| \frac{R}{Ls} \right| \ll 1 \qquad \text{and} \qquad \left| \frac{G}{Cs} \right| \ll 1,$$

both γ and Z_0 can be developed in a series:

$$\gamma = \frac{s}{c} \left[1 + \frac{1}{2} \left(\frac{R}{L} + \frac{G}{C} \right) \frac{1}{s} + \cdots \right]$$

and

$$Z_0 = \sqrt{\frac{L}{C}} \left[1 + \frac{1}{2} \left(\frac{R}{L} - \frac{G}{C} \right) \frac{1}{s} + \cdots \right].$$

These lead to the following useful approximations:

$$\gamma \cong \frac{s}{c} + \alpha$$

where

$$\alpha = \frac{1}{2} \left(\frac{R}{L} + \frac{G}{C} \right) \sqrt{LC} \qquad \text{and} \qquad Z_0 \cong \sqrt{\frac{L}{C}}.$$

For the range in which these approximations are valid a line with small losses will have the same behavior as a distortionless line.

If the line is infinitely long or terminated in a *matched load* ($Z_l = Z_0$), the reflection coefficient Γ_l and consequently V_- vanish. This can also be seen if it is noted that V_+ and V_- represent the amplitude of the incident and reflected waves, respectively. For an infinitely long or matched line, there is no reflected wave and $V_- = 0$. The voltage transform is then

$$V(x, s) = V_+ e^{-\gamma x}.$$

If a voltage source $v_g(t)$ is applied at $x = 0$, the boundary condition requires that $V_+ = V_g(s)$. Thus

$$V(x, s) = V_g(s)e^{-\alpha x}e^{-xs/c}. \tag{11-16}$$

In order to find the inverse transform of (11–16) the *t-translation theorem* is required. This states that if

$$V(s) = V_g(s)e^{-Ts},$$

where

$$v_g(t) = \frac{1}{2\pi j} \int_{c-j\infty}^{c+j\infty} V_g(s)e^{ts}\, ds,$$

then

$$\mathcal{L}^{-1}[V_g(s)e^{-Ts}] = \frac{1}{2\pi j} \int_{c-j\infty}^{c+j\infty} V_g(s)e^{(t-T)s}\, ds$$

$$= v_g(t - T). \tag{11-17}$$

Thus a translation of $-T$ in the time domain is represented by an exponential factor e^{-Ts} in the s-domain. The exponential factor $e^{-xs/c}$ in (11–16) represents a delay of x/c seconds in the time domain. Thus

$$v(x, t) = e^{-\alpha x}v_g(\tau),$$

where $\tau = t - x/c$. To interpret this result it should be noted that $v_g(\tau) = 0$ if $\tau < 0$. Thus $v(x, t) = 0$ if $t < x/c$. This means that a time interval x/c is required before the applied voltage wave reaches a position x on the line. The quantity c therefore represents the velocity of propagation of the wave. Due to the line losses, the amplitude decreases by the factor $e^{-\alpha x}$ in the distance x. However, except for the decrease of amplitude and the time delay, the waveform of $v(x, t)$ is the same at every point on the line for the incident wave. Hence the designation *distortionless* for the line in which $R/L = G/C$.

Equations (11–11) and (11–12) are not, in general, suitable forms for obtaining the inverse Laplace transforms. More convenient forms are obtainable by substituting $x = \Gamma_0\Gamma_l e^{-2\gamma l}$. If Re $[s] > 0$, it follows that

$|x| < 1$. Thus the factor $(1 - x)^{-1}$ in (11–11) and (11–12) can be expanded in a series of the form

$$\frac{1}{1 - x} = 1 + x + x^2 + x^3 + \cdots .$$

Substituting this series into the equations for $V(x, s)$ and $I(x, s)$ yields

$$V(x, s) = \frac{Z_0 V_g(s)}{Z_0 + Z_g} [e^{-\gamma x} + \Gamma_l e^{-\gamma(2l-x)}]$$
$$\times [1 + \Gamma_0 \Gamma_l e^{-2\gamma l} + \Gamma_0^2 \Gamma_l^2 e^{-4\gamma l} + \cdots]$$
$$= \frac{Z_0 V_g(s)}{Z_0 + Z_g} [e^{-\gamma x} + \Gamma_l e^{-\gamma(2l-x)} + \Gamma_0 \Gamma_l e^{-\gamma(2l+x)} + \Gamma_0 \Gamma_l^2 e^{-\gamma(4l-x)}$$
$$+ \Gamma_0^2 \Gamma_l^2 e^{-\gamma(4l+x)} + \cdots] \quad (11\text{–}18)$$

and

$$I(x, s) = \frac{V_g(s)}{Z_0 + Z_g} [e^{-\gamma x} - \Gamma_l e^{-\gamma(2l-x)}]$$
$$\times [1 + \Gamma_0 \Gamma_l e^{-2\gamma l} + \Gamma_0^2 \Gamma_l^2 e^{-4\gamma l} + \cdots]$$
$$= \frac{V_g(s)}{Z_0 + Z_g} [e^{-\gamma x} - \Gamma_l e^{-\gamma(2l-x)} + \Gamma_0 \Gamma_l e^{-\gamma(2l+x)} - \Gamma_0 \Gamma_l^2 e^{-\gamma(4l-x)}$$
$$+ \Gamma_0^2 \Gamma_l^2 e^{-\gamma(4l+x)} + \cdots]. \quad (11\text{–}19)$$

The first forms of (11–18) and (11–19) yield the following voltage and current transforms at the load end:

$$V(l, s) = \frac{Z_0 V_g(s)}{Z_0 + Z_g} (1 + \Gamma_l) e^{-\gamma l} [1 + \Gamma_0 \Gamma_l e^{-2\gamma l} + \Gamma_0^2 \Gamma_l^2 e^{-4\gamma l} + \cdots],$$
$$(11\text{–}20)$$

$$I(l, s) = \frac{V_g(s)}{Z_0 + Z_g} (1 - \Gamma_l) e^{-\gamma l} [1 + \Gamma_0 \Gamma_l e^{-2\gamma l} + \Gamma_0^2 \Gamma_l^2 e^{-4\gamma l} + \cdots].$$
$$(11\text{–}21)$$

EXAMPLE 1. Consider the case where $Z_g = R_g$ and $Z_l = R_l$ are both resistive. In this case both Γ_0 and Γ_l are real. The voltage response to a suddenly applied voltage $v_g(t)$ can be obtained from (11–18) by substituting (11–15) for γ and interpreting the factor e^{-Ts} in the time domain as a time delay of T seconds. Equation (11–18) yields

$$v(x, t) = \frac{Z_0}{Z_0 + R_g} \left[e^{-\alpha x} v_g \left(t - \frac{x}{c} \right) + \Gamma_l e^{-\alpha(2l-x)} v_g \left(t - \frac{2l - x}{c} \right) \right.$$
$$\left. + \Gamma_0 \Gamma_l e^{-\alpha(2l+x)} v_g \left(t - \frac{2l + x}{c} \right) + \Gamma_0 \Gamma_l^2 e^{-\alpha(4l-x)} v_g \left(t - \frac{4l - x}{c} \right) + \cdots \right].$$

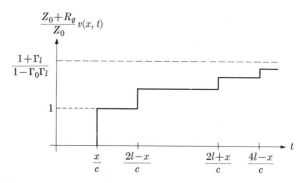

FIG. 11–3. Transmission line response to a step input.

If $\alpha = 0$, the response to a unit-step input is shown in Fig. 11–3. The sudden jumps in the voltage waveform are due to a succession of incident waves from the generator and reflected waves from the load. The first incident wave arrives at x after a time interval x/c. The amplitude of this wave can be normalized to unity as shown in the figure. This wave continues down to the load where it is reflected. The reflected wave has a normalized amplitude of Γ_l and arrives at x after a time interval $(2l - x)/c$. This wave is reflected at the generator end with a normalized amplitude $\Gamma_l\Gamma_0$. The steady-state voltage can be obtained by the superposition of all these waves, resulting in a geometric series which can be summed:

$$\frac{Z_0 + R_g}{Z_0} v(x, \infty) = 1 + \Gamma_l + \Gamma_0\Gamma_l + \Gamma_0\Gamma_l^2 + \Gamma_0^2\Gamma_l^2 + \cdots = \frac{1 + \Gamma_l}{1 - \Gamma_0\Gamma_l}.$$

Substituting from (11–9) and (11–10) yields

$$v(x, \infty) = \frac{R_l}{R_l + R_g}.$$

This result is easily verified by considering the voltage-divider action of the network under d-c conditions. ▲

EXAMPLE 2. Consider the case where $Z_g = 0$ and the line is terminated in a capacitance C_l. Thus $\Gamma_0 = -1$ and

$$\Gamma_l = -\frac{s - a}{s + a}$$

where $a = 1/Z_0C_l$. Equation (11–20) yields

$$V(l, s) = V_g(s) \frac{2a}{s + a}\left[e^{-\gamma l} + \left(\frac{s - a}{s + a}\right)e^{-3\gamma l} + \left(\frac{s - a}{s + a}\right)^2 e^{-5\gamma l} + \cdots\right].$$

$$(11–22)$$

The inverse transforms of these terms can be found with the aid of Appendix (B–8):

$$\mathcal{L}^{-1}\left[\frac{(s+b)^n}{(s+a)^{n+1}}\right] = e^{-at}L_n[(a-b)t],$$

where $L_n(x)$ is the Laguerre polynomial of order n. The convolution theorem yields

$$\mathcal{L}^{-1}\left[\frac{(s+b)^n}{(s+a)^{n+1}}V_g(s)\right] = \int_0^t e^{-a\tau}L_n[(a-b)\tau]v_g(t-\tau)\,d\tau = v_n(t),$$
$$(11\text{–}23)$$

where $v_n(t) = 0$ for $t < 0$. In applying (11–23) to (11–22), we substitute $b = -a$. The inverse transform of (11–22) is

$$v(l, t) = 2a\sum_{n=0}^{\infty} e^{-(2n+1)al}v_n\left[t - (2n+1)\frac{l}{c}\right]. \; \blacktriangle$$

11–3 Transmission line discontinuities. A general type of discontinuity between two different transmission lines can be represented by a two-terminal-pair network, as shown in Fig. 11–4. The propagation function, characteristic impedance, and velocity of wave propagation of the two lines will be designated by $\gamma_1, \gamma_2, Z_{01}, Z_{02}, c_1$, and c_2, respectively. For the two-terminal network we have

$$V_1 = AV_2 + BI_2, \qquad I_1 = CV_2 + DI_2.$$

The load impedance of line 1 as defined by (11–8) is

$$Z_l = \frac{V_1(l, s)}{I_1(l, s)} = \frac{V_1}{I_1} = \frac{AZ_{02} + B}{CZ_{02} + D},$$

where we have assumed that the line 2 is infinitely long or terminated in a matched load so that

$$\frac{V_2}{I_2} = \frac{V_2(0, s)}{I_2(0, s)} = Z_{02}.$$

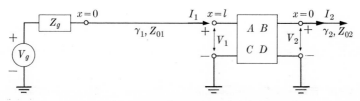

FIG. 11–4. Transmission line discontinuity.

EXAMPLE 3. Consider the case where the discontinuity is due to simple mismatch between the lines so that $A = D = 1$ and $B = C = 0$. If $Z_g = 0$, the reflection coefficients are

$$\Gamma_0 = -1 \quad \text{and} \quad \Gamma_l = \frac{Z_{02} - Z_0}{Z_{02} + Z_0},$$

respectively. Equation (11–20) yields

$$V_2(0, s) = V_1(l, s)$$
$$= V_g(s)(1 + \Gamma_l)e^{-\gamma_1 l}[1 - \Gamma_l e^{-2\gamma_1 l} + \Gamma_l^2 e^{-4\gamma_1 l} - \cdots].$$

If the first line is distortionless and Γ_l is a constant, the inverse transform of $V_2(0, s)$ is easily obtained with the aid of the t-translation theorem (11–17). For example, if the first line is lossless and a unit step is applied, we have

$$v_2(0, t) = (1 + \Gamma_l)(1 - \Gamma_l + \Gamma_l^2 - \Gamma_l^3 + \cdots + (-1)^n \Gamma_l^n)$$
$$= 1 + (-1)^n \Gamma_l^{n+1}$$

for the time interval

$$(2n + 1)\frac{l}{c_1} < t < (2n + 3)\frac{l}{c_1}.$$

The cases where $\Gamma_l > 0$ and $\Gamma_l < 0$ are shown in Figs. 11–5 and 11–6. ▲

EXAMPLE 4. If the two transmission lines are joined by an inductance L_1, the parameters are $A = D = 1, C = 0$, and $B = L_1 s$. The reflection coefficient at the load end of line 1 is

$$\Gamma_l = \frac{s + b}{s + a},$$

where

$$a = \frac{Z_{01} + Z_{02}}{L_1} \quad \text{and} \quad b = \frac{Z_{02} - Z_{01}}{L_1}.$$

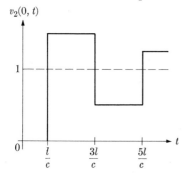

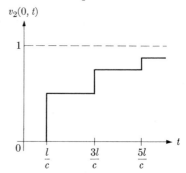

FIG. 11–5. Response to a unit step, Example 3, $\Gamma_l > 0$.

Fig. 11–6. Response to a unit step, Example 3, $\Gamma_l < 0$.

The input voltage transform for line 2 is

$$V_2(0, s) = Z_{02}I_2(0, s) = Z_{02}I_1(l, s)$$

$$= \frac{Z_{02}}{Z_{01}} V_g(s)(1 - \Gamma_l)e^{-\gamma_1 l}[1 + \Gamma_0\Gamma_l e^{-2\gamma_1 l} + \cdots],$$

where (11–21) has been used. If $\Gamma_0 = -1$, we obtain

$$V_2(0, s) = \frac{2Z_{02}}{L_1} V_g(s) \left[\frac{e^{-\gamma_1 l}}{s+a} - \frac{s+b}{(s+a)^2} e^{-3\gamma_1 l} + \cdots \right.$$

$$\left. + (-1)^n \frac{(s+b)^n}{(s+a)^{n+1}} e^{-(2n+1)\gamma_1 l} + \cdots \right].$$

$$(11\text{–}24)$$

Equation (11–23) can be used to obtain the inverse transform of the terms of (11–24). Thus

$$v_2(0, t) = \frac{2Z_{02}}{L_1} \sum_{n=0}^{\infty} (-1)^n e^{-(2n+1)al} v_n \left[t - (2n+1)\frac{l}{c} \right] \cdot \blacktriangle \qquad (11\text{–}25)$$

PROBLEMS

11–1. A unit-step voltage is applied to a lossless transmission line of length l. If $Z_g = R$, determine the voltage $v(0, t)$ if (a) $Z_l = 0$ (b) $Z_l = \infty$. Sketch the waveforms for the cases $R < Z_0$, $R = Z_0$, $R > Z_0$.

11–2. Solve Problem 11–1 if the voltage $v(l/2, t)$ is to be determined.

11–3. An input voltage $v_g(t)$ is applied to a distortionless transmission line of length l. If $Z_l = R_l$ and $Z_g = Z_0$, determine the voltage response at a position x. Discuss the cases $R_l > Z_0$, $R_l = Z_0$, $R_l < Z_0$.

11–4. A distortionless transmission line is open circuited at the load end and is suddenly excited at the generator end by a voltage $v_g(t)$. If $Z_g = L_1 s$, determine the voltage response of the transmission line.

11–5. If $Z_g = Z_l = 1/C_1 s$, determine the current response at the load end of a distortionless transmission line due to a unit-step voltage input.

11–6. Determine from (11–25) explicit expressions for the first two terms in the incident-voltage waveform at the load end. The input voltage is taken to be a unit step.

11–7. Two distortionless lines with parameters γ_1, Z_{01}, c_1, γ_2, Z_{02}, and c_2, respectively, are connected together with a shunt capacitance C_1 at the junction (Fig. 11–7). The second line is infinitely long. Compute the waveform $v_1(l, t)$ due to a unit-step input voltage for the interval $0 \leq t < 3l/c_1$. Take $Z_g = 0$.

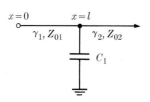

FIGURE 11–7

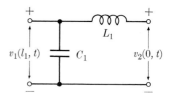

FIGURE 11–8

11–8. A transmission line of length l is connected to an infinitely long transmission line by means of the network shown in Fig. 11–8. Both lines are distortionless and have parameters γ_1, Z_{01}, c_1, γ_2, Z_{02}, and c_2, respectively. If the input is a unit-step voltage and $Z_g = 0$, determine the waveform $v_2(0, t)$ for the interval $0 \leq t < 3l/c_1$.

GENERAL REFERENCES

BEWLEY, L. V., *Travelling Waves on Transmission Systems*, Wiley and Sons, New York, 1951.

MOORE, R. K., *Traveling-Wave Engineering*, McGraw-Hill, New York, 1961.

REFERENCES

1. R. KING, *Transmission Line Theory*, McGraw-Hill, New York, 1955.
2. R. ADLER, L. CHU, and R. FANO, *Electromagnetic Energy Transmission and Radiation*, Wiley and Sons, New York, 1960.

CHAPTER 12

COMPARISON OF MODE AND LAPLACE
TRANSFORM METHODS

12–1 Introduction. In Chapters 10 and 11 two different methods for the solution of the differential equations of distributed-parameter systems were discussed. Expressing the solution as a superposition of modes which represent standing waves, as was done in Chapter 10, is readily visualized physically. The results obtained by means of the Laplace transform (Chapter 11) are easily interpreted in terms of traveling waves. However, there is a more fundamental difference which becomes evident when the examples of Chapter 10 are solved using the Laplace transform. Boundary-value problems of this type can be solved with the aid of the so-called *Green's function*, which is a function satisfying the boundary conditions and the equation of motion where the forcing term has an impulse-type distribution at a single point. Laplace transform methods can be used to determine the Green's function for a particular system. It is then possible to determine the response to an arbitrary input with the aid of the super-position principle.

12–2 The longitudinal vibrations of a uniform rod. The uniform rod discussed in Section 10–6 will once more be considered. The equation of motion is given by [see (10–37) and (10–38)]

$$\frac{\partial^2 u}{\partial t^2} = a^2 \frac{\partial^2 u}{\partial x^2} + \frac{1}{A\rho} f, \tag{12-1}$$

where

$$a^2 = \frac{E}{\rho}, \tag{12-2}$$

$u = u(x, t)$ is the displacement, and $f = f(x, t)$ is the force density. The Laplace transform of (12–1) yields

$$\frac{\partial^2 U}{\partial x^2} - \left(\frac{s}{a}\right)^2 U = -\frac{1}{Aa^2\rho} F, \tag{12-3}$$

where $U = U(x, s) = \mathcal{L}[u(x, t)]$ and $F = F(x, s) = \mathcal{L}[f(x, t)]$.

Green's function, $g(x, x_0, t)$, is defined to be a function which satisfies the boundary conditions and (12–1), where the force density f is considered to be an impulse-type function of x at x_0. Thus, the Laplace transform of Green's function is the solution of

$$\frac{\partial^2 G}{\partial x^2} - \frac{s^2 G}{a^2} = \delta(x - x_0), \tag{12-4}$$

which also satisfies the Laplace transform of the boundary conditions (10–39). If (12–4) is integrated over the impulse, we obtain

$$\lim_{\epsilon \to 0} \frac{\partial G}{\partial x}\bigg]_{x_0-\epsilon}^{x_0+\epsilon} = 1. \tag{12-5}$$

An equivalent and more convenient definition of Green's function follows from (12–4) and (12–5). The function G is continuous and satisfies the boundary conditions and the differential equation

$$\frac{\partial^2 G}{\partial x^2} - \frac{s^2 G}{a^2} = 0 \tag{12-6}$$

in the intervals $0 \le x < x_0$, $x_0 < x \le l$ and has a discontinuity in its derivative at x_0 given by (12–5). Physically, this discontinuity is a consequence of the impulsive force density at x_0.

The solution of (12–6) meeting the boundary conditions (which require that $G = 0$ at $x = 0$ and $dG/dx = 0$ at $x = l$) in each interval is

$$G(x, x_0, s) = \begin{cases} C_1 \sinh \dfrac{sx}{a}, & 0 \le x < x_0, \\[2mm] C_2 \cosh \dfrac{s}{a}(l - x), & x_0 < x \le l. \end{cases} \tag{12-7}$$

The continuity of G requires that

$$C_1 \sinh \frac{sx_0}{a} = C_2 \cosh \frac{s}{a}(l - x_0).$$

From condition (12–5) we obtain

$$-C_2 \frac{s}{a} \sinh \frac{s}{a}(l - x_0) - C_1 \frac{s}{a} \cosh \frac{sx_0}{a} = 1.$$

Solving for C_1 and C_2 and substituting into (12–7) yields

$$G(x, x_0, s) = \begin{cases} -\dfrac{a}{s} \dfrac{\cosh (s/a)(l - x_0) \sinh (sx/a)}{\cosh (sl/a)}, & 0 \le x < x_0, \\[4mm] -\dfrac{a}{s} \dfrac{\cosh (s/a)(l - x) \sinh (sx_0/a)}{\cosh (sl/a)}, & x_0 < x \le l. \end{cases} \tag{12-8}$$

In (12–3) the transform of the force density, $F(x_0, s)$, can be considered to be the transform of a distribution of infinitesimal impulses $F(x_0, s)\,dx_0$ $\delta(x - x_0)$ along the rod. The solution of (12–3) can then be found with the aid of (12–8) and the principle of superposition. Thus

$$U(x, s) = -\frac{1}{Aa^2\rho} \int_0^l G(x, x_0, s)F(x_0, s)\,dx_0. \tag{12–9}$$

The inverse transform of (12–9) can be found with the aid of the convolution theorem. This yields

$$u(x, t) = -\frac{1}{Aa^2\rho} \int_0^t \int_0^l g(x, x_0, t - \tau)f(x_0, \tau)\,dx_0\,d\tau. \tag{12–10}$$

The form of this solution differs considerably from that given in Section 10–6 where $u(x, t)$ was represented in terms of modes [see (10–42) and (10–44)]. It will now be shown that these solutions are identical. By using the Heaviside expansion we have, for the interval $0 \le x < x_0$,

$$g(x, x_0, t) = \mathcal{L}^{-1}\left[-\frac{a}{s}\frac{\cosh (s/a)(l - x_0)\sinh (sx/a)}{\cosh (sl/a)}\right]$$

$$= -a \sum_n \frac{1}{s_n}\frac{\cosh (s_n/a)(l - x_0)\sinh (s_n x/a)}{[(d/ds)\cosh (sl/a)]_{s=s_n}} e^{s_n t}. \tag{12–11}$$

The poles of $G(x, x_0, s)$ are the roots of the equation

$$\cosh \frac{sl}{a} = 0.$$

These are given by

$$s_n = \pm j\frac{\pi a n}{2l} = \pm j\omega_n, \qquad n = 1, 3, 5, \ldots \tag{12–12}$$

(note that $s = 0$ is not a pole since it is cancelled by the zero of the sinh s term in the numerator). Substituting (12–12) into (12–11) yields

$$g(x, x_0, t) = -\frac{2a^2}{l} \sum_{n=1,3,5,\ldots}^{\infty} \frac{1}{\omega_n} \sin \frac{\omega_n x_0}{a} \sin \frac{\omega_n x}{a} \sin \omega_n t. \tag{12–13}$$

A similar argument for the interval

$$x_0 < x \le l$$

leads to the same result. Thus (12–13) is valid for the whole interval

$$0 \le x \le l.$$

If this equation is substituted into (12–10) and the factors are suitably grouped, we obtain

$$u(x, t) = \frac{2}{A\rho l} \sum_{n=1,3,5,\ldots}^{\infty} \frac{1}{\omega_n} \sin \frac{\omega_n x}{a} \int_0^l f_n(\tau) \sin \omega_n(t - \tau) \, d\tau$$

$$= \sum_{n=1,3,5\ldots,}^{\infty} u_n(t) y_n(x), \qquad (12\text{–}14)$$

where

$$f_n(\tau) = \frac{2}{l} \int_0^l \sin \frac{\omega_n x_0}{a} f(x_0, \tau) \, dx_0 = \frac{(f, y_n)}{(y_n, y_n)},$$

$$u_n(t) = \frac{1}{A\rho \omega_n} \int_0^l f_n(\tau) \sin \omega_n(t - \tau) \, d\tau,$$

and

$$y_n(x) = \sin \frac{\omega_n x}{a}.$$

Equation (12–14) is the solution in terms of the modes. The function $f_n(\tau)$ is expressed in terms of the scalar product notation used previously [see (10–42) and (10–44)].

On comparison of these two methods it is apparent that the direct expansion in terms of modes is considerably simpler. The Laplace transform method requires the use of the Green's function and also considerable mathematical manipulations, which ultimately results in the same form of solution. However, this latter method does offer some advantages when the forcing function is concentrated at the ends of the interval. Analogies with the traveling waves on transmission lines are then possible. As an example, we consider an external concentrated force $h(t)$ applied at $x = l$. The force density is

$$f(x, t) = h(t) \, \delta(x - l). \qquad (12\text{–}15)$$

Taking the Laplace transform of (12–15) and substituting into (12–9) yields

$$U(x, s) = \frac{a}{AE} H(s) \frac{\sinh (sx/a)}{\cosh (sl/a)}, \qquad (12\text{–}16)$$

where the relation (12–2) has been used. Comparing this with (11–14) shows that an analogy with the transmission line current is possible if $\Gamma_l = 1$, $\Gamma_0 = -1$, and $Z_g = 0$ so that

$$I(x, s) = \frac{V_g(s)}{Z_0} \frac{\sinh \gamma(l - x)}{\cosh \gamma l}. \qquad (12\text{–}17)$$

The transmission line is open circuited at $x = l$ and is driven directly by a voltage source $v_g(t)$. Equations (12–16) and (12–17) can be compared by using the substitution $sU(l - x, s) = I(x, s)$ and choosing $V_g(s) = H(s)$ and $Z_0 = AE/a$. Since $\gamma = s/a$, the velocity of wave propagation is

$$c = a = \sqrt{E/\rho}. \tag{12–18}$$

It is seen that the velocity of the cross section is analogous to the current and that the external force is analogous to the voltage source. Equation (12–17) can be expanded into the form (11–19), and from this the response of the rod in terms of incident and reflected waves can be determined.

12–3 The inertia-loaded rod. The transmission line equations for the case where $G = R = 0$ and where there is no distributed external driving voltage along the line are obtained from (11–1) and (11–2). Thus

$$\frac{\partial V}{\partial x} = -LIs, \qquad \frac{\partial I}{\partial x} = -CVs. \tag{12–19}$$

These can be compared with the transform of the equations for the free longitudinal oscillations of a uniform rod (see Section 10–6)

$$\frac{\partial U}{\partial x} = \frac{1}{AE} F, \tag{12–20a}$$

$$\frac{\partial F}{\partial x} = A\rho s^2 U. \tag{12–20b}$$

We choose $L = A\rho$, $C = 1/AE$, $I = sU$, and $V = -F$. The current is then analogous to the velocity of the cross section and the voltage is analogous to the internal force acting on the cross section of the rod.

To obtain a transmission line analog of the inertia-loaded rod (see Section 9–7 and Fig. 10–7) it is convenient to change the coordinate system so that $x = 0$ corresponds to the position of the mass loading M and the concentrated applied force $h(t)$ (see Fig. 12–1). The force density is given by

$$f(x, t) = h(t)\, \delta(x),$$

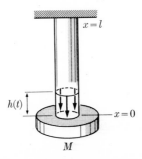

Fig. 12–1. The inertia-loaded rod with a concentrated forcing function.

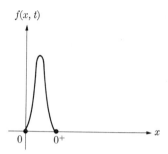

FIG. 12–2. The distribution of the force density.

where $\delta(x)$ is a unit impulse of the form shown in Fig. 12–2. Integrating (12–1) over the interval 0 to 0^+ and noting that this interval is an infinitesimal, we obtain

$$-a^2 \frac{\partial u}{\partial x}\Big]_0^{0^+} = \frac{1}{A\rho} h(t). \tag{12–21}$$

For the boundary condition at $x = 0$ we use (10–47) with a sign reversal due to the reversed coordinate system. Thus

$$\frac{M}{AE} \frac{\partial^2 u}{\partial t^2}\Big]_{x=0} = \frac{\partial u}{\partial x}\Big]_{x=0}. \tag{12–22}$$

Taking the Laplace transform of (12–21) and (12–22), we obtain

$$\frac{M}{AE} s^2 U(0, s) = \frac{\partial U(x, s)}{\partial x}\Big]_{x=0} = \frac{\partial U(x, s)}{\partial x}\Big]_{x=0^+} + \frac{1}{AE} H(s).$$

Substituting $I = sU$ into this equation and using (12–19) yields

$$MsI(0, s) + V(0^+, s) = H(s) = V_g(s),$$

which is the voltage relation for the input network of a transmission line where $Z_g = Ms$. The inductance $L_g = M$ is the analog for the inertia load (Fig. 12–3).

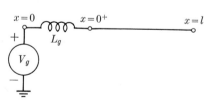

FIG. 12–3. Transmission line analog for the inertia-loaded rod.

We have discussed two methods of solving for the response of distributed-parameter systems. One method is based on a representation of the solution in terms of modes. The second method uses the Laplace transform and, in general, requires determining the Green's function. The results of Section 12–2 and this section indicate the circumstances under which the mode or Laplace transform method is preferable. In the general case, the forcing function is distributed over the system and the mode method is simpler. However, if the boundary conditions can be represented by network equations and if the externally applied forcing function can be considered to drive the system through the network, the Laplace transform method leads to the simplest representation. The problem of determining the Green's function is then avoided and the simpler problem of finding suitable terminating networks is considered.

EXAMPLE 1. Consider the transmission line analog of the inertia-loaded rod to be suddenly excited by a voltage $v_g(t) = h(t)$. The terminal conditions yield $\Gamma_l = 1$ and

$$\Gamma_0 = \frac{sL_g - Z_0}{sL_g + Z_0} = \frac{s - b}{s + b},$$

where $b = (A\rho a/M)$. Substituting into (11–19) and dividing by s yields

$$U(x, s) = \frac{I(x, s)}{s} = \frac{1/L_g}{s + b}\frac{V_g(s)}{s}\left[e^{-\gamma x} - e^{-\gamma(2l-x)} + \left(\frac{s - b}{s + b}\right)e^{-\gamma(2l+x)}\right.$$

$$- \left(\frac{s - b}{s + b}\right)e^{-\gamma(4l-x)} + \left(\frac{s - b}{s + b}\right)^2 e^{-\gamma(4l+x)}$$

$$\left. - \left(\frac{s - b}{s + b}\right)^2 e^{-\gamma(6l-x)} + \cdots\right]. \qquad (12\text{--}23)$$

The terms in this transform have the form

$$V_n(s)e^{-sT} = \frac{F(s)}{s + b}\left(\frac{s - b}{s + b}\right)^n e^{-sT},$$

where we have set

$$f(t) = \int_0^t v_g(\tau)\, d\tau,$$

so that $F(s) = (1/s)V_g(s)$. The inverse transform of $V_n(s)e^{-sT}$ can be found with the aid of Appendix (B–8) and application of the t-translation and convolution theorems. Thus

$$v_n(t) = \int_0^t e^{-b\tau}L_n(2b\tau)f(t - \tau)\, d\tau,$$

where $v_n(t) = 0$ if $t < 0$. Using this result, we obtain the inverse transform of (12–23)

$$u(x, t) = \frac{1}{L_g} \sum_{n=0}^{\infty} \left[v_n \left(t - \frac{2nl + x}{a} \right) - v_n \left(t - \frac{2(n + 1)l - x}{a} \right) \right]. \; \blacktriangle$$

12–4 Terminal conditions for an electromechanical filter. An electromechanical filter is usually driven by means of the *magnetostrictive effect*. The boundary conditions for this type of excitation are relatively complicated and can best be represented by a network analog [1]. Figure 12–4 illustrates the drive system where a coil excites the ferrite or nickel alloy rod. The coil is considered to be uniformly wound with n turns per unit length. The parameters for the rod are again taken as A, E, l, and ρ, and it is biased by means of a permanent magnet to a suitable operating point on its magnetization curve. The linearized equations for incremental operation take the form

$$\text{strain} = \frac{1}{E} \text{ (stress)} + b_1 \text{ (magnetic field intensity)},$$

$$\text{magnetic flux density} = \mu \text{ (magnetic field intensity)} + b_1 \text{ (stress)}.$$

In transform notation these equations are

$$\frac{\partial U(x, s)}{\partial x} = \frac{1}{E} \frac{F(x, s)}{A} + b_1 n I_0(s) \tag{12–24a}$$

$$B(x, s) = \mu n I_0(s) + b_1 \frac{F(x, s)}{A} = (\mu - E b_1^2) n I_0(s) + b_1 E \frac{\partial U(x, s)}{\partial x}. \tag{12–24b}$$

The magnetic field intensity is considered to be uniform over the length of the rod and is taken to be $n i_0(t)$. Newton's law of motion, applied to an element of the rod, results in (12–20b). If we eliminate F and then U from

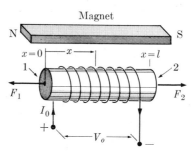

Fig. 12–4. Excitation for a magnetostrictive rod.

(12–20b) and (12–24a), we obtain the equations

$$\frac{\partial^2 U}{\partial x^2} = \left(\frac{s}{a}\right)^2 U = \gamma^2 U, \tag{12–25}$$

$$\frac{\partial^2 F}{\partial x^2} = \left(\frac{s}{a}\right)^2 F + A\rho b_1 n s^2 I_0, \tag{12–26}$$

where $a = \sqrt{E/\rho}$. The magnetostrictive drive results in a forcing term on the right-hand side of (12–26). However, (12–25) still has the same form as in the case of free vibrations. The solution of (12–25) consists of a linear combination of the exponentials $e^{\pm\gamma x}$. We can choose a transmission line analog and take $I = sU$. If we express the current I in terms of the input and output currents (designated by I_1 and I_2, respectively) we have

$$I = \frac{I_1 \sinh \gamma(l - x) + I_2 \sinh \gamma x}{\sinh \gamma l}.$$

The voltage is determined by $V = -F$. This can be obtained from the inhomogeneous equation (12–26). However, it is more conveniently obtained from (12–24a) by noting that

$$\frac{\partial U}{\partial x} = \frac{1}{s}\frac{\partial I}{\partial x}.$$

This yields

$$V_1 = V(0, s) = NI_0 + Z_0\left(I_1 \coth \gamma l - \frac{I_2}{\sinh \gamma l}\right) \tag{12–27a}$$

$$V_2 = V(l, s) = NI_0 + Z_0\left(\frac{I_1}{\sinh \gamma l} - I_2 \coth \gamma l\right), \tag{12–27b}$$

where

$$N = AEb_1 n \quad \text{and} \quad Z_0 = AE/a.$$

The remaining equation for this system relates the applied voltage $v_0(t)$ to the input current $i_0(t)$. This is obtained by computing the rate of change of flux linking the coil. In transform notation this yields

$$V_0 = sAn\int_0^l B(x, s)\,dx = N(I_2 - I_1) + sL_0 I_0, \tag{12–28}$$

where $L_0 = A(\mu - Eb_1^2)n^2 l$ and where (12–24b) has been substituted into the integral. After the integration is performed, sU is replaced by I.

A network analog which yields (12–27) and (12–28) is shown in Fig. 12–5. The transformer is ideal and has a turns ratio of N. The T-equivalent network is obtained with the aid of Appendix (A–12). If we let V_{22} and I_{22} be the primary voltage and current, respectively, and set $V_{11} = I_{22}$,

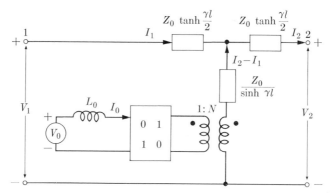

FIG. 12–5. Network analog for the excitation of a magnetostrictive rod.

$I_{11} = I_0$, it follows that

$$\begin{pmatrix} V_{11} \\ I_{11} \end{pmatrix} = \begin{pmatrix} 0 & 1 \\ 1 & 0 \end{pmatrix} \begin{pmatrix} V_{22} \\ I_{22} \end{pmatrix}.$$

This two-terminal-pair network is shown in Fig. 12–5. If this network is represented in terms of impedance elements [see (9–1)] we find that $z_{12} = -1$ and $z_{21} = 1$. A network of this type is known as a *gyrator*.

The cross section at 1 is suitably terminated to secure a good match between the source and the filter which is connected to the cross section at 2. The physical conditions for these connections require equilibrium for the forces and continuity for the displacements at each of the cross sections. In the transmission line analog these conditions are equivalent to continuity of voltage and current. The load termination of the filter is very much the same as at the generator end. Conditions are chosen so that the combined electrical and mechanical damping results in a reasonable impedance match to the filter over the bandwidth of the system.

The reason that a simple network analog can represent these terminal conditions is due to the fact that the magnetic field intensity has been taken to be uniform. If this is not the case, (12–25) and (12–26) will both have forcing terms on the right-hand side which are functions of x. The problem must then be solved by using the mode method or by determining a Green's function. A simple network analog is then no longer possible.

PROBLEMS

12–1. Figure 12–6 illustrates a uniform rod of length l and rectangular cross section which has a conductive coat on two sides and is driven by means of the piezoelectric effect. The linearized equations for incremental operation have the form

$$\text{strain} = \frac{1}{E}\ (\text{stress}) + b\ (\text{electric field intensity}),$$

electric flux density $= b$ (strain) $+ \epsilon$ (electric field intensity), where b, E, and ϵ are constants. The electric field intensity is approximately uniform and is taken to be $v_0(t)/d$. Determine a network analog which will approximate the conditions at the input and at the cross sections 1 and 2 of the rod. [*Hint:* Assume the electric flux density to be normal to the conducting surface so that it equals the surface charge density. Then note that $i_0 = dq/dt$, where q is the charge on the conducting surface.]

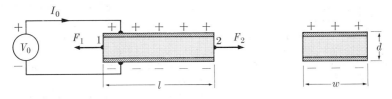

FIGURE 12–6

12–2. Determine a transmission line analog for the angular oscillations of a uniform rod. Find expressions for the characteristic impedance, the propagation function, and determine the velocity of wave propagation. Compare these with the corresponding expressions for longitudinal oscillations. (The shear modulus can be found from $G = E/2(1 + k)$, where $k \cong 0.3$ for metals.)

12–3. Consider a rod which has piecewise uniform sections (Fig. 12–7). (a) Show that the transmission line analog for the longitudinal or angular oscillations takes the form illustrated in Fig. 9–29. (b) This rod can be used as a section of a bandpass filter. Show that the pass band is determined by the real values of β which satisfy the equation (see Problem 9–8)

$$\cos \beta = \cos 2\beta_1 \cos \beta_2 - \frac{1}{2}\left(\frac{Z_2}{Z_1} + \frac{Z_1}{Z_2}\right) \sin 2\beta_1 \sin \beta_2,$$

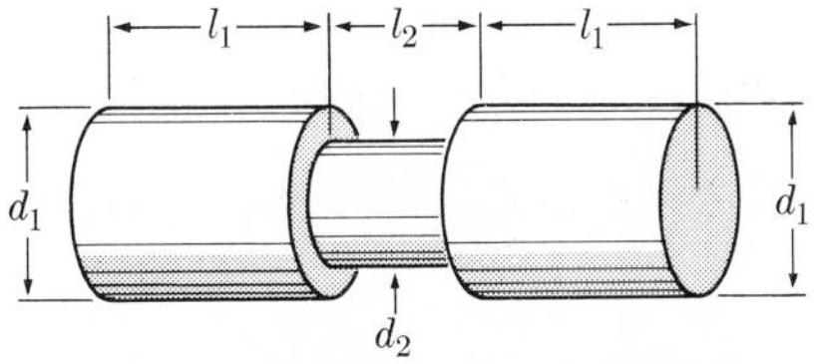

FIGURE 12–7

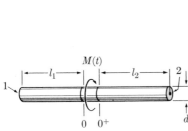

FIGURE 12–8   FIGURE 12–9

where $\beta_k = \omega l_k / a_k$ and a_k is the velocity of wave propagation for the subsection k. (c) Use the result of part (b) to determine the time delay for one section. (d) The fractional bandwidth is defined to be $K = \Delta\omega/\omega_0$, where ω_0 is the value of ω at the band center and $\Delta\omega$ is the difference in the values of ω at the band edges. Sketch the phase characteristic and determine K for the following cases (1) $Z_2/Z_1 \gg 1$, $\beta_1 = \beta_2 = \pi/2$; (2) $Z_2/Z_1 \ll 1$, $\beta_1 = 2\beta_2 = \pi$.

12–4. (a) A concentrated external moment, $M(t)$, is applied over an infinitesimal segment (designated by $0^+ - 0$) of a uniform rod (Fig. 12–8). Determine a transmission line analog which will represent the conditions at the cross sections 0, 1, and 2. (b) An approximate means of realizing the moment $M(t)$ is illustrated in Fig. 12–9, where two magnetostrictive rods which operate in the longitudinal mode apply push-pull forces [2]. Determine a network analog which will approximate the conditions at the cross sections 0, 1, 2, and 3 of these rods.

12–5. An electromechanical filter is to operate in the torsional mode at a center frequency of 100 kc. It is to have a fractional bandwidth of 0.05. The desired attenuation characteristic outside of the pass band is obtained by choosing 9 sections of the type shown in Fig. 12–7, where $\beta_1 = \beta_2 = \pi/2$. The material used is the alloy Ni-Span-C which has a velocity of wave propagation (for the torsional mode) of 2.9×10^5 cm/sec. Determine the linear dimensions l_1 and d_1 if $d_2 = 0.54$ cm. What is the time delay for the filter? (Use the results of Problem 12–3.)

REFERENCES

1. H. KATZ, *Solid State Magnetic and Dielectric Devices*, Wiley and Sons, New York, 1959.

2. R. W. GEORGE, "Electromechanical filters," *Proc. IRE*, **44**, 14–18 (January 1956).

CHAPTER 13

STEADY-STATE RESPONSE OF SYSTEMS

13–1 Introduction. A frequently occurring problem in system analysis is the determination of the steady-state response when the input is periodic. It is possible to solve this problem using Laplace transform and superposition methods. Let the recurrent input waveform be represented by $v_T(t)$, where, by definition, $v_T(t) = 0$ for $t < 0$ (see Fig. 13–1). The Laplace transform $V_T(s)$ will be subject to the condition that it be a rational function of s with poles in the left half of the s-plane only. The input can then be represented in the form

$$v_i(t) = \cdots + v_T(t + 2T) + v_T(t + T) + v_T(t), \qquad 0 \le t < T, \quad (13\text{–}1)$$

where $v_T(t)$ is the last recurrent waveform of the sequence and T is the period.

Let $g(t)$ be the system response (with all initial conditions taken to be identically zero) due to the input $v_T(t)$. Thus, if $H(s)$ is the system transfer function, we have

$$G(s) = H(s)V_T(s).$$

The output response due to the sequence of recurrent inputs represented by the series (13–1) can then be found by superposition. Thus

$$v_o(t) = \cdots + g(t + 2T) + g(t + T) + g(t).$$

The Laplace transform of this expression can be obtained with the aid

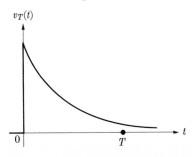

Fig. 13–1. Recurrent input waveform.

267

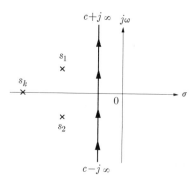

FIG. 13–2. Path of integration in the s-plane.

of the t-translation theorem (11–17). Thus

$$V_o(s) = \cdots + G(s)e^{2Ts} + G(s)e^{Ts} + G(s)$$
$$= H(s)V_T(s)(1 + e^{Ts} + e^{2Ts} + \cdots). \qquad (13\text{–}2)$$

If

$$\mathrm{Re}[s] < 0, \qquad (13\text{–}3)$$

the series (13–2) can be summed into the forms

$$V_o(s) = H(s)V_T(s)\left(\frac{1}{1 - e^{Ts}}\right), \qquad (13\text{–}4a)$$

$$V_o(s) = H(s)V_T(s)\left(1 + \frac{e^{Ts}}{1 - e^{Ts}}\right). \qquad (13\text{–}4b)$$

Equation (13–4a) represents the Laplace transform of the system response due to all recurrent inputs both present and past. In (13–4b) the first term represents the Laplace transform of the system response due to the input $v_T(t)$, while the remaining term represents the Laplace transform of the system response due to all recurrent inputs applied in the past. Both of these forms will be of subsequent use.

The output response can be determined from the inverse transform

$$v_o(t) = \mathcal{L}^{-1}[V_o(s)] = \frac{1}{2\pi j}\int_{c-j\infty}^{c+j\infty} V_o(s)e^{st}\,ds. \qquad (13\text{–}5)$$

Careful consideration must be given to the path of integration used to evaluate (13–5). Since $g(t) = 0$ for $t < 0$, it follows that the poles of $G(s)$ must be to the left of the path of integration. Condition (13–3), which permits the series (13–2) to be summed, requires that the path of integration lie in the left half of the s-plane. Figure 13–2 shows the type of path required, where the poles of $G(s)$ are designated by s_k. For lumped-parameter networks with losses, as a consequence of the conditions on $V_T(s)$, there is no difficulty in choosing a path of this kind. However, in order to simplify the analysis, it is often desirable to neglect losses or to idealize the input waveform. This can be accounted for by a limiting procedure. Several examples will be used to illustrate the method to be used in evaluating (13–5).

13–2 Applications to linear lumped-parameter networks [1, 2].

EXAMPLE 1. Consider a periodic sequence of unit voltage impulses applied to the RC-network shown in Fig. 13–3. In this case $V_T(s) = 1$ and

$$H(s) = \frac{V_o}{V_i} = \frac{s}{s + a} = 1 - \frac{a}{s + a},$$

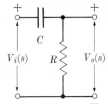

where $a = 1/RC$. The difficulty with the convergence in the integral (13–5) due to the use of impulses is avoided by considering the two terms of $H(s)$ separately. The inverse transform of 1 is $\delta(t)$. The inverse transform of the remaining term is found with the aid of (13–4a). Thus

FIG. 13–3. RC-network.

$$v_o(t) = \delta(t) - \frac{1}{2\pi j} \int_{c-j\infty}^{c+j\infty} \frac{a}{s + a} \frac{e^{st}}{1 - e^{Ts}} ds$$

$$= \delta(t) - \frac{ae^{-at}}{1 - e^{-aT}}, \qquad 0 \le t < T. \qquad (13\text{–}6)$$

Note that the integral is evaluated by completing the path of integration in the left half of the s-plane so that the pole at $s = -a$ is enclosed and that the pole coefficient is $F(s) = ae^{st}/(1 - e^{sT})$. The restriction on t given in (13–6) is a consequence of the representation of $v_i(t)$ in the form (13–1), where the recurrent inputs for $t \ge T$ are not considered. However, due to the periodic nature of the signals, it is sufficient to restrict t to the interval $0 \le t < T$. It is interesting to note that if the interval $0 \le t < +\infty$ is chosen, the output response obtained from (13–5) is that which results from a sequence of recurrent inputs starting at $t = -\infty$ and stopping at $t = T$.

Suppose now that the recurrent input is

$$v_T(t) = e^{-bt}, \qquad t > 0.$$

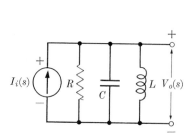

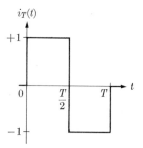

FIG. 13–4. Parallel RLC-network.   FIG. 13–5. Square-wave recurrent input.

Then $V_T(s) = 1/(s + b)$ and, with the aid of (13–4a) we obtain

$$V_o(s) = \frac{s}{(s + a)(s + b)} \frac{1}{1 - e^{Ts}}.$$

The poles in the left half of the s-plane are at $s = -a$ and $s = -b$. Thus

$$v_o(t) = \left[\frac{se^{st}}{(s + b)(1 - e^{Ts})}\right]_{s=-a} + \left[\frac{se^{st}}{(s + a)(1 - e^{Ts})}\right]_{s=-b}$$

$$= \frac{ae^{-at}}{(a - b)(1 - e^{-aT})} + \frac{be^{-bt}}{(b - a)(1 - e^{-bT})}, \qquad 0 \le t < T.$$

The previous result (13–6) can be obtained by considering the recurrent input to be $v_T(t) = be^{-bt}$ and taking the limit $\lim_{b \to \infty} v_T(t) = \delta(t)$. The fact that the limit is a unit impulse can be seen by integrating $v_T(t)$ with respect to t. ▲

EXAMPLE 2. Suppose the network shown in Fig. 13–4 is excited by a periodic current waveform and it is desired to determine the voltage response. The recurrent waveform is taken to be the square wave shown in Fig. 13–5 and its Laplace transform is

$$I_T(s) = \frac{1 - 2e^{-Ts/2} + e^{-Ts}}{s} = \frac{(1 - e^{-Ts/2})^2}{s}. \tag{13–7}$$

This result can be seen by noting that the waveform consists of a positive unit step at $t = 0$, a negative double step at $t = T/2$, and a positive unit step at $t = T$. The exponential factors in (13–7) arise from the time delays associated with these steps. The transfer function in this case is the impedance function

$$Z(s) = \frac{V_o}{I_i} = \frac{1}{C} \frac{s}{s^2 + 2\zeta\omega_n s + \omega_n^2},$$

where $\omega_n^2 LC = 1$ and $2\zeta\omega_n = 1/RC$. The voltage transform is obtained from (13–4b) and can be written in the form

$$V_o(s) = H(s)\left[I_T(s) - \frac{I_T(s)}{1 - e^{-Ts}}\right]$$

$$= \frac{1}{C}\frac{s}{s^2 + 2\zeta\omega_n s + \omega_n^2}\left[I_T(s) - \frac{1}{s}\frac{1 - e^{-Ts/2}}{1 + e^{-Ts/2}}\right]. \qquad (13–8)$$

The first term in the brackets is the Laplace transform of $i_T(s)$, while the second term is the Laplace transform of all the past $(t < 0)$ recurrent inputs.* If we restrict ourselves to the interval $0 \le t < T/2$, where $i_T(t) = 1$, we can consider the first term as a unit step and take $I_T(s) = 1/s$. While this seems intuitively obvious, it will nevertheless be subsequently proved. For the second term in (13–8) a path of the type shown in Fig. 13–2 is required. Thus

$$v_o(t) = \frac{1}{C}\mathcal{L}^{-1}\left[\frac{1}{s^2 + 2\zeta\omega_n s + \omega_n^2}\left(1 - \frac{1 - e^{-Ts/2}}{1 + e^{-Ts/2}}\right)\right]$$

$$= \frac{1}{C}\mathcal{L}^{-1}\left[\frac{1}{s^2 + 2\zeta\omega_n s + \omega_n^2}\frac{2}{1 + e^{Ts/2}}\right]$$

$$= \frac{4}{C}\operatorname{Re}\left[\frac{e^{st}}{(s - s_1^*)}\frac{1}{1 + e^{Ts/2}}\right]_{s=s_1}$$

$$= \frac{2}{\beta C}e^{-\sigma t}\frac{\sin \beta t - e^{-\sigma t/2}\sin \beta(T/2 - t)}{1 + 2e^{-\sigma T/2}\cos(\beta T/2) + e^{-\sigma T}}, \qquad 0 \le t < \frac{T}{2},$$

$$(13–9)$$

where

$$s_1 = -\sigma + j\beta = -\omega_n(\zeta + j\sqrt{1 - \zeta^2})$$

and s_1^* are the poles of $Z(s)$.

The fact that the integrals containing the exponential terms of (13–7) vanish for $t < T/2$ follows from (2–17). The exponential factors in the integrands of these integrals are $e^{(t-T/2)s}$ and $e^{(t-T)s}$, respectively. Thus, if $t < T/2$, the path of integration for these terms can be completed in the right half of the s-plane. Since this path encloses no poles, the integrals are, by Cauchy's theorem, identically zero.

Due to the symmetry in the input $[i_T(t - T/2) = -i_T/(t)]$, the output response for the interval $T/2 \le t < T$ is simply $-v_o(t - T/2)$. A plot of the output response is shown in Fig. 13–6. ▲

---

* In this case the lower limit in the Laplace transform integral must be extended to $-\infty$.

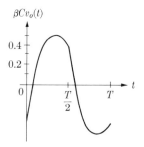

$\beta C v_o(t)$

FIG. 13–6. Voltage response for a parallel RLC-network when $\sigma = \beta$, $\sigma T = \pi$. The input is shown in Fig. 13–5.

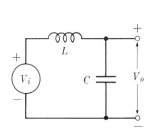

FIG. 13–7. Series LC-network.

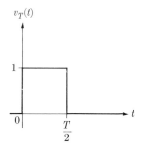

$v_T(t)$

FIG. 13–8. Square-wave recurrent input.

EXAMPLE 3. Consider now the lossless LC-network shown in Fig. 13–7. The transfer function is

$$H(s) = \frac{V_o}{V_i} = \frac{a^2}{s^2 + a^2},$$

where $a^2 LC = 1$. The recurrent input waveform is taken to be the square wave shown in Fig. 13–8. The Laplace transform is

$$V_T(s) = \frac{1 - e^{-Ts/2}}{s},$$

which follows from the fact that $v_T(t)$ consists of a positive unit step at $t = 0$ and a negative unit step at $t = T/2$. It should be noted that $s = 0$ is not a pole of $V_T(s)$, since it is cancelled by a numerator zero, which can be seen by considering the series expansion for $e^{-Ts/2}$. Substituting $V_T(s)$ into (13–4b) yields

$$V_o(s) = \frac{a^2}{s^2 + a^2}\, V_T(s) - \frac{a^2}{s(s^2 + a^2)}\, \frac{1}{1 + e^{-Ts/2}}. \qquad (13\text{–}10)$$

Consider the first term of (13–10), which is the Laplace transform of the

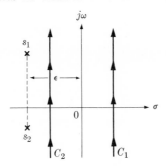

Fɪɢ. 13–9. Paths of integration.

system response to the input $v_T(t)$. The path of integration for this term (designated by C_1) must have all poles to the left as shown in Fig. 13–9. If we restrict t to the interval $0 \le t < T/2$, the integral containing the exponential term $e^{-Ts/2}$ vanishes. Thus

$$\mathcal{L}_1^{-1}\left[\frac{a^2}{s^2+a^2}\left(\frac{1}{s}-\frac{1}{s}e^{-Ts/2}\right)\right] = \mathcal{L}_1^{-1}\left[\frac{a^2}{s^2+a^2}\frac{1}{s}\right], \qquad 0 \le t < \frac{T}{2},$$

(13–11)

where the index on $\mathcal{L}^{-1}$ corresponds to that on the path of integration used. The path C_1 can be completed by a contour enclosing the poles at $s = \pm ja$ and at $s = 0$. For the second term of (13–10), we first consider losses to be present so that the poles of $H(s)$ are at $s_{1,2} = -\epsilon \pm jw$ with $\epsilon > 0$ and then let $\epsilon \to 0$. This makes it possible to choose the path C_2 for this term in the left half of the s-plane as required by condition (13–3). This path can then be completed by a contour enclosing the poles at $s = \pm ja$. Thus

$$v_o(t) = \left[\frac{a^2 e^{st}}{s^2+a^2}\right]_{s=0} + 2\,\mathrm{Re}\left[\frac{a^2 e^{st}}{s(s+ja)}\left(1-\frac{1}{1+e^{-Ts/2}}\right)\right]_{s=ja}$$

$$= 1 - \frac{1}{2}\frac{\cos at + \cos a(T/2 - t)}{1 + \cos (aT/2)}, \qquad 0 \le t < \frac{T}{2}.$$

(13–12)

For the interval $T/2 \le t < T$, the exponential term in (13–11) must be considered. Since

$$\mathcal{L}^{-1}\left[\frac{a^2}{s(s^2+a^2)}\right] = 1 - \cos at, \qquad t > 0,$$

the t-translation theorem yields

$$\mathcal{L}^{-1}\left[\frac{a^2 e^{-Ts/2}}{s(s^2+a^2)}\right] = 1 - \cos a\left(\frac{T}{2}-t\right), \qquad t > \frac{T}{2}.$$

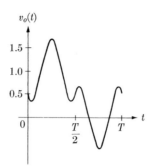

FIG. 13–10. Voltage response of a series LC-network when $aT = 5\pi$. The input is shown in Fig. 13–8.

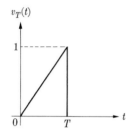

FIG. 13–11. Saw-tooth waveform.

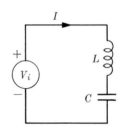

FIG. 13–12. An LC-network.

Thus

$$v_o(t) = \cos a\left(\frac{T}{2} - t\right) - \frac{1}{2}\frac{\cos at + \cos a(T/2 - t)}{1 + \cos (aT/2)}, \qquad \frac{T}{2} \leq t < T.$$
(13–13)

The results (13–12) and (13–13) are plotted in Fig. 13–10. ▲

EXAMPLE 4. A recurrent waveform of the type shown in Fig. 13–11 is applied to the network shown in Fig. 13–12. The transform of the current response can be obtained with the aid of (13–4b), which takes the form

$$I(s) = Y(s)V_T(s)\left[1 + \frac{1}{e^{-sT} - 1}\right],$$
(13–14)

where

$$TV_T(s) = \int_0^T te^{-st}\, dt = \frac{1 - e^{-sT} - sTe^{-sT}}{s^2},$$

and $Y(s)$ is the admittance function

$$Y(s) = \frac{1}{L}\frac{s}{s^2 + a^2},$$

with $a^2LC = 1$.

The two terms in (13–14) will be considered separately. The path of integration for the first term is C_1 (see Fig. 13–9). This results from the fact that this term represents the transform of the current response due to the input $v_T(t)$. If $t < T$, the integrals containing the factor e^{-sT} vanish. For the second term the path must be chosen as C_2, where $\text{Re}[s] < 0$. Thus

$$LTi(t) = \mathcal{L}_1^{-1}\left[\frac{1}{s^2 + a^2}\frac{1}{s}\right] + \mathcal{L}_2^{-1}\left[\frac{1}{s^2 + a^2}\left(-\frac{1}{s} + \frac{T}{e^{sT} - 1}\right)\right].$$

The path C_1 can be completed in the left half of the s-plane and encloses the poles at $s = 0$ and $s = \pm ja$. Completing the path C_2, we see that only the poles at $s = \pm ja$ are enclosed. Thus

$$LTi(t) = \frac{1}{a^2} + 2\,\text{Re}\left[\frac{e^{jat}}{s + ja}\left(\frac{1}{s} - \frac{1}{s} + \frac{T}{e^{sT} - 1}\right)\right]_{s=ja}$$

$$= \frac{1}{a^2}\left[1 - \frac{aT}{2}\frac{\sin a(T - t) + \sin at}{1 - \cos aT}\right], \qquad 0 \le t < T. \blacktriangle$$

On the basis of these examples it becomes evident how general expressions can be found. It is usually necessary to consider the past inputs $(t < 0)$ separately from the present input $(0 \le t < T)$. Thus, if the input is the square wave shown in Fig. 13–5, (13–4b) has the form

$$V_o(s) = H(s)\frac{(1 - e^{-Ts/2})^2}{s}\left[1 + \frac{1}{e^{-Ts} - 1}\right] \tag{13–15}$$

[note that $s = 0$ is not a pole of $V_o(s)$, since it is cancelled by a numerator zero]. The inverse transform of (13–15) is

$$v_o(t) = \mathcal{L}_1^{-1}\left[H(s)\frac{(1 - e^{-Ts/2})^2}{s}\right] - \mathcal{L}_2^{-1}\left[\frac{H(s)}{s}\frac{1 - e^{-Ts/2}}{1 + e^{-Ts/2}}\right],$$
$$0 \le t < T, \tag{13–16a}$$

$$= \mathcal{L}_1^{-1}\left[\frac{H(s)}{s}\right] - \mathcal{L}_2^{-1}\left[\frac{H(s)}{s}\frac{1 - e^{-Ts/2}}{1 + e^{-Ts/2}}\right], \qquad 0 \le t < \frac{T}{2}, \tag{13–16b}$$

$$= \mathcal{L}_3^{-1}\left[\frac{H(s)}{s}\left(1 - \frac{1 - e^{-Ts/2}}{1 + e^{-Ts/2}}\right)\right] = \mathcal{L}_3^{-1}\left[\frac{H(s)}{s}\frac{2}{1 + e^{Ts/2}}\right],$$
$$0 \le t < \frac{T}{2}. \tag{13–16c}$$

The step from (13–16a) to (13–16b) follows from the fact that for $t < T/2$, the additional integrals in (13–16a) vanish. Equation (13–16c) follows from (13–16b) because $s = 0$ is not a pole for the integrand of the second

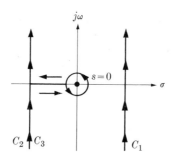

FIG. 13–13. Paths of integration.

integral, so that C_2 can be replaced by C_3. These paths are shown in Fig. 13–13. The path C_3 is identical with C_2 with the exception that it includes a small path enclosing the origin.

In the derivation of (13–16c) it was assumed that all poles of $H(s)$ are in the left half of the s-plane, so that it is possible to choose $\mathrm{Re}[s] < 0$ for the path C_2. We can, in the final result, permit these poles to approach the $j\omega$-axis, so that in the limit, this restriction can be removed.

EXAMPLE 5. Let $H(s) = 1/s$. Using (13–16c) and completing the path of integration in the left half of the s-plane, we see that a second-order pole is enclosed at $s = 0$. The pole coefficient is

$$F(s) = \frac{2e^{st}}{1 + e^{sT/2}}.$$

Thus

$$v_o(t) = \frac{dF}{ds}\bigg]_{s=0} = t - \frac{T}{4}, \qquad 0 \le t < \frac{T}{2}. \, \blacktriangle \qquad (13\text{–}17)$$

It is also possible to complete the path C_3 in the right half of the s-plane (see Section 2–8). In this case the poles at

$$s_n = \pm j(2\pi n/T),$$

where $n = 1, 3, 5, \ldots$, are enclosed. These are the zeros of the denominator term $1 + e^{Ts/2}$. The resulting terms obtained are of the form $a_n \sin (2\pi nt/T)$. Thus this yields the Fourier series for the periodic waveform $v_o(t)$. In general, the closed form of the solution as, for example, given by (13–17) is more desirable than the Fourier series. It is for this reason that the path is completed in the left half of the s-plane. The fact that there are poles of $V_o(s)$ on both sides of the path C_3 indicates the necessity of careful consideration of the path of integration to be used. For this reason an index is used on the $\mathcal{L}$-transform to indicate this.

13–3 Applications to distributed-parameter networks [3]. Let us consider a finite transmission line of length l driven by a voltage source $V_g(s)$ and terminated in an open circuit. Thus $\Gamma_0 = -1$, $\Gamma_l = 1$, and, from (11–13), we obtain

$$V(x, s) = V_g(s) \frac{\cosh \gamma(l - x)}{\cosh \gamma l}. \tag{13–18}$$

If the line is distortionless, γ has the form given by (11–15), $\gamma = s/c + \alpha$, where c is the velocity of wave propagation and α is the attenuation constant. If the recurrent input waveform is $v_T(t)$, we have

$$V_g(s) = V_T(s)[1 + e^{Ts} + e^{2Ts} + \cdots]. \tag{13–19}$$

The sequence of input waves represented by (13–19) and the multiplicity of reflections at both ends of the transmission line result in a wave pattern which, in general, is very complicated. One method of solution is to use a series expansion. Thus, for $x = l$, (13–18) and (13–19) yield

$$V(l, s) = 2V_T(s)[1 + e^{Ts} + e^{2Ts} + \cdots][e^{-\gamma l} - e^{-3\gamma l} + e^{-5\gamma l} - \cdots]$$

$$= 2V_T(s) \sum_{n=0}^{\infty} e^{nTs} \sum_{k=0}^{\infty} (-1)^k e^{-(2k+1)\gamma l}$$

$$= 2V_T(s) \sum_{n=0}^{\infty} \sum_{k=0}^{\infty} (-1)^k e^{-(2k+1)\sigma} e^{[n-(2k+1)/\beta]Ts}, \tag{13–20}$$

where we have set $\sigma = \alpha l$ and $\beta = cT/l$.

The inverse transform of (13–20) can be found with the aid of the t-translation theorem. Thus

$$v(l, t) = 2 \sum_{n=0}^{\infty} \sum_{k=0}^{\infty} (-1)^k e^{-(2k+1)\sigma} v_T(\tau_{nk}), \tag{13–21}$$

where

$$\tau_{nk} = t + \left(n - \frac{2k + 1}{\beta}\right) T. \tag{13–22}$$

If $v_T(\tau) = 0$ for $\tau < 0$ and $\tau > T$, we need consider only those terms in the sum for which

$$\left| n - \frac{2k + 1}{\beta}\right| < 1. \tag{13–23}$$

EXAMPLE 6. Consider the case where $\beta = 6$. By substituting $k = 3n + m$, it is seen that

$$\tau_{nk} = t - \left(\frac{2m + 1}{6}\right) T$$

and that condition (13–23) is satisfied for $m = 0, \pm1, \pm2$, and -3. If $m < 0$, the terms in the sum (13–21) which have a common value of τ_{nk} are

$$\sum_{n=1}^{\infty} (-1)^{3n+m} e^{-(6n+2m+1)\sigma}$$

$$= (-1)^{m-1} e^{-(6+2m+1)\sigma}[1 - e^{-6\sigma} + e^{-12\sigma} - \cdots]$$

$$= (-1)^{m-1} \frac{e^{-(6+2m+1)\sigma}}{1 + e^{-6\sigma}}.$$

If $m \geq 0$, the terms are

$$\sum_{n=0}^{\infty} (-1)^{3n+m} e^{-(6n+2m+1)\sigma} = (-1)^m \frac{e^{-(2m+1)\sigma}}{1 + e^{-6\sigma}}.$$

Thus, (13–21) yields

$$\frac{1 + e^{-6\sigma}}{2} v(l, t) = e^{-\sigma}[v_T(t + \tfrac{5}{6}T) + v_T(t - \tfrac{1}{6}T)]$$

$$- e^{-3\sigma}[v_T(t + \tfrac{1}{2}T) + v_T(t - \tfrac{1}{2}T)]$$

$$+ e^{-5\sigma}[v_T(t + \tfrac{5}{6}T) + v_T(t - \tfrac{1}{6}T)], \quad 0 \leq t < T. \; \blacktriangle$$

Suppose now that the transmission line is driven by a current source $I_g(s)$. Equation (11–13) can be used by considering the current source to be replaced by a voltage source $V_g(s) = Z_g I_g(s)$ and taking $Z_g \to \infty$. Thus $\Gamma_0 = \Gamma_l = 1$ and

$$V(x, s) = Z_0 I_g(s) \frac{\cosh \gamma(l - x)}{\sinh \gamma l}. \tag{13–24}$$

If $i_T(t)$ is the recurrent input waveform, we have

$$I_g(s) = I_T(s)(1 + e^{Ts} + e^{2Ts} + \cdots). \tag{13–25}$$

From (13–24) and (13–25) we obtain, for $x = l$,

$$V(l, s) = Z_0 I_T(s)(1 + e^{Ts} + e^{2Ts} + \cdots)(e^{-\gamma l} + e^{-3\gamma l} + \cdots)$$

$$= 2Z_0 I_T(s) \sum_{n=0}^{\infty} \sum_{k=0}^{\infty} e^{-(2k+1)\sigma} e^{[n-(2k+1)/\beta]Ts}. \tag{13–26}$$

The inverse transform of (13–26) is

$$v(l, t) = 2Z_0 \sum_{n=0}^{\infty} \sum_{k=0}^{\infty} e^{-(2k+1)\sigma} i_T(\tau_{nk}),$$

where τ_{nk} is given by (13–22). If $i_T(\tau) = 0$ for $\tau < 0$ and $\tau > T$, we need consider only those terms in the sum which satisfy the condition (13–23).

EXAMPLE 7. Consider the case where $\beta = 12$. By substituting $k = 6n + m$ it is seen that

$$\tau_{nk} = t - \left(\frac{2m + 1}{12}\right) T$$

and that condition (13–23) is satisfied if $m = 0, \pm 1, \pm 2, \pm 3, \pm 4, \pm 5,$ and -6. If $m < 0$, the terms in the sum (13–26) which have a common value of τ_{nk} are

$$\sum_{n=1}^{\infty} e^{-(12n+2m+1)\sigma} = e^{-(12+2m+1)\sigma}(1 + e^{-12\sigma} + e^{-24\sigma} + \cdots)$$

$$= \frac{e^{-(12+2m+1)\sigma}}{1 - e^{-12\sigma}}.$$

If $m \geq 0$, the terms are

$$\sum_{n=0}^{\infty} e^{-(12+2m+1)\sigma} = \frac{e^{-(2m+1)\sigma}}{1 - e^{-12\sigma}}.$$

Thus (13–26) yields

$$\begin{aligned}
v(l, t) \frac{1 - e^{-12\sigma}}{2Z_0} = {}& e^{-\sigma}[i_T(t - \tfrac{1}{12}T) + i_T(t + \tfrac{11}{12}T)] \\
& + e^{-3\sigma}[i_T(t - \tfrac{3}{12}T) + i_T(t + \tfrac{9}{12}T)] \\
& + e^{-5\sigma}[i_T(t - \tfrac{5}{12}T) + i_T(t + \tfrac{7}{12}T)] \\
& + e^{-7\sigma}[i_T(t - \tfrac{7}{12}T) + i_T(t + \tfrac{5}{12}T)] \\
& + e^{-9\sigma}[i_T(t - \tfrac{9}{12}T) + i_T(t + \tfrac{3}{12}T)] \\
& + e^{-11\sigma}[i_T(t - \tfrac{11}{12}T) + i_T(t + \tfrac{1}{12}T)], \quad 0 \leq t < T. \blacktriangle
\end{aligned}$$

It is possible to solve these problems by means of contour integration, which yields a representation in terms of standing waves. For example, if we consider (13–16c) and take $H(s)$ to be the voltage transfer function for the transmission line, which is given by (13–18), we have

$$v(x, t) = \mathcal{L}_3^{-1}\left[\frac{1}{s} \frac{\cosh \gamma(l - x)}{\cosh \gamma l} \frac{2}{1 + e^{Ts/2}}\right]. \tag{13–27}$$

By completing the path C_3 in the right half of the s-plane, the poles determined by $1 + e^{Ts/2} = 0$ will be enclosed.

The methods developed here yield the same results as the so-called steady-state operational calculus as developed by Waidelich [4, 5]. Integrals of the type (13–5), where the integrand is given by (13–4a), occur in the modified z-transform theory [6]. However, the solution of the problems discussed here by means of the modified z-transform represents a considerable complication, both from the mathematical and the physical point of view.

PROBLEMS

13-1. Consider the LC-network shown in Fig. 13-7 to be excited by a sequence of unit voltage impulses with period T. Determine the steady-state voltage response across the inductance and capacitance.

13-2. A network with a transfer function

$$H(s) = \frac{1}{(s + a)(s + b)}$$

is excited by a recurrent square wave which has a transform

$$V_T(s) = \frac{(1 - e^{-sT/2})^2}{s}.$$

Determine the output response. Consider the limiting case $a \to 0$, $b \to 0$ and determine the response for this case directly. Sketch the paths of integration used.

13-3. A recurrent waveform

$$v_T(t) = \begin{cases} \sin \dfrac{\pi t}{T}, & 0 \le t \le T, \\ 0, & t > T, \end{cases}$$

FIGURE 13-14

is applied as an input to the network shown in Fig. 13-14. Determine the steady-state output response.

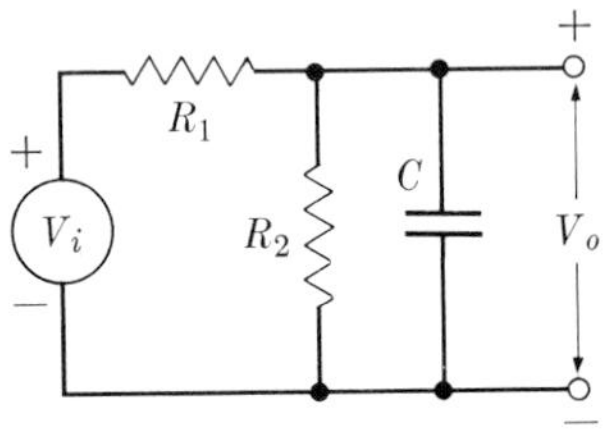

13-4. Solve Example 7 of this chapter for the case where $\beta = 8$. Sketch the waveform of the voltage response if $\sigma = 0.2$ and if the recurrent input waveform $i_T(t)$ is a unit impulse.

13-5. Evaluate the inverse transform (13-27) by completing the path of integration in the right half of the s-plane.

REFERENCES

1. D. L. WAIDELICH, "Response of circuits to steady-state pulses," *Proc. IRE,* **37,** 1396–1401 (December 1949).

2. D. L. WAIDELICH, "Steady-state currents of electrical networks," *J. Appl. Phys.,* **13,** 706–712 (November 1942).

3. D. L. WAIDELICH, "Steady-state waves on transmission lines," *Trans. AIEE,* **69,** 1521–1524 (1950).

4. D. L. WAIDELICH, "Steady-state operational calculus," *Proc. IRE,* **34,** 78–83 (February 1946).

5. D. L. WAIDELICH, "Steady-state transforms," *Proc. IRE,* **48,** 2039 (December 1960).

6. E. I. JURY, "A note on the steady-state response of linear time-invariant systems to general periodic inputs," *Proc. IRE,* **48,** 942–944 (May 1960).

CHAPTER 14

THE DIFFUSION EQUATION

14–1 Introduction. Many physical phenomena are the result of the motion of material particles due to density gradients. The mathematical description of these phenomena requires the use of an equation of continuity which accounts for the generation, decay, and transport of the material particles under consideration. Heat flow, the charging of a transmission line with negligible inductance, the diffusion of liquids, and the flow of mobile charges in semiconductors are examples of this type of process.

14–2 The leakage-free noninductive transmission line. If $G = 0$, the transmission line is called *leakage-free*. If, in addition, $L = 0$, it is also noninductive. The propagation function and characteristic impedance for this line are

$$\gamma = \sqrt{sRC} \quad \text{and} \quad Z_0 = \sqrt{\frac{R}{sC}},$$

respectively.

If the line is considered to be infinitely long and if a unit-step voltage is applied at the input, we have

$$V(x, s) = \frac{1}{s} e^{-\sqrt{as}} \tag{14–1}$$

and

$$\sqrt{\frac{R}{C}}\, I(x, s) = \frac{1}{\sqrt{s}} e^{-\sqrt{as}}, \tag{14–2}$$

where

$$a = RCx^2. \tag{14–3}$$

The inverse transform of (14–2) is

$$\sqrt{\frac{R}{C}}\, i(x, t) = \frac{1}{2\pi j} \int_{c-j\infty}^{c+j\infty} \frac{e^{-\sqrt{as}}}{\sqrt{s}} e^{st}\, ds. \tag{14–4}$$

The path of integration is shown in Fig. 14–1. The integrand is a multivalued function of s and has a branch point at $s = 0$ (see Section 2–7). Thus with the aid of (2–26) the path of integration for the integral (14–4) can be transformed, yielding the integral (note that $t > 0$)

$$\frac{1}{2\pi j} \int_{C_- + C_0 + C_+} \frac{e^{-\sqrt{as}} e^{st}}{\sqrt{s}}\, ds,$$

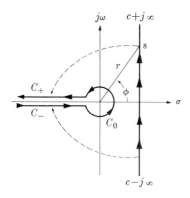

FIG. 14–1. Transformation of the path of integration.

where the paths C_-, C_0, and C_+ are as shown in Fig. 14–1. These paths enclose the singularity at $s = 0$. Consider first the path C_0, which is a small circle of radius r_0. If $r_0 \rightarrow 0$, the exponentials in the integrand can be replaced by unity. The integral along C_0 is then

$$\frac{1}{2\pi j} \int_{-\pi}^{+\pi} \frac{j r_0 e^{j\phi}\, d\phi}{\sqrt{r_0}\, e^{j\phi/2}} = 2\frac{\sqrt{r_0}}{\pi},$$

which approaches zero if $r_0 \rightarrow 0$. The remaining two integrals are along the paths C_- and C_+, which are taken to be an infinitesimal distance below and above the real axis, respectively. At first sight it might appear that these two integrals should cancel each other, since ds is oppositely directed on the two paths. This would be the case if the integrand were a single-valued function of s. However, due to the factor $\sqrt{s}$, the integrand is a double-valued function of s, and careful consideration must be given to its value. If we let

$$s = re^{j\phi}, \qquad |\phi| < \frac{\pi}{2}, \tag{14–5}$$

it follows that

$$\sqrt{s} = \sqrt{r}\, e^{j(\phi/2)}.$$

The original path of integration is transformed into C_-, C_0, and C_+ as indicated by the dotted lines in Fig. 14–1. Thus, along C_+, we have $\phi = \pi$ and

$$\sqrt{s} = j\sqrt{r}. \tag{14–6}$$

On C_- we have

$$\phi = -\pi$$

and

$$\sqrt{s} = -j\sqrt{r}. \tag{14–7}$$

Using the appropriate value of $\sqrt{s}$, we obtain

$$\frac{1}{2\pi j} \int_{C_-} \frac{e^{-\sqrt{as}} e^{st}}{\sqrt{s}} \, ds = \frac{1}{2\pi} \int_0^\infty \frac{e^{j\sqrt{ar} - rt}}{\sqrt{r}} \, dr \qquad (14\text{–}8)$$

and

$$\frac{1}{2\pi j} \int_{C_+} \frac{e^{-\sqrt{as}} e^{st}}{\sqrt{s}} \, ds = \frac{1}{2\pi} \int_0^\infty \frac{e^{-j\sqrt{ar} - rt}}{\sqrt{r}} \, dr. \qquad (14\text{–}9)$$

To evaluate (14–8) we use the substitution

$$u = \frac{1}{2j} \sqrt{\frac{a}{t}} + \sqrt{rt},$$

which yields the integral

$$\frac{1}{\pi\sqrt{t}} e^{-a/4t} \int_z^\infty e^{-u^2} \, du, \qquad (14\text{–}10)$$

where

$$z = \frac{1}{2j} \sqrt{\frac{a}{t}}.$$

This integral can be evaluated with the aid of the *error function* [see Appendix (C-1)]

$$\operatorname{erf} z = \frac{2}{\sqrt{\pi}} \int_0^z e^{-u^2} \, du.$$

Since erf $\infty = 1$, the integral (14–10) takes the form

$$\frac{1}{2\sqrt{\pi t}} e^{-a/4t} [1 - \operatorname{erf} z].$$

The integral (14–9) can be evaluated by noting that it is the complex conjugate of (14–8). Since $z^* = -z$, we find that (14–4) yields

$$\sqrt{\frac{R}{C}} \, i(x, t) = \mathcal{L}^{-1}\left[\frac{e^{-\sqrt{as}}}{\sqrt{s}}\right] = \frac{e^{-a/4t}}{\sqrt{\pi t}}, \qquad t > 0. \qquad (14\text{–}11)$$

In deriving (14–11), use has been made of the fact that erf z is an odd function, that is, erf $(-z) = -\operatorname{erf} z$. The inverse transform given by (14–11) is of considerable importance and is used in Appendix C to derive many other useful transforms.

The inverse transform of (14–1) can be found with the aid of Appendix (C-10). Thus

$$v(x, t) = \operatorname{erfc}\left(\frac{1}{2} \sqrt{\frac{a}{t}}\right), \qquad t > 0, \qquad (14\text{–}12)$$

where erfc z is the *complementary error function* defined by

$$\text{erfc } z = 1 - \text{erf } z.$$

Numerical values of the error functions can be found in standard tables [1]. For small and large values of z, power series and asymptotic expansions can be used to approximate the functions [see Appendix (C–5)].

From (14–8), (14–9), and (14–11) it follows that

$$\frac{1}{\pi} \int_0^\infty \frac{\cos \sqrt{ar}}{\sqrt{r}} e^{-rt} \, dr = \frac{1}{\sqrt{\pi t}} e^{-a/4t}. \tag{14–13}$$

This relation is of interest, since by substituting $t = p$ and $r = \tau$, the transform

$$\sqrt{\frac{\pi}{p}} \, e^{-a/4p} = \int_0^\infty \frac{\cos \sqrt{a\tau}}{\sqrt{\tau}} e^{-p\tau} \, d\tau$$

is obtained. By means of integral relations of this kind, extensive transform tables have been derived and compiled [2].

Suppose the input voltage to the transmission line is now taken to be

$$v_g(t) = \begin{cases} \sin \omega t, & t > 0, \\ 0, & t < 0. \end{cases}$$

The voltage transform is then

$$V(x, s) = \frac{\omega}{s^2 + \omega^2} e^{-\sqrt{as}}. \tag{14–14}$$

There are simple poles at $s = \pm j\omega$ and a branch cut in the s-plane is also required to make $V(x, s)$ a single-valued function of s. By means of (2–26), the path of integration for the inverse transform can be transformed into contours enclosing the poles and a path along the branch cut (see Fig. 14–2). The Heaviside expansion is used to evaluate the contour integrals. The integral along the branch cut requires separate consideration and is evaluated using the substitutions (14–6) and (14–7). Thus

$$v(x, t) = e^{-\sqrt{a\omega/2}} \sin\left(\omega t - \sqrt{\frac{a\omega}{2}}\right) + \frac{1}{\pi} \int_0^\infty \frac{\omega}{r^2 + \omega^2} \sin \sqrt{ar} \, e^{-rt} \, dr,$$
$$t > 0.$$

The integral in this expression represents the distortion in the waveshape of the applied sine wave. An integral of this type is not generally suitable for numerical computation. However, for large t, it can be used to obtain an *asymptotic expansion*. This is due to the fact that $e^{-rt} \to 0$ if $r > 0$ and $t \to +\infty$. The value of the integral I_1 is then mainly due to a small

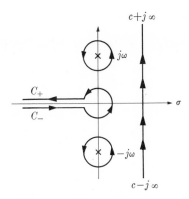

Fig. 14–2. Path of integration around poles and along the branch cut.

region at the origin. In this region the term $(r^2 + \omega^2)^{-1}$ can be expanded in a power series in r. Thus

$$I_1 \cong \frac{1}{\omega\pi} \int_0^\infty \left\{ 1 - \left(\frac{r}{\omega}\right)^2 + \left(\frac{r}{\omega}\right)^4 - \cdots \right\} \sin \sqrt{ar} \, e^{-rt} \, dr.$$

To determine the asymptotic expansion, I_1 is written in the equivalent form

$$\frac{1}{\omega\pi} \left\{ 1 - \frac{1}{\omega^2} \frac{d^2}{dt^2} + \frac{1}{\omega^4} \frac{d^4}{dt^4} - \cdots \right\} \int_0^\infty \sin \sqrt{ar} \, e^{-rt} \, dr. \qquad (14\text{–}15)$$

The formal equivalence of these forms is seen by carrying out the differentiation under the integral sign. The integral in (14–15) can be determined by differentiating (14–13) with respect to a. This yields

$$\frac{1}{\pi} \int_0^\infty \sin \sqrt{ar} \, e^{-rt} \, dr = \frac{1}{2t} \sqrt{\frac{a}{\pi t}} \, e^{-a/4t}.$$

Substitution of this integral into (14–15) results in the asymptotic expansion

$$I_1 \sim \left(1 - \frac{1}{\omega^2} \frac{d^2}{dt^2} + \frac{1}{\omega^4} \frac{d^4}{dt^4} - \cdots \right) \frac{1}{2\omega t} \sqrt{\frac{a}{\pi t}} \, e^{-a/4t}$$

$$= \left[1 - \frac{1 \cdot 3 \cdot 5}{(2\omega t)^2} + \frac{10a\omega}{(2\omega t)^3} + \cdots \right] \frac{1}{2\omega t} \sqrt{\frac{a}{\pi t}} \, e^{-a/4t}, \qquad (14\text{–}16)$$

where the symbol $\sim$ is used to indicate the asymptotic equality of the functions (see Section 14–8).

A different form for the solution is obtained if the convolution theorem is applied to (14–14). The voltage response to a unit-step input is given by [see (14–12)]

$$g_v(x, t) = \operatorname{erfc}\left(\frac{1}{2}\sqrt{\frac{a}{t}}\right), \qquad t > 0$$

$$= \operatorname{erfc}\left(\frac{1}{\sqrt{u}}\right),$$

where

$$u = \frac{4t}{a} = \frac{4t}{RCx^2}.$$

The impulse response is then

$$h_v(x, t) = \frac{dg_v(x, t)}{dt},$$

and the convolution theorem yields

$$v(x, t) = \int_0^t \sin \omega(t - \tau)h_v(x, \tau)\, d\tau = C_1 \sin \omega t - S_1 \cos \omega t,$$

where

$$C_1 = \frac{1}{\sqrt{\pi}}\int_0^u \cos\frac{a\omega u}{4}\,\frac{e^{-1/u}}{u\sqrt{u}}\, du,$$

$$S_1 = \frac{1}{\sqrt{\pi}}\int_0^u \sin\frac{a\omega u}{4}\,\frac{e^{-1/u}}{u\sqrt{u}}\, du. \qquad (14\text{–}17)$$

The quantities C_1 and S_1 can be evaluated by numerical integration.

The telegraphist's equation (11–4) reduces to

$$\frac{\partial^2 v}{\partial x^2} = RC\,\frac{\partial v}{\partial t}$$

for the leakage-free noninductive cable. This is a special case of the *diffusion equation* (14–45) and is also applicable to one-dimensional heat-flow problems. An analogy between one-dimensional heat-flow problems and the examples just discussed is possible if $v(x, t)$ is taken to represent the temperature, $1/R$ the thermal conductivity per unit length, and C the thermal capacity per unit length.

14–3 The leakage-free noninductive transmission line with various input and output terminations. Consider an infinitely long transmission line with $G = L = 0$ driven by a voltage source having an internal impedance Z_g (Fig. 14–3). The voltage and current transforms are

$$V(x, s) = \frac{V_g(s)}{1 + Z_g/Z_0}\, e^{-\gamma x} \qquad (14\text{–}18)$$

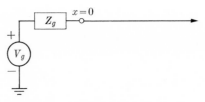

FIG. 14–3. Infinite transmission line.

and

$$I(x, s) = \frac{V(x, s)}{Z_0},\qquad(14\text{–}19)$$

respectively.

EXAMPLE 1. Let us determine the input current response to a unit-step input voltage if $Z_g = 1/sC_g$. Substituting

$$s = ap,\qquad \text{where}\qquad a = \frac{C}{C_g}\frac{1}{RC_g},$$

into (14–18) and (14–19) yields, for $x = 0$,

$$I(0, s) = I[p] = \frac{C_g}{1 + \sqrt{p}}.\qquad(14\text{–}20)$$

With the aid of the identity

$$(\sqrt{p} - 1)(\sqrt{p} + 1) = p - 1,$$

(14–20) can be transformed into

$$I[p] = C_g\left[-\frac{1}{p - 1} + \left(1 + \frac{1}{p - 1}\right)\frac{1}{\sqrt{p}}\right].\qquad(14\text{–}21)$$

We have

$$\mathcal{L}^{-1}\left[\frac{1}{p - 1}\right] = e^{\tau},\qquad(14\text{–}22)$$

since there is a simple pole at $p = 1$. Equation (14–11) yields, with $a = 0$,

$$\mathcal{L}^{-1}\left[\frac{1}{\sqrt{p}}\right] = \frac{1}{\sqrt{\pi\tau}}.\qquad(14\text{–}23)$$

The inverse transform of (14–21) can be obtained by using (14–22) and (14–23) for the first two terms and using the convolution theorem for the remaining term. Thus

$$i[\tau] = C_g\left[-e^{\tau} + \frac{1}{\sqrt{\pi\tau}} + \int_0^{\tau} e^{(\tau - u)}\frac{1}{\sqrt{\pi u}}\,du\right].\qquad(14\text{–}24)$$

The integral in (14–24) can be expressed in terms of the error function by means of the substitution $u = y^2$. To determine $i(t)$, the scaling theorem must be applied. Thus

$$i(t) = ai[\tau] = \frac{C}{RC_g}\left[\frac{1}{\sqrt{\pi\tau}} - e^\tau \operatorname{erfc}(\sqrt{\tau})\right], \qquad t > 0,$$

where

$$\tau = at = \frac{C}{C_g}\frac{t}{RC_g}.$$

Similarly, substituting $s = ap$ into (14–18) yields

$$V(0, s) = V[p] = \frac{1/a}{\sqrt{p}(1 + \sqrt{p})} = \left[\frac{1}{p - 1} - \frac{1}{p - 1}\frac{1}{\sqrt{p}}\right]\frac{1}{a}.$$

The inverse transform can be found with the aid of (14–22) and (14–23). The input voltage response is thus

$$v(0, t) = av[\tau] = e^\tau \operatorname{erfc}(\sqrt{\tau}), \qquad t > 0.$$

These results may also be obtained directly from the transform tables in Appendix F. However, the problem has been discussed in this manner to illustrate typical substitutions and algebraic manipulations which reduce the transform to simpler terms. ▲

EXAMPLE 2. As a second example, we take $Z_g = L_g s$ and determine the transmission line input-voltage response to a unit-step voltage, $V_g(s) = 1/s$. Equation (14–18) will now have the form

$$aV(0, s) = aV[p] = \frac{1}{p}\frac{1}{1 + p\sqrt{p}} = \frac{1}{p}\frac{1}{D(p)},$$

where $s = ap$ and

$$a^{3/2} = \frac{1}{L_g}\sqrt{\frac{R}{C}}. \tag{14–25}$$

The path of integration is shown in Fig. 14–4. A branch cut is required to make $V[p]$ a single-valued function in the cut p-plane. Cauchy's integral theorem can then be applied and the path of integration transformed into contours enclosing the three poles at $p = 0$, p_1, p_2, and a path along the branch cut. The two poles p_1 and p_2 are the principal roots of

$$D(p) = 1 + p\sqrt{p} = 0,$$

which are

$$p_1 = -\frac{1}{2} + j\frac{\sqrt{3}}{2}, \qquad p_2 = -\frac{1}{2} - j\frac{\sqrt{3}}{2}.$$

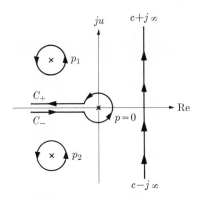

FIG. 14–4. Path of integration around poles and along the branch cut.

The contour integrals can be evaluated using the Heaviside expansion. The integral along the branch cut must be considered separately. Thus

$$v(t) = av[\tau] = 1 + 2\,\mathrm{Re}\left[\frac{1}{p_1}\frac{e^{p_1\tau}}{D'(p_1)}\right] + \frac{1}{2\pi j}\int_{C_-+C_+}\frac{e^{p\tau}}{p(1+p\sqrt{p})}\,dp.$$

$$(14\text{–}26)$$

We now consider the value of the integrand.

On C_-, we have

$$p = re^{-j\pi}, \qquad p\sqrt{p} = r^{3/2}e^{-j3\pi/2}.$$

On C_+, we have

$$p = re^{j\pi}, \qquad p\sqrt{p} = r^{3/2}e^{j3\pi/2}.$$

Substituting these values into (14–26) yields

$$v(t) = 1 - \frac{4}{3}e^{-\tau/2}\cos\frac{\sqrt{3}}{2}\tau + \frac{1}{\pi}\int_0^\infty\frac{\sqrt{r}\,e^{-r\tau}}{1+r^3}\,dr, \qquad t > 0, \quad (14\text{–}27)$$

where $\tau = at$ and a is given by (14–25).

For large τ the contribution to the value of the integral I_1 in (14–27) comes mainly from a small region near the origin. Expanding the term $(1 + r^3)^{-1}$ in a power series in r, we obtain

$$I_1 \cong \frac{1}{\pi}\int_0^\infty\sqrt{r}\,e^{-r\tau}[1 - r^3 + r^6 - r^9 + \cdots]\,dr,$$

$$\sim -\frac{1}{\pi}\frac{d}{d\tau}\left[1 + \frac{d^3}{d\tau^3} + \frac{d^6}{d\tau^6} + \cdots\right]\int_0^\infty\frac{e^{-r\tau}}{\sqrt{r}}\,dr.$$

The formal equivalence of these two forms is seen by carrying out the differentiation under the integral sign. The integral can be evaluated by substituting $a = 0$ into (14–13). Thus

$$I_1 \sim -\frac{1}{\pi}\left[\frac{d}{d\tau} + \frac{d^4}{d\tau^4} + \frac{d^7}{d\tau^7} + \cdots\right]\sqrt{\frac{\pi}{\tau}}$$

$$= \frac{1}{\sqrt{\pi\tau}}\left[\frac{1}{2\tau} - \frac{1\cdot 3\cdot 5\cdot 7}{(2\tau)^4} + \frac{1\cdot 3\cdot 5\cdot 7\cdot 9\cdot 11\cdot 13}{(2\tau)^7} - \cdots\right]. \blacktriangle$$

$$(14\text{–}28)$$

EXAMPLE 3. If the transmission line is finite, (11–12) can be used to determine the current at $x = l$. Thus

$$I(l, s) = \frac{V_g(s)}{(Z_0 + Z_g)}\frac{(1 - \Gamma_l)e^{-\gamma l}}{(1 - \Gamma_0\Gamma_l e^{-2\gamma l})}. \tag{14–29}$$

As an example let (see Fig. 14–5)

$$Z_g = Z_l = \frac{1}{C_g s}.$$

Then

$$\Gamma_0 = \Gamma_l = \frac{1 - \sqrt{p}}{1 + \sqrt{p}},$$

where the substitution

$$s = ap = \frac{C}{RC_g^2}\,p \tag{14–30}$$

has been used. If the input is taken to be a unit-step voltage, we can use (14–30) to transform (14–29) into

$$I(l, s) = I[p] = \frac{C_g}{2\cosh b\sqrt{p} + [(1 + p)/\sqrt{p}]\sinh b\sqrt{p}} = \frac{C_g}{D(p)},$$

$$(14\text{–}31)$$

where

$$b = \frac{Cl}{C_g} \tag{14–32}$$

is the ratio of the total transmission-line capacitance and the capacitance C_g. Due to the appearance of the factor $\sqrt{p}$, it would seem that $I[p]$ is a

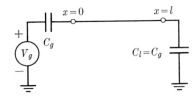

FIG. 14–5. Finite transmission line.

multivalued function of p. However, if the denominator is expanded in powers of $\sqrt{p}$, it becomes evident that it is a single-valued function of p. (Only even powers of $\sqrt{p}$ appear in the expansion.) Thus, Cauchy's integral theorem and the Heaviside expansion can be used without the necessity of first introducing a branch cut. The inverse transform of (14–31) is thus

$$i[\tau] = C_g \sum_{n=0}^{\infty} \frac{e^{p_n \tau}}{D'(p_n)}, \tag{14–33}$$

where the poles p_n are the roots of the equation

$$\frac{\sinh b\sqrt{p}}{\cosh b\sqrt{p}} = -\frac{2\sqrt{p}}{1+p}. \tag{14–34}$$

To solve this equation let $b\sqrt{p_n} = j\beta_n$. Equation (14–34) will then reduce to the form

$$\tan \beta_n = \frac{2(\beta_n/b)}{(\beta_n/b)^2 - 1}, \qquad n = 0, 1, 2, \ldots. \tag{14–35}$$

With the aid of (14–34) we find that

$$D'(p_n) = \frac{-b}{\sqrt{p_n}\,\sinh b\sqrt{p_n}} \left[1 - \left(1 - \frac{1}{p_n}\right)\frac{\sinh^2 b\sqrt{p_n}}{2b}\right]$$

$$= \frac{b^2}{\beta_n \sin \beta_n}\left[1 + \frac{2}{b}\frac{1}{1+(\beta_n/b)^2}\right].$$

Substituting this into (14–33) yields

$$i(l, t) = ai[\tau] = \frac{1}{Rl}\sum_{n=0}^{\infty}\frac{\beta_n}{b}\frac{\sin \beta_n e^{-(\beta_n/b)^2\tau}}{1+(2/b)1/[1+(\beta_n/b)^2]}, \tag{14–36}$$

where $\tau = at$ and $b/aC_g = Rl$ is the total resistance of the transmission line.

Consider now the limiting case where $C_g \to +\infty$. It follows from (14–32) that $b \to 0$. Thus (14–35) leads to the approximation

$$\frac{\beta_n}{b}\sin \beta_n \cong 2\cos \beta_n. \tag{14–37}$$

Equation (14–37) yields $\beta_0^2/b \cong 2$ and $\beta_n \cong \pi n$ for $n > 0$. If the limit of (14–36) is taken as $b \to 0$, we obtain

$$i(l, t) = \frac{1}{Rl}\left[1 + 2\sum_{n=1}^{\infty}(-1)^n e^{-n^2 z}\right], \qquad z > 0,$$

where

$$z = \pi^2 \frac{t}{RCl^2}.$$

This series will converge rapidly for large t. However, it is not a suitable expression for small t. An alternative result, suitable for small t, can be derived by using the expansion (11–21), which in this case reduces to

$$I(l, s) = 2 \sqrt{\frac{C}{R}} \frac{1}{\sqrt{s}} \left[e^{-l\sqrt{RCs}} + e^{-3l\sqrt{RCs}} + e^{-5l\sqrt{RCs}} + \cdots \right].$$

The inverse transform of each of the terms of this series can be obtained with the aid of (14–11). Thus

$$i(l, t) = \frac{2}{Rl} \sqrt{\frac{\pi}{z}} [e^{-\pi^2/4z} + e^{-9\pi^2/4z} + e^{-25\pi^2/4z} + \cdots], \qquad z > 0. \ \blacktriangle$$

14–4 The noninductive transmission line. If $L = 0$, the propagation function and the characteristic impedance are

$$\gamma = \sqrt{R(G + sC)} \qquad \text{and} \qquad Z_0 = \sqrt{\frac{R}{G + sC}},$$

respectively. If the input voltage is a unit step and the line is considered to be infinitely long, we have

$$V(x, s) = \frac{1}{s} e^{-\sqrt{a(s+b)}},$$

where $a = x^2 RC$ and $b = G/C$.

With the aid of Appendix (C-15) we obtain, for $t > 0$,

$$\mathcal{L}^{-1} \left[\frac{e^{-\sqrt{a(s+b)}}}{s} \right] = v(x, t) = \frac{e^{\sqrt{ab}}}{2} \operatorname{erfc} z_1 + \frac{e^{-\sqrt{ab}}}{2} \operatorname{erfc} z_2, \qquad (14\text{--}38)$$

where

$$z_1 = \frac{1}{2} \sqrt{\frac{a}{t}} + \sqrt{bt}, \qquad z_2 = \frac{1}{2} \sqrt{\frac{a}{t}} - \sqrt{bt}. \qquad (14\text{--}39)$$

The current transform is

$$I(x, s) = \sqrt{\frac{C}{R}} \frac{\sqrt{s + b}}{s} e^{-\sqrt{a(s+b)}}.$$

One possibility for determining the inverse transform of $I(x, s)$ is to note that

$$-Ri(x, t) = \frac{\partial v(x, t)}{\partial x} = \frac{\partial v(x, t)}{\partial a} (2x RC)$$

and substitute (14–38) into this equation.

A different form for $i(x, t)$ is obtained by means of the convolution theorem: $I(x, s)$ is first rearranged as

$$I(x, s) = \sqrt{\frac{C}{R}} \left(\frac{s + b}{s} \right) \frac{1}{\sqrt{s + b}} e^{-\sqrt{a(s+b)}}. \qquad (14\text{--}40)$$

The s-translation theorem applied to (14–11) yields

$$\mathcal{L}^{-1}\left[\frac{1}{\sqrt{s+b}}\,e^{-\sqrt{a(s+b)}}\right] = e^{-bt}\mathcal{L}^{-1}\left[\frac{e^{-\sqrt{as}}}{\sqrt{s}}\right]. \qquad (14\text{–}41)$$

Applying the convolution theorem to (14–40) and using (14–41) yields

$$i(x,\,t) = \sqrt{\frac{C}{R}}\left[\frac{e^{-bt-a/4t}}{\sqrt{\pi t}} + b\int_0^t \frac{e^{-b\tau-a/4\tau}}{\sqrt{\pi\tau}}\,d\tau\right], \qquad t > 0.$$

14–5 The coaxial cable with frequency-dependent loss. In the derivation of the transmission-line equations (11–1) and (11–2), it was assumed that the line parameters R, L, G, and C were constants. These parameters arise out of the attempt to represent the wave propagation in terms of a single dominant mode. In practice, suitable values are usually determined experimentally. However, if a more accurate analysis of wave propagation is required, the values of these parameters must be determined from Maxwell's equations. The parameter G is usually negligible, while L and C are reasonably constant. However, R, the series resistance per unit length, is frequency dependent. A suitable high-frequency approximation is obtained by using the formula [3]

$$R = K\sqrt{s},$$

where

$$K = \frac{1}{2\pi r}\sqrt{\frac{\mu}{\sigma}}.$$

This is the skin-effect formula for the case of a plane electromagnetic wave propagating along a plane lossy conductor. Here σ is the conductivity, μ is the permeability, and r is taken as the average radius of the cable.

The propagation function and characteristic impedance are

$$\gamma = \sqrt{(K\sqrt{s} + Ls)Cs}, \quad \text{and} \quad Z_0 = \sqrt{\frac{K\sqrt{s} + Ls}{Cs}},$$

respectively. At high frequencies we have the approximations

$$\gamma \cong \frac{s}{c} + \frac{K}{2R_0}\sqrt{s}, \quad \text{and} \quad Z_0 \cong R_0 + \frac{Kc}{2\sqrt{s}},$$

where

$$c = \frac{1}{\sqrt{LC}}$$

is the velocity of propagation and

$$R_0 = \sqrt{\frac{L}{C}} = \mathop{\mathrm{Lim}}_{s \to \infty} Z_0$$

is the limiting characteristic impedance at infinite frequency.

The transform of the incident voltage wave due to a unit-step voltage input is

$$V(x, s) = \frac{1}{s} e^{-sx/c} e^{-\sqrt{as}},$$

where

$$a = \left(\frac{Kx}{2R_0}\right)^2.$$

The inverse transform can be obtained by applying the t-translation theorem and using (14–1) and (14–12). Thus

$$v(x, t) = \mathrm{erfc}\ \frac{1}{2} \sqrt{\frac{a}{t - (x/c)}}, \qquad t > \frac{x}{c},$$

where $v(x, t) = 0$, for $t < x/c$.

The transform of the incident current wave is

$$I(x, s) = \frac{1}{R_0} e^{-sx/c} \frac{1}{\sqrt{s}} \frac{e^{-\sqrt{as}}}{(\sqrt{s} + \sqrt{b})},$$

where

$$\sqrt{b} = \frac{K}{2L}.$$

The inverse transform can be obtained by applying the t-translation theorem and using Appendix (C-17). Thus noting that $\sqrt{ab} = bx/c$, we obtain

$$R_0 i(x, t) = e^{bt} \mathrm{erfc}\ z, \qquad t > \frac{x}{c},$$

where

$$z = \sqrt{b(t - x/c)} + \frac{1}{2} \sqrt{\frac{a}{t - x/c}}.$$

The fact that both the voltage and current response are zero for $t < x/c$ is a consequence of (2–17). The paths of integration can then be completed in the right half of the s-plane. Since no poles are enclosed, the integrals vanish.

It should be noted that in this approximate model, the arrival of the wavefront is governed by the wave equation, while the buildup of the voltage and current after the arrival of the wave is governed by the diffusion equation. The infinite current response for $t \to +\infty$ is due to the fact that the d-c resistance of the cable has been taken to be zero.

14–6 Transients in junction transistors. An approximate mathematical model for the base region of a junction transistor results from the equation of continuity [4]

$$-\frac{1}{q}\frac{\partial j_p}{\partial x} - \frac{p - p_n}{\tau_p} = \frac{\partial p}{\partial t} \tag{14–42}$$

and the equation for the hole current density

$$\frac{1}{q} j_p = \mu_p p E - D_p \frac{\partial p}{\partial x}. \tag{14–43}$$

The constants are defined as follows (see Fig. 14–6):

$p_n = $ the equilibrium hole density in the n-type base material,

$p = p(x, t) = $ the hole density in the base,

$j_p = j_p(x, t) = $ the hole current density,

$D_p = $ the diffusion constant for holes,

$\tau_p = $ the hole lifetime in the base,

$q = $ the electronic charge,

$\mu_p = $ the hole mobility in the base,

$E = $ the built-in electric field intensity in the base region.

The base region is considered to be of constant width W. This is a valid approximation for small collector loads. The boundary conditions are constraints imposed on the hole density by the applied emitter-base and collector-base voltages and are given by

$$p(0, t) = p_n \cdot e^{q v_e / kT},$$

$$p(W, t) = p_n \cdot e^{q v_c / kT} \cong 0.$$

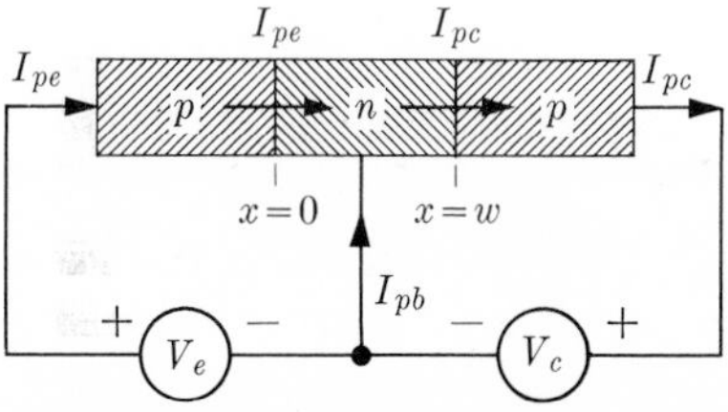

FIG. 14–6. Junction transistor model.

In normal operation, the collector is reversed biased so that v_c is negative. The hole density at $x = W$ is then negligible.

It is convenient to introduce the *excess hole density*

$$p_1 = p - p_n. \tag{14-44}$$

For a diffusion transistor, the internal field E is negligible. Substituting $E = 0$ and eliminating the hole current density from (14-42) and (14-43) yields the diffusion equation

$$\frac{\partial^2 p_1}{\partial x^2} - \frac{1}{L_p^2} p_1 = \frac{1}{D_p} \frac{\partial p_1}{\partial t}, \tag{14-45}$$

where $L_p = \sqrt{D_p \tau_p}$ is the *diffusion length* of the holes in the base region. The boundary conditions for p_1 are

$$p_1(0, t) = p_n(e^{qv_e/kT} - 1),$$

$$p_1(W, t) = p_n(e^{qv_c/kT} - 1) \cong -p_n. \tag{14-46}$$

The transistor is normally biased to a suitable operating point, and the problem is to determine the response to suddenly applied external changes in voltages or currents. Let $p_0(x)$ be the excess hole density for steady conditions and let $p_2(x, t)$ be defined by the equation

$$p_1(x, t) = p_0(x) + p_2(x, t). \tag{14-47}$$

Thus p_2 is the *incremental hole density* resulting from the suddenly applied external changes. The diffusion equation contains a steady component

$$\frac{\partial^2 p_0}{\partial x^2} - \frac{1}{L_p^2} p_0 = 0$$

and a time varying component

$$\frac{\partial^2 p_2}{\partial x^2} - \frac{1}{L_p^2} p_2 = \frac{1}{D_p} \frac{\partial p_2}{\partial t}. \tag{14-48}$$

It is the solution of this latter equation which is to be determined. Let

$$P_2(x, s) = \mathcal{L}[p_2(x, t)].$$

The Laplace transform of (14-48) yields

$$\frac{\partial^2 P_2}{\partial x^2} - \alpha^2 P_2 = 0, \tag{14-49}$$

where

$$\alpha = \sqrt{\frac{1 + \tau_p s}{L_p^2}}. \tag{14-50}$$

The solution of (14–49) which satisfies the boundary conditions is

$$P_2(x, s) = \frac{P_2(0, s) \sinh \alpha(W - x) + P_2(W, s) \sinh \alpha x}{\sinh \alpha W} . \qquad (14\text{–}51)$$

It follows from (14–46) that $p_2(W, t) \cong 0$. Thus $P_2(W, s) \cong 0$ and (14–51) simplifies to

$$P_2(x, s) \cong P_2(0, s) \frac{\sinh \alpha(W - x)}{\sinh \alpha W} . \qquad (14\text{–}52)$$

The incremental emitter and collector hole current densities are obtained from (14–43) with $E = 0$. Thus

$$j_{pe}(t) = -qD_p \left. \frac{\partial p_2(x, t)}{\partial x} \right]_{x=0} ,$$

$$j_{pc}(t) = -qD_p \left. \frac{\partial p_2(x, t)}{\partial x} \right]_{x=W} .$$

Taking the Laplace transform of these equations and substituting (14–52) yields

$$J_{pe}(s) = qD_p\alpha P_2(0, s) \coth \alpha W,$$

$$J_{pc}(s) = qD_p\alpha P_2(0, s) \operatorname{csch} \alpha W.$$

The ratio of these quantities yields

$$\frac{J_{pc}}{J_{pe}} = \frac{I_{pc}}{I_{pe}} = \frac{1}{\cosh \alpha W} , \qquad (14\text{–}53)$$

where i_{pc} and i_{pe} are the incremental collector and emitter hole currents, respectively. There is also a contribution to the incremental emitter and collector currents (designated by i_e and i_c) due to electron flow through the junctions. However, for efficient transistor action this must be small. We can then set $i_{pc} \cong i_c$ and $i_{pe} \cong i_e$. Equation (14–53) is suitable for the grounded-base connection where an external current source supplies the emitter current.

We consider now the problem of determining the incremental collector current response if $i_{pe}(t)$ is a unit-step current. The function $1/\cosh z$ can be expanded in the following series:

$$\frac{1}{\cosh z} = \frac{2}{e^z + e^{-z}} = 2 \sum_{n=1}^{\infty} (-1)^{n+1} e^{-(2n-1)z}.$$

Using this in (14–53) yields

$$I_{pc}(s) = \frac{2}{s} \sum_{n=1}^{\infty} (-1)^{n+1} e^{-(2n-1)z},$$

where $z = \alpha W$. Using the substitutions $b = 1/\tau_p$ and

$$\sqrt{a_n b} = (2n - 1)\frac{W}{L_p},$$

we obtain

$$I_{pc}(s) = \frac{2}{s}\sum_{n=1}^{\infty}(-1)^{n+1}e^{-\sqrt{a_n(s+b)}}.$$

The inverse transform of each of the terms in this series can be obtained by means of (14–38). Thus

$$i_{pc}(t) = \sum_{n=1}^{\infty}(-1)^{n+1}\left[e^{\sqrt{a_n b}}\,\text{erfc}\left\{\frac{1}{2}\sqrt{\frac{a_n}{t}} + \sqrt{bt}\right\}\right.$$
$$\left. + e^{-\sqrt{a_n b}}\,\text{erfc}\left\{\frac{1}{2}\sqrt{\frac{a_n}{t}} - \sqrt{bt}\right\}\right].$$

Numerical results obtained from this equation are discussed in the literature [5, 6, 7].

A different form for the solution is obtained by noting that (15–53), which has the form

$$I_{pc}(s) = \frac{1}{s\cosh\alpha W} = \frac{1}{sD(s)},$$

is a single-valued function of s. This can be seen by expanding $\cosh z$ in a power series in z and then substituting $z = \alpha W$. Thus the Heaviside expansion can be used, and we obtain

$$i_{pc}(t) = \frac{1}{\cosh(W/L_p)} + \sum_{n=0}^{\infty}\frac{e^{s_n t}}{s_n D'(s_n)}. \qquad (14\text{–}54)$$

The poles s_n are the roots of

$$\cosh\alpha W = 0.$$

These roots are determined by

$$\alpha W = j\frac{(2n+1)}{2}\pi, \qquad n = 0, 1, 2, \ldots.$$

Eliminating α by means of (14–50) and squaring the result yields

$$s_n = -b(1 + \sigma_n), \qquad (14\text{–}55)$$

where

$$\sigma_n = \left(\frac{2n+1}{2}\pi\frac{L_p}{W}\right)^2, \qquad n = 0, 1, 2, \ldots$$

(it should be noted that no additional poles arise due to a choice of $n < 0$).

With the aid of these quantities we obtain

$$D'(s_n) = \frac{d \cosh \alpha W}{ds}\Bigg]_{s=s_n} = \frac{1}{\pi} \frac{(-1)^n}{2n+1} \left(\frac{W}{L_p}\right)^2 \frac{1}{b}. \qquad (14\text{–}56)$$

Substituting (14–55) and (14–56) into (14–54) yields

$$i_{pc}(t) = \frac{1}{\cosh (W/L_p)} - \pi \left(\frac{L_p}{W}\right)^2 e^{-bt} \sum_{n=0}^{\infty} \frac{(-1)^n(2n+1)}{1+\sigma_n} e^{-b\sigma_n t}.$$

If the collector load is not negligible, complications such as base-width variations must be accounted for [8]. However, a useful approximation can be obtained from (14–53) by expanding $\cosh \alpha W$ in a power series in s:

$$\cosh \alpha W = \frac{1}{\alpha_0}\left[1 + a_1 \left(\frac{s}{\omega_0}\right) + a_2 \left(\frac{s}{\omega_0}\right)^2 + \cdots\right].$$

Differentiating successively with respect to s and substituting $s = 0$ yields

$$\frac{1}{\alpha_0} = \cosh u \cong 1 \qquad\qquad a_1 = \frac{\tanh u}{u} \cong 1$$

$$a_2 = \frac{1}{2u^3}(u - \tanh u) \cong \tfrac{1}{6} \qquad \omega_0 = \frac{2}{\tau_p u^2},$$

where $u = W/L_p \ll 1$. Equation (14–53) has the approximate form [9]

$$\frac{1}{\cosh \alpha W} \cong \frac{\alpha_0}{1 + (s/\omega_0) + \tfrac{1}{6}(s/\omega_0)^2}$$

$$= \frac{\alpha_0}{[1 + (s/1.268\omega_0)][1 + (s/4.732\omega_0)]}.$$

14–7 Transients in drift transistors. In the drift transistor an internal built-in electric field E is produced in the base region by a controlled variation in donor concentration. In the following discussion we consider E to be constant. Substituting (14–43) into (14–42) yields

$$\frac{\partial^2 p}{\partial x^2} - \frac{\mu_p E}{D_p} \frac{\partial p}{\partial x} - \frac{p - p_n}{D_p \tau_p} = \frac{1}{D_p} \frac{\partial p}{\partial t}.$$

Using the substitutions (14–44) and (14–47) and introducing the Laplace transform yields

$$\frac{d^2 P_2}{dx^2} - 2\beta \frac{dP_2}{dx} - \frac{1 + \tau_p s}{L_p^2} P_2 = 0, \qquad (14\text{–}57)$$

where

$$\beta = \frac{1}{2} \frac{\mu_p E}{D_p}. \qquad (14\text{–}58)$$

The solution of (14–57) which satisfies the boundary condition is

$$P_2(x, s) = e^{\beta x} \frac{P_2(0, s) \sinh \alpha(W - x) + P_2(W, s) \sinh \alpha x}{\sinh \alpha W}$$

$$\cong P_2(0, s) e^{\beta x} \frac{\sinh \alpha(W - x)}{\sinh \alpha W}, \tag{14–59}$$

where

$$\alpha = \sqrt{\beta^2 + \frac{1 + \tau_p s}{L_p^2}}. \tag{14–60}$$

Equation (14–59) follows from the fact that $P_2(W, s) \cong 0$. The incremental hole density can be determined from (14–43). Taking the Laplace transform and using (14–58) yields

$$J_p(x, s) = qD_p \left[-\frac{\partial P_2}{\partial x} + 2\beta P_2 \right],$$

from which the transforms of the incremental emitter and collector hole current densities are obtained:

$$J_{pe} = J_p(0, s) = \frac{qD_p P_2(0, s)}{\sinh \alpha W} [\beta \sinh \alpha W + \alpha \cosh \alpha W],$$

$$J_{pc} = J_p(W, s) = \frac{qD_p P_2(0, s)}{\sinh \alpha W} \alpha e^{\beta W}.$$

The ratio of these quantities yields

$$\frac{J_{pc}}{J_{pe}} = \frac{I_{pc}}{I_{pe}} = \frac{e^{\beta W}}{\cosh \alpha W + (\beta/\alpha) \sinh \alpha W} = \frac{e^{\beta W}}{D(s)}.$$

If the incremental emitter current is a unit step, the collector current response can be found by means of the Heaviside expansion (note that I_{pc} is a single-valued function of s). Thus

$$i_{pc}(t) = \frac{e^{\beta W}}{D(0)} + \sum_{n=0}^{\infty} \frac{e^{\beta W} e^{s_n t}}{s_n D'(s_n)}. \tag{14–61}$$

The poles s_n are the roots of

$$\frac{\cosh \alpha W}{\sinh \alpha W} = -\frac{\beta}{\alpha}. \tag{14–62}$$

The solution of this equation can be found by substituting

$$\alpha W = jy \tag{14–63}$$

into (14–62), which yields

$$\tan y = -\frac{y}{\beta W}. \tag{14-64}$$

Let the roots of this equation be designated by y_n, $(n = 0, 1, 2, \ldots)$. The poles s_n are determined by (14–60) and (14–63). Thus

$$\tau_p s_n = -1 - \left[\left(\frac{y_n}{W}\right)^2 + \beta^2\right]L_p^2.$$

For $D'(s_n)$, we have

$$D'(s_n) = \left[-1 - \beta W \left(\frac{\sinh \alpha W}{\alpha W}\right)^2\right]\frac{W}{\sinh \alpha W}\frac{d\alpha}{ds}$$

$$= \left[-1 - \beta W \frac{1}{y_n^2 + (\beta W)^2}\right]\frac{W}{j \sin y_n}\frac{d\alpha}{ds}, \tag{14-65}$$

where (14–60), (14–62), and (14–63) have been used to simplify the result. From (14–60) we obtain

$$\frac{d\alpha}{ds} = \frac{1}{2\alpha}\frac{\tau_p}{L_p^2} = \frac{W}{j2y_n}\frac{\tau_p}{L_p^2}. \tag{14-66}$$

Substituting (14–65) and (14–66) into (14–61) yields the result

$$i_{pc}(t) = \frac{e^{\beta W}}{D(0)} + \frac{2}{\tau_p}\left(\frac{L_p}{W}\right)^2 e^{\beta W} \sum_{n=0}^{\infty} \frac{y_n \sin y_n e^{s_n t}}{s_n\left[1 + \dfrac{1}{\beta W}\dfrac{1}{1 + (y_n/\beta W)^2}\right]}.$$

This equation is discussed by Johnston [10], who also considers a suitable model for the common-emitter configuration.

14–8 Asymptotic expansions. The method used in deriving the asymptotic expansions (14–16) and (14–28) is easily generalized. Consider the inverse transform

$$g(t) = \frac{1}{2\pi j}\int_{c-j\infty}^{c+j\infty} \frac{N(s)}{D(s)} H(s)e^{st}\,ds, \tag{14-67}$$

where $N(s)$ and $D(s)$ are polynomials in s. Let the zeros of $D(s)$ be simple and designated by s_k $(k = 1, 2, \ldots, n)$; $H(s)$ is considered to have no poles, but is a multivalued function of s of the type discussed in Section 14–2. A branch cut C is thus required to make $H(s)$ into a single-valued function (see Fig. 14–7). In this cut s-plane, Cauchy's integral theorem

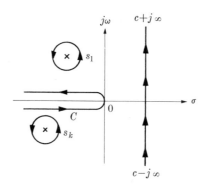

FIG. 14–7. Path of integration around poles and along the branch cut.

can be used to transform (14–67) into

$$g(t) = \sum_{k=1}^{n} \frac{N(s_k)H(s_k)}{D'(s_k)} e^{s_k t} + \frac{1}{2\pi j} \int_C \frac{N(s)}{D(s)} H(s)e^{st}\, ds, \quad (14\text{–}68)$$

where the sum originates from the contour integrals taken around the poles and represents the Heaviside expansion for these terms. The remaining integral is along the branch cut and does not vanish, since $H(s)$ has different values for corresponding points on the two sides of the cut. Since C is in the left half of the s-plane, Re $[s] < 0$. Thus, for large t, due to the factor e^{st}, it is mainly the region close to the origin which contributes to the value of the integral. If $s_k \neq 0$, a power-series expansion of the form

$$\frac{N(s)}{D(s)} = a_0 + a_1 s + a_2 s^2 + \cdots$$

is possible. The integral in (14–68) is then equal to

$$\frac{1}{2\pi j} \int_C (a_0 + a_1 s + a_1 s^2 + \cdots)H(s)e^{st}\, ds. \qquad (14\text{–}69)$$

The integral (14–69) is formally equivalent to

$$\left(a_0 + a_1 \frac{d}{dt} + a_2 \frac{d^2}{dt^2} + \cdots\right) h(t), \qquad (14\text{–}70)$$

where

$$h(t) = \frac{1}{2\pi j} \int_C H(s)e^{st}\, ds = \frac{1}{2\pi j} \int_{c-j\infty}^{c-j\infty} H(s)e^{st}\, ds. \qquad (14\text{–}71)$$

In general, the series (14–70) diverges. However, for a suitable number of terms and sufficiently large t, it may approximate very accurately the integral in (14–69). This type of approximation is indicated by the symbol $\sim$. A series with this type of behavior is called an asymptotic expansion.

It is of interest to make some further comments. In the so-called operational calculus as formulated by Heaviside, asymptotic expansions were derived by direct expansion of the Laplace transform and subsequent interpretation of the terms. This method does not use the integral representation (14–67) and is now only of historical interest. Thus, the result (14–68) with the asymptotic expansion (14–70) was often obtainable only by the unjustifiable introduction and dropping of terms. To some extent this method is still popular, largely due to its apparent simplicity and a lack of understanding of the formally more rigorous method based on (14–69) and (14–70), which is equally as simple.

In applied mathematics a quick and easily understood method of obtaining a solution to a problem is desirable. It is usually taken for granted that the mathematical manipulations can be justified by a more rigorous analysis, even though this is seldom undertaken, particularly when it detracts from understanding the method as a mathematical tool. Once a result has been obtained, the mathematical manipulations should, in principle, be rigorously justified. The justifications for the integral transformations of (14–67) into (14–68) and of $h(t)$ into (14–71) is relatively simple, provided that suitable assumptions are made concerning the integrand (see Section 2–6). However, a rigorous proof for the equality of (14–69) and (14–70) is not a simple matter. For a finite number of terms, there is obviously no difficulty. However, for an infinite number of terms (14–70) is, in general, a divergent series. It has been assumed, but not proven, that this series approximates (14–69) in an asymptotic sense. In particular cases, a simple proof is possible by considering the remainder term of (14–69) [11]. However, a general discussion requires the use of the method of steepest descent [12].

PROBLEMS

14–1. If a unit-step input voltage is applied to an infinitely long leakage-free noninductive transmission line, the voltage transform is given by (14–1). (a) Show that

$$v(x, t) = 1 - \frac{1}{\pi} \int_0^\infty \frac{\sin \sqrt{ar}}{r} e^{-rt} \, dr.$$

(b) Using the result of part (a), show that

$$\operatorname{erf} \frac{1}{2} \sqrt{\frac{a}{s}} = \frac{1}{\pi} \int_0^\infty \frac{\sin \sqrt{at}}{t} e^{-st} \, dt.$$

14–2. Derive an asymptotic expansion for $v(x, t)$ from the result given in Problem 14–1(a).

14–3. A voltage

$$v_g(t) = \begin{cases} \sin \omega t, & t > 0, \\ 0, & t < 0, \end{cases}$$

is applied to an infinitely long leakage-free noninductive transmission line. Use the convolution theorem to show that the current response is

$$i(x, t) = C_2 \sin \omega t - S_2 \cos \omega t,$$

where

$$C_2 = \frac{2}{x R \sqrt{\pi}} \int_0^u \left\{ \frac{1}{u} - \frac{1}{2} \right\} \frac{e^{-1/u}}{u\sqrt{u}} \cos \frac{a\omega u}{4} \, du,$$

$$S_2 = \frac{2}{x R \sqrt{\pi}} \int_0^u \left\{ \frac{1}{u} - \frac{1}{2} \right\} \frac{e^{-1/u}}{u\sqrt{u}} \sin \frac{a\omega u}{4} \, du,$$

and

$$u = \frac{4t}{RCx^2} = \frac{4t}{a}.$$

14–4. Use the approximation $e^{-1/u} \cong 1 - 1/u$ ($u \gg 1$) to approximate the integrals C_1, S_1 (14–17), and C_2, S_2 of Problem 14–3 by means of the Fresnel integrals

$$C(u) = \int_0^u \frac{\cos z}{\sqrt{z}} \, dz, \qquad S(u) = \int_0^u \frac{\sin z}{\sqrt{z}} \, dz.$$

14–5. Find an alternative representation for the solution of Problem 14–3 by integrating the inverse Laplace transform integral around the poles and along a suitable branch cut. From this result determine an asymptotic expansion for the current.

14–6. Derive an asymptotic expansion for

$$\int_0^\infty \frac{e^{-rt}}{1+r^2} \, dr,$$

where t is real and positive.

14–7. Determine the input voltage and current for an infinitely long leakage-free noninductive cable if $V_g(s) = 1/s$ and $Z_g = R_g$. Find an asymptotic expansion for both the current and voltage response.

14–8. A voltage waveform of unit height and width T is applied to an infinitely long leakage-free noninductive transmission line. Determine the voltage response of the line.

14–9. A noninductive transmission line of length l is short circuited at the receiving end. Find the current response to a unit-step input voltage using the Heaviside expansion.

14–10. Consider the cable discussed in Section 14–5. A voltage waveform of the type shown in Fig. 14–8 is applied at the input. Determine (a) the current response and (b) the voltage response.

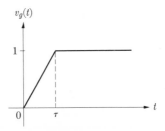

FIGURE 14–8

14–11. Determine the impulse response of the grounded-base junction transistor (a) by expanding $(\cosh z)^{-1}$ in powers of e^{-z}, and, (b) by means of the Heaviside expansion.

14–12. (a) Determine the coefficients c_n in the partial fraction expansion

$$\frac{1}{\cosh \alpha W} = \sum_{n=0}^\infty \frac{c_n}{s - s_n}$$

[for the values of s_n see (14–55)]. (b) Use the first two terms of the series in part (a) to show that

$$\frac{1}{\cosh \alpha W} \cong \frac{8}{3\pi} \frac{1 - (8/3\pi^2)(s/\omega_0)}{\left(1 + (8/\pi^2)(s/\omega_0)\right)\left(1 + (8/9\pi^2)(s/\omega_0)\right)},$$

where

$$\omega_0 = \frac{2}{\tau_p} \left(\frac{L_p}{W}\right)^2 \quad \text{and} \quad \frac{W}{L_p} \ll 1.$$

This expression can be used to approximate the alpha of a junction transistor.

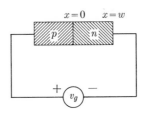

FIGURE 14–9

Compare this with the approximation given in the text and discuss the relative merits of both.

14–13. Figure 14–9 illustrates a model for a junction diode which has a uniform cross-sectional area A. The constraint imposed on the hole density at $x = 0$ by the applied voltage v_g is $p(0, t) = p_n e^{q v_g / kT}$. If $W/L_p \gg 1$, the hole density at $x = W$ is negligible. Consider the incremental operation about a fixed voltage v_o by taking $v_g = v_o + v$, where

$$\left| \frac{qv}{kT} \right| \ll 1.$$

(a) Prove that the transform of the incremental hole current is

$$I_p = G_p (1 + \tau_p s)^{1/2} V,$$

where

$$G_p = \left(\frac{q}{kT} \right) \left(\frac{q D_p}{L_p} \right) (p_n + p_0) A$$

and $V = \mathcal{L}[v(t)]$ (see Section 14–6). (b) The transform of the total incremental current is

$$I = I_p + I_e = [G_p (1 + \tau_p s)^{1/2} + G_e (1 + \tau_e s)^{1/2}] V,$$

where i_e is the incremental current due to the diffusion of electrons into the p region. Determine the current response to a unit-step voltage ($V = 1/s$) [see Appendix (C–27)].

14–14. Consider the transform given in Problem 14–13(b). If the input current is taken to be a unit impulse, show that the voltage response is

$$v(t) = \frac{1}{a - c} \left[\sqrt{\frac{a}{\pi t}} e^{-bt} - \sqrt{\frac{c}{\pi t}} e^{-dt} \right] + \frac{\sqrt{ack}}{a - c} e^{-\alpha t} [\operatorname{erfc} \sqrt{akt} - \operatorname{erfc} \sqrt{ckt}],$$

where

$$\alpha = \frac{ab - cd}{a - c}, \qquad k = \frac{d - b}{a - c},$$

and

$$a = G_p^2 \tau_p, \qquad b = \frac{1}{\tau_p}, \qquad c = G_e^2 \tau_e, \qquad d = \frac{1}{\tau_e}.$$

[see Appendix (C–28)].

References

1. E. Jahnke and F. Emde, *Tables of Functions*, Dover Publications, New York, 1943.

2. A. Erdelyi, *Tables of Integral Transforms*, Vol. I, McGraw-Hill, New York, 1954.

3. R. L. Wigington and N. S. Nahman, "Transient analysis of coaxial cables considering skin effect," *Proc. IRE*, **45**, 166–174 (February 1957).

4. A. Van Der Ziel, *Solid State Physical Electronics*, Prentice-Hall, Englewood Cliffs, New Jersey, 1957, p. 96.

5. J. Schaffner and J. Suran, "Transient response of the grounded base transistor amplifier with small load impedance," *J. Appl. Phys.*, **29**, 1355–1357 (November 1953).

6. R. D. Middlebrook, *An Introduction to Junction Transistor Theory*, Wiley and Sons, New York, 1957, p. 204.

7. E. L. Steele and B. R. Gossick, "On the response time of junction transistors," *Proc. Solid State Phenomena*, **7**, 163–173, Polytechnic Institute of Brooklyn, Interscience Publishers, New York, 1957.

8. Ref. 6, p. 177.

9. A. B. Macnee, "Approximating the alpha of a junction transistor," *Proc. IRE*, **45**, 91 (January 1957).

10. R. C. Johnston, "Transient response of drift transistors," *Proc. IRE*, **46**, 830–838 (May 1958).

11. S. Goldman, *Transformation Calculus and Electrical Transients*, Prentice-Hall, Englewood Cliffs, New Jersey, 1955, p. 316.

12. P. Morse and H. Feshback, *Methods of Theoretical Physics, Part 1*, McGraw-Hill, New York, 1953.

General References

Chow, W. F., and J. J. Suran, "Transient analysis of junction transistor amplifiers," *Proc. IRE*, **41**, 1125–1129 (September 1953).

Easley, J. W., "The effect of collector capacity on the transient response of junction transistors," *Trans. IRE, PGED*–4, 6–14 (January 1957).

Ebers, J. J., and J. L. Moll, "Large-signal behaviour of junction transistors," *Proc. IRE*, **42**, 1761–1772 (December 1954).

Enenstein, N. H., and M. E. McMahon, "Pulse response of junction transistors," *Trans. IRE, PGED*–3, 5–8 (June 1953).

Gartner, W. W., "Large-signal rise-times in junction transistors," *Trans. IRE, PGED*–5, 316 (October 1958).

Macdonald, J. R., "Solution of a transistor transient response problem," *Trans. IRE, PGCT*–3, 54–57 (March 1956).

Moll, J. L., "Large-signal transient response of junction transistors," *Proc. IRE*, **42**, 1773–1784 (December 1954).

CHAPTER 15

THE GENERAL TRANSMISSION LINE

15-1 Introduction. The equations for the voltage and current transforms for a general type of transmission line are given by (11–11) and (11–12). Since Γ_0, Γ_l, γ, and Z_0 are, in general, irrational functions of s, it becomes difficult to obtain useful solutions in terms of tabulated functions. We now discuss certain cases where solutions are possible.

15-2 The infinite transmission line with $G = 0$. If the shunt conductance per unit length, G, is taken to be zero, the propagation function and characteristic impedance are

$$\gamma = \frac{1}{c} \sqrt{(s + b)^2 - b^2} \tag{15-1}$$

and

$$Z_0 = \frac{R_0}{s} \sqrt{(s + b)^2 - b^2}, \tag{15-2}$$

respectively, where c is the velocity of propagation for the wavefront,

$$b = R/2L,$$

and

$$R_0 = \sqrt{L/C} = \lim_{s \to \infty} Z_0$$

is the so-called *surge impedance*. If the limit $s \to \infty$ is taken, it is seen that $\gamma \to s/c$. Thus c represents the limiting velocity of propagation for the waves associated with the exponential spectral terms in the signal (see Section 11–2).

If the line is infinitely long, there is no reflected wave. Thus $\Gamma_l = 0$ and, if $Z_g = 0$, the current and voltage transforms (11–11) and (11–12) are

$$I(x, s) = \frac{s V_g(s)}{R_0} \frac{e^{-x/c \sqrt{(s+b)^2 - b^2}}}{\sqrt{(s + b)^2 - b^2}} \tag{15-3}$$

and

$$V(x, s) = V_g(s) e^{-x/c \sqrt{(s+b)^2 - b^2}}. \tag{15-4}$$

If the input is a unit-step voltage, the inverse transform of (15–3) and (15–4) can be obtained with the aid of the transforms [see (D–41), (D–47), and (D–48)]

$$\mathcal{L}\left[u\left(t - \frac{x}{c}\right)I_0(z)\right] = \frac{e^{-x/c\sqrt{s^2-a^2}}}{\sqrt{s^2 - a^2}}, \tag{15-5}$$

$$\mathcal{L}\left[u\left(t - \frac{x}{c}\right)\frac{a^2x}{c}\frac{I_1(z)}{z}\right] = e^{-x/c\sqrt{s^2-a^2}} - e^{-xs/c}, \tag{15-6}$$

$$\mathcal{L}\left[u\left(t - \frac{x}{c}\right)\left(\frac{t - x/c}{t + x/c}\right)^{1/2}aI_1(z)\right] = \frac{s - \sqrt{s^2 - a^2}}{\sqrt{s^2 - a^2}}e^{-(x/c)\sqrt{s^2-a^2}}$$
$$\tag{15-7}$$

where

$$z = a\sqrt{t^2 - (x/c)^2}, \tag{15-8}$$

$I_n(z)$ is the modified Bessel function of order n, and $u(t)$ is the unit-step function, that is, $u(t) = 1$ for $t > 0$ and $u(t) = 0$ for $t < 0$.

Applying the s-translation theorem to (15–3) and taking $a = b$ in (15–5) yields

$$i(x, t) = \frac{e^{-bt}}{R_0}\mathcal{L}^{-1}\left[\frac{e^{-(x/c)\sqrt{s^2-b^2}}}{\sqrt{s^2 - b^2}}\right] = \frac{e^{-bt}}{R_0}I_0(z), \qquad t > \frac{x}{c}. \tag{15-9}$$

The voltage transform (15–4) can be written in the form

$$V(x, s) = \frac{1}{s}[e^{-(x/c)(s+b)} + (e^{-(x/c)\sqrt{(s+b)^2-b^2}} - e^{-(x/c)(s+b)})].$$

The term $e^{-xs/c}/s$ is the Laplace transform of a unit step occurring at $t = x/c$. The second term can be evaluated by using the s-translation theorem, taking $a = b$ in (15–6), and considering $1/s$ to represent integration in the time domain. Thus

$$v(x, t) = e^{-xb/c} + \frac{b^2x}{c}\int_{x/c}^{t}e^{-b\tau}\frac{I_1(z)}{z}\,d\tau, \qquad t > \frac{x}{c}.$$

For $t < x/c$, we obtain $i(x, t) = 0 = v(x, t)$. This result can be easily seen from (15–3). For large s, we have $I(x, s) \cong e^{-xs/c}/R_0s$. Thus, if $t < x/c$, the path of integration for the inverse Laplace transform can be completed in the right half of the s-plane. Since no singularities are enclosed, it follows from Cauchy's theorem that $i(x, t) = 0$. The same conclusion holds for $v(x, t)$. From a physical point of view this results from the finite velocity of wave propagation for the wavefront. It takes a time interval of x/c seconds for the wavefront to reach a position x. These results are also valid for the incident wave on a finite line. If the line length is l, a time interval of $(2l - x)/c$ seconds is required before the reflected wave reaches the position x and affects the resultant wave form.

15–3 The infinite general transmission line driven by an arbitrary voltage source. In the general case, the propagation function and characteristic impedance are

$$\gamma = \frac{1}{c} \sqrt{(s+b)^2 - a^2}$$

and

$$Z_0 = R_0 \frac{\sqrt{(s+b)^2 - a^2}}{(s+b) - a},$$

where

$$b = \frac{1}{2}\left(\frac{R}{L} + \frac{G}{C}\right) \quad \text{and} \quad a = \frac{1}{2}\left(\frac{R}{L} - \frac{G}{C}\right).$$

The current transform is

$$I(x, s) = \frac{1}{R_0} \frac{V_g(s)}{A(s+b) + \dfrac{\sqrt{(s+b)^2 - a^2}}{(s+b) - a}} e^{-(x/c)\sqrt{(s+b)^2-a^2}}, \qquad (15\text{–}10)$$

where

$$A(s+b) = \frac{Z_g(s)}{R_0} \qquad (15\text{–}11)$$

is considered to be a rational function of s.

The transform $I(x, s)$ is first simplified by means of the s-translation theorem. This yields

$$i(x, t) = \frac{e^{-bt}}{R_0} \mathcal{L}^{-1}[F(s)], \qquad (15\text{–}12)$$

where

$$F(s) = \frac{(s-a) V_g(s-b)}{(s-a) A(s) + \sqrt{s^2 - a^2}} e^{-(x/c)\sqrt{s^2-a^2}}.$$

Algebraic manipulation of $F(s)$ yields the following expressions, where, for convenience, $A = A(s)$ is used.

$$F(s) = \frac{(s-a) V_g(s-b)}{(1 - A^2)s + (1 + A^2)a} \frac{(s+a) - A\sqrt{s^2 - a^2}}{\sqrt{s^2 - a^2}} e^{-(x/c)\sqrt{s^2-a^2}}$$

$$= \frac{(s-a) V_g(s-b)}{(1 - A^2)s + (1 + A^2)a}$$

$$\times \left[\left(1 - A + \frac{a}{\sqrt{s^2 - a^2}} + \frac{s - \sqrt{s^2 - a^2}}{\sqrt{s^2 - a^2}}\right) e^{-(x/c)\sqrt{s^2-a^2}}\right].$$

$$(15\text{–}13)$$

A variety of forms for $F(s)$ is possible. The choice is governed largely by the attempt to obtain factors which are listed in transform tables. However, it is also desirable to arrange the solution in a form where the various factors can be interpreted in terms of their physical significance. These are the reasons for the choice of the form (15–13). The quantity A is a measure of the mismatch between the internal impedance of the generator and the surge impedance of the line. The inverse transform of (15–13) can be obtained with the aid of the convolution theorem and (15–5), (15–6), and (15–7). The first term in the brackets of (15–13) can be expressed in the form

$$(1 - A)e^{-xs/c} + (1 - A)[e^{-(x/c)\sqrt{s^2 - a^2}} - e^{-xs/c}]. \qquad (15\text{–}14)$$

The first exponential in this expression represents a delay of x/c seconds, i.e., the t-translation theorem can be applied to this term. The inverse transform of the remaining two exponentials in (15–14) is obtained from (15–6). The inverse transforms of the remaining two terms in the bracket of (15–13) are found using (15–5) and (15–7).

The function

$$\frac{(s - a)V_g(s - b)}{(1 - A^2)s + (1 + A^2)a} = \frac{N(s)}{D(s)}$$

is a rational function of s and thus can be expressed as the ratio of polynomials $N(s)$ and $D(s)$. The poles of this function are the zeros of $D(s)$. Let these zeros be simple and designated by $s_k (k = 1, 2, \ldots, n)$.

The Heaviside expansion can be used to determine the inverse transform of the first factor of (15–13). The inverse transforms of the terms making up the second factor have been discussed. Applying the convolution theorem yields

$$f(t) = \sum_{k=1}^{n} \frac{N(s_k)}{D'(s_k)} e^{s_k t} \left\{ [1 - A(s_k)]e^{-xs_k/c} + a\int_{x/c}^{t} e^{-s_k \tau} \right.$$

$$\left. \times \left[(1 - A(s_k))\frac{ax}{c}\frac{I_1(z)}{z} + I_0(z) + a\left(\tau - \frac{x}{c}\right)\frac{I_1(z)}{z} \right] d\tau \right\},$$

$$t > \frac{x}{c}.$$

For the voltage transform we have

$$V(x, s) = Z_0 I(x, s) = R_0 \frac{\sqrt{(s + b)^2 - a^2}}{(s + b) - a} I(x, s).$$

With the aid of the s-translation theorem we obtain

$$v(x, t) = e^{-bt}\mathcal{L}^{-1}[G(s)], \qquad (15\text{–}15)$$

where

$$G(s) = \frac{V_g(s-b)}{(1-A^2)s+(1+A^2)a}[(s+a)-A\sqrt{s^2-a^2}]e^{-(x/c)\sqrt{s^2-a^2}}$$

$$= \frac{(s+a)V_g(s-b)}{(1-A^2)s+(1+A^2)a}A$$

$$\times\left[\frac{1}{A}-1+\frac{a}{\sqrt{s^2-a^2}}-\frac{s-\sqrt{s^2-a^2}}{\sqrt{s^2-a^2}}\right]e^{-(x/c)\sqrt{s^2-a^2}}.$$

$$(15\text{--}16)$$

EXAMPLE 1. Suppose that the input voltage is a unit step and that $Z_g = R_0$ and $G = 0$. It follows that $A = 1$, $a = b$, and $(s-a)V_g(s-b) = 1$. Equation (15–13) is then

$$F(s) = \frac{1}{2a}\left[\frac{a}{\sqrt{s^2-a^2}}+\frac{s-\sqrt{s^2-a^2}}{\sqrt{s^2-a^2}}\right]e^{-(x/c)\sqrt{s^2-a^2}}.$$

The inverse transform of $F(s)$ can be found by using (15–5) and (15–7). Substituting this into (15–12) yields

$$i(x,t) = \frac{e^{-bt}}{2R_0}\left[I_0(z)+a\left(t-\frac{x}{c}\right)\frac{I_1(z)}{z}\right], \qquad t > \frac{x}{c}, \qquad (15\text{--}17)$$

where z is given by (15–8).

To determine the voltage response, we have, from (15–16),

$$G(s) = \frac{1}{2a}\left[\frac{a}{\sqrt{s^2-a^2}}-\frac{s-\sqrt{s^2-a^2}}{\sqrt{s^2-a^2}}\right]e^{-(x/c)\sqrt{s^2-a^2}}.$$

Thus, using (15–5), (15–7), and (15–15), we obtain

$$v(x,t) = \frac{e^{-bt}}{2}\left[I_0(z)-a\left(t-\frac{x}{c}\right)\frac{I_1(z)}{z}\right], \qquad t > \frac{x}{c}. \qquad (15\text{--}18)$$

At $z = 0^+$ the ratio of (15–17) and (15–18) yields $v/i = R_0$. Thus the initial rate of rise of the waveform is due to the high-frequency spectral terms of the waveforms. This is seen by noting that $V/I \rightarrow R_0$ as $s \rightarrow \infty$. ▲

15–4 The response of the infinite transmission line to a voltage source with $Z_g = 0$.

In the special case where $Z_g = 0$, we have $A = 0$ [see (15–11)] and (15–10) has the form

$$R_0 I(x,s) = \frac{N(s)}{D(s)}H(s)$$

where

$$H(s) = \frac{e^{-(x/c)\sqrt{(s+b)^2 - a^2}}}{\sqrt{(s+b)^2 - a^2}}$$

and

$$\frac{N(s)}{D(s)} = (s + b - a)V_g(s) = a_0 + a_1 s + a_2 s^2 + \cdots.$$

The resultant response can be found from the general expression (14–68) and, if the asymptotic expansion (14–70) is used for the integral, we obtain

$$R_0 i(x, t) \sim \sum_{k=1}^{n} \frac{N(s_k)}{D'(s_k)} H(s_k)e^{s_k t} + \left(a_0 + a_1 \frac{d}{dt} + a_2 \frac{d^2}{dt^2} + \cdots \right) h(t).$$

$$(15–19)$$

EXAMPLE 2. Suppose that the input voltage is

$$v_g(t) = \begin{cases} \sin \omega_c t, & t > 0, \\ 0, & t < 0, \end{cases}$$

and that $G = 0$. Then $a = b$ and [see (15–9)]

$$h(t) = e^{-bt}I_0(z), \qquad t > \frac{x}{c},$$

where z is given by (15–8). We also have $N(s) = \omega_c s$ and $D(s) = s^2 + \omega_c^2$. The poles are at $s = \pm j\omega_c$ and

$$\frac{N(s)}{D(s)} = \frac{s}{\omega_c} - \left(\frac{s}{\omega_c}\right)^3 + \left(\frac{s}{\omega_c}\right)^5 - \cdots.$$

For large t we can use the asymptotic expansion

$$I_0(z) \sim \frac{e^{zt}}{\sqrt{2\pi z}} \cong \frac{e^{bt}}{\sqrt{2\pi bt}}.$$

Substituting these results into (15–19) yields

$$R_0 i(x, t) \sim \omega_c \, \mathrm{Re}[H(j\omega_c)e^{j\omega_c t}]$$

$$- \frac{1}{\sqrt{2\pi bt}}\left[\frac{1}{(2\omega_c t)} - \frac{1 \cdot 3 \cdot 5}{(2\omega_c t)^3} + \frac{1 \cdot 3 \cdot 5 \cdot 7 \cdot 9}{(2\omega_c t)^5} - \cdots \right].$$

The first term in this expression is the steady-state sinusoidal response of the transmission line, while the second term is the asymptotic expansion for the transient response. ▲

It is seen from Example 2 that an asymptotic expansion, when obtainable, leads to a considerable simplification of the solution. This is very convenient when numerical results are required. The exact solution, which contains an integral along the branch cut, is, in general, not suitable for numerical computations.

15–5 The response of a finite transmission line terminated in a lumped-parameter network. A general expression for the transform of the transmission-line current is given by (11–19). If $Z_g = 0$ so that $\Gamma_0 = -1$, this takes the form

$$I(x, s) = \frac{V_g(s)}{Z_0}\left[e^{-\gamma x} + \sum_{n=1}^{\infty} (-\Gamma_l)^n (e^{-\gamma x_n} + e^{-\gamma y_n})\right], \qquad (15\text{–}20)$$

where $x_n = 2nl - x$ and $y_n = 2nl + x$. If $G = 0$, the propagation function and characteristic impedance are given by (15–1) and (15–2). Substituting into (15–20) yields

$$I(x, s) = \frac{1}{R_0}\left\{ F_0(x, s+b) + \sum_{n=1}^{\infty} [F_n(x_n, s+b) + F_n(y_n, s+b)]\right\},$$

$$(15\text{–}21)$$

where

$$F_n(x, s) = G_n(s)\,\frac{e^{-(x/c)\sqrt{s^2-b^2}}}{\sqrt{s^2-b^2}} \qquad (15\text{–}22)$$

and

$$G_n(s) = (s-b)V_g(s-b)\left[\frac{\sqrt{s^2-b^2} - (s-b)Z_l(s-b)/R_0}{\sqrt{s^2-b^2} + (s-b)Z_l(s-b)/R_0}\right]^n.$$

$$(15\text{–}23)$$

The s-translation theorem can be applied to (15–21), and we obtain

$$i(x, t) = \frac{1}{R_0}\,e^{-bt}\left\{ f_0(x, t) + \sum_{n=1}^{\infty} [f_n(x_n, t) + f_n(y_n, t)]\right\}.$$

In order to determine the inverse transform of (15–22), we use the substitution

$$s = \frac{b(1+p^2)}{2p}, \qquad (15\text{–}24)$$

which yields

$$\sqrt{s^2-b^2} = s - bp. \qquad (15\text{–}25)$$

Substituting this into (15–23) yields an expression which is a rational function of p and s (note that $Z_l(s)$ is a rational function of s, since it is the impedance function of a lumped-parameter network). If s is now eliminated by means of (15–24) and the terms in p suitably grouped, we obtain a rational function of p which can be expanded in a power series

$$G_n(s) = \sum_{k=0}^{\infty} c_{nk} p^k. \tag{15-26}$$

An expansion of this form is usually possible if p is sufficiently small. It is seen from (15–24) that s is then large. This implies that the result should be valid for small t. If, on the other hand, t is large, an asymptotic expansion can be used. Equation (15–26) can be expressed in terms of s by means of (15–25). Thus

$$F_n(x, s) = \sum_{k=0}^{\infty} c_{nk} \left(\frac{s - \sqrt{s^2 - b^2}}{b} \right)^k \frac{e^{-(x/c)\sqrt{s^2 - b^2}}}{\sqrt{s^2 - b^2}}.$$

The inverse transform of the terms of this series can be found with the aid of Appendix (D–47). This yields

$$f_n(x, t) = \sum_{k=0}^{\infty} c_{nk} u \left(t - \frac{x}{c} \right) \left(\frac{t - x/c}{t + x/c} \right)^{k/2} I_k(b\sqrt{t^2 - (x/c)^2}), \tag{15-27}$$

where $u(t)$ is the unit-step function.

PROBLEMS

15–1. Determine expressions for the current and voltage response for an infinitely long transmission line if the input is a unit-step voltage and $Z_g = 0$. All four of the parameters R, G, L, and C are taken to be nonzero.

15–2. An infinitely long transmission line with $G = 0$ is driven from a voltage source where $V_g = 1/s$ and $Z_g = 1/C_g s$. Determine the current response.

15–3. Solve Problem 15–2 if $Z_g = R_g$.

15–4. Determine an asymptotic expansion for the voltage response of an infinitely long transmission line if $G = 0$, $Z_g = 0$, and if V_g has simple poles. Apply this to the case where the input voltage is a suddenly applied sine wave.

15–5. A finite transmission line of length l is terminated in a load $Z_l = R_0$. Consider the expansion (11–19) for the current transform. If $G = 0$, $Z_g = 0$ and $V_g = 1/s$, show that the inverse transform of the first two terms is identical with (15–17) when $x = l$.

15–6. Consider a transmission line of length l. If $V_g = 1/s$, $Z_g = 0$, and $G = 0$, determine the coefficients in the expansion (15–26) if (a) $Z_l = 0$ and (b) $Z_l = \infty$.

15–7. A transmission line of length l has a load impedance $Z_l = 1/C_l s$. If $V_g = 1/s$, $Z_g = 0$, and $G = 0$, determine the coefficients in the expansion (15–26).

GENERAL REFERENCES

CARSON, J. R., *Electric Circuit Theory and Operational Calculus*, McGraw-Hill, New York, 1926.

McLACHLAN, N. W., *Complex Variable Theory and Transform Calculus*, 2nd ed., Cambridge University Press, 1953.

WAGNER, K. W., *Operatorenrechnung nebst Anwendungen in Physik und Technik*, Barth, Leipzig, 1940.

WEBER, E., *Linear Transient Analysis*, Vol. II, Wiley and Sons, New York, 1956.

CHAPTER 16

LINEAR SYSTEMS WITH RANDOM INPUTS

16–1 Introduction. The input signal to a system is often incompletely known and can be described only by its statistical properties. A signal of this type is called a *random signal*. Evidently the system response will also be a random signal. In this chapter we shall develop suitable mathematical techniques for describing the properties of random input and output signals.

16–2 Probability distribution functions. Let us consider a set $v_k(t)$ $(k = 1, 2, \ldots, n)$ of random signals, where n is to be a large number (see Fig. 16–1). These could, for example, represent the measured current fluctuations in n different diodes under similar conditions. The physical process which causes the random fluctuations is called a random process. We let $v(t)$ represent any of the measured signal values at time t. Suppose that we are interested in determining the probability $\Pr(v \leq x)$ that $v(t)$ does not exceed a specified value $x(t)$. This probability will be called the first *distribution function*, $F_1(x, t)$, and can be obtained from

$$F_1(x, t) = \Pr(v \leq x) = \frac{m}{n}, \tag{16–1}$$

where m is the number of the n signals which have a measured value

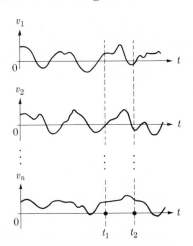

FIG. 16–1. A set of n random signals.

$v(t) \leq x(t)$. Equation (16–1) implies that the distribution function is obtained experimentally. However, a function so obtained is not, in general, suitable for problems in analysis. A suitable function is usually postulated mathematically. We consider this function to be differentiable and define the *first probability density function* by

$$p_1(x, t) = \frac{\partial F_1(x, t)}{\partial x}. \qquad (16\text{–}2)$$

Equations (16–1) and (16–2) show that the probability of finding a measured value in the range

$$x \leq v \leq x + \Delta x \qquad (16\text{–}3)$$

is given by

$$p_1(x, t) \, \Delta x \cong \text{Pr} \, (v \leq x + \Delta x) - \text{Pr} \, (v \leq x),$$

provided that Δx is small. It is evident that the probability density function must satisfy the condition

$$\int_{-\infty}^{+\infty} p_1(x, t) \, dx = 1,$$

since $\text{Pr} \, (v < +\infty) = 1$.

Suppose that we have a function $f = f(v)$ and wish to determine the average or expected value. We divide the range of v-values into small intervals Δx. If we have n signals, the number of signals having a measured value falling in the interval (16–3) is $np_1(x, t) \, \Delta x$. Each of these measurements yields $f(x)$. Thus the average or *expected value* of f is

$$E(f) = \lim_{\Delta x \to 0} \frac{1}{n} \sum [np_1(x, t) \, \Delta x] f(x) = \int_{-\infty}^{+\infty} f(x) p_1(x, t) \, dx. \qquad (16\text{–}4)$$

It should be noted that all quantities under discussion are functions of t, the instant at which the signals are measured. In a mathematical sense, (16–4) is used to define the expected value of f.

We consider now two different instants of time t_1 and t_2. We use the notation $v_k = v(t_k) \, (k = 1, 2)$ for the values of $v(t)$ at these instants. The *second probability distribution function*

$$F_2(x_1, t_1; x_2, t_2) = \text{Pr} \, (v_1 \leq x_1; v_2 \leq x_2)$$

gives the probability that $v_1 \leq x_1$ and $v_2 \leq x_2$, where x_1 and x_2 are specified. The *second probability density function* is

$$p_2(x_1, t_1; x_2, t_2) = \frac{\partial^2 F_2}{\partial x_1 \partial x_2}.$$

The expected value of the function $f = f(v_1, v_2)$ is

$$E(f) = \int_{-\infty}^{+\infty} \int_{-\infty}^{+\infty} f(x_1, x_2) p_2(x_1, t_1; x_2, t_2) \, dx_1 \, dx_2, \qquad (16\text{–}5)$$

which is an extension of (16–4) to two variables.

In many practical situations it is sufficient to consider the probability density functions as being independent of time. The random process is then defined as being *stationary*. It should be noted that for a stationary random process, the second probability density function can be represented in the form

$$p_2(x_1, t_1; \ x_2, t_2) = p_2(x_1, x_2, \tau),$$

where $\tau = t_1 - t_2$, since a translation in time does not change the statistics.

16–3 Time averages. Instead of considering the expected values to be determined from measurements carried out on n signals, we can select one signal, for example, $v(t) = v_1(t)$, and define the *average value* by

$$\bar{v} = \lim_{T \to \infty} \frac{1}{2T} \int_{-T}^{+T} v(t) \, dt. \qquad (16\text{–}6)$$

An important quantity is the average value of the product $u(t)v(t + \tau)$, which is called the *correlation function:*

$$\phi_{uv}(\tau) = \overline{u(t)v(t + \tau)} = \lim_{T \to \infty} \frac{1}{2T} \int_{-T}^{+T} u(t)v(t + \tau) \, dt. \qquad (16\text{–}7)$$

On an intuitive basis it would seem that the averages of a stationary random process computed on the basis of one signal (time averages) or on the basis of an assembly of functions (expected values) should be identical. This would be the case if the signals $v_k(t)$ (see Fig. 16–1) represent, in a statistical sense, segments of one signal. The *ergodic hypothesis* postulates the equality of these averages so that we have

$$E(v) = \bar{v}. \qquad (16\text{–}8)$$

Considerable care must be taken in the interpretation of this equality since it is not valid for all functions. Consider the case where $E(v) \neq 0$. The function $v(t) = 0$ has an average value $\bar{v} = 0$ and it would seem that $E(v) \neq \bar{v}$. However, the probability of occurrence of the function $v(t) = 0$ is zero. It is therefore essential to interpret (16–8) in a statistical sense and assign a statistical weight or probability to the possible functions $v(t)$ used in computing the time averages in (16–8). The mathematical complications arising from this interpretation of (16–8) are considerable. For our purposes it is sufficient to note that we need only to restrict $v(t)$ to a class of random functions having the necessary statistical properties. A function of the type $v(t) = 0$ is thus ruled out.

As an example consider a random-phase sine wave

$$v(t) = \sin(\omega_c t + \phi), \tag{16-9}$$

where the phase ϕ has a fixed value for each member function of the assembly of functions. The correlation function is obtained from (16–7), where $u = v$:

$$\phi_{vv}(\tau) = \tfrac{1}{2} \cos \omega_c \tau.$$

Suppose that the first probability density function for ϕ is

$$p_1(\phi) = \begin{cases} \dfrac{1}{2\pi}, & -\pi < \phi < \pi, \\ 0, & |\phi| > \pi. \end{cases} \tag{16-10}$$

We obtain, from (16–4),

$$E(v_1 v_2) = \int_{-\infty}^{+\infty} p_1(\phi) \sin(\omega_c t_1 + \phi) \sin[\omega_c(t_1 + \tau) + \phi] \, d\phi = \tfrac{1}{2} \cos \omega_c \tau.$$

The ergodic hypothesis is thus satisfied. It should be noted that this is a consequence of the use of $v(t)$ in the form (16–9) in conjunction with the postulated probability function (16–10). In the remainder of this chapter we shall assume that the random process is stationary and that the ergodic hypothesis is valid.

16–4 Spectral density. In Chapter 1 we discussed the spectral resolution of a signal into exponential terms. Two possible representations were obtained. The Laplace transformation proves useful if $v(t) = 0$ for $t < 0$. However, this is not the situation for the signals considered here. Thus the Fourier transform must be used. The conditions for the convergence of this transform places restrictions on $v(t)$ which are seldom met in practice. To overcome this difficulty we choose a large interval $2T$ and take

$$v_T(t) = \begin{cases} v(t), & |t| \le T, \\ 0, & |t| > T. \end{cases}$$

This is a truncated function and its Fourier transform [see (1–19)] is

$$V_T(\omega) = \int_{-\infty}^{+\infty} v_T(t) e^{-j\omega t} \, dt = \int_{-T}^{+T} v(t) e^{-j\omega t} \, dt. \tag{16-11}$$

Since $v(t)$ is real it follows that

$$V_T^*(\omega) = V_T(-\omega). \tag{16-12}$$

The inverse transform is

$$v_T(t) = \frac{1}{2\pi} \int_{-\infty}^{+\infty} V_T(\omega) e^{j\omega t}\, d\omega. \tag{16-13}$$

There are a number of important statistical relations which can be obtained from these transforms. Consider the following integral and its transformations:

$$\int_{-\infty}^{+\infty} U_T(-\omega) V_T(\omega)\, d\omega = \int_{-\infty}^{+\infty} \left[\int_{-\infty}^{+\infty} u_T(t) e^{j\omega t}\, dt \right] V_T(\omega)\, d\omega$$

$$= \int_{-\infty}^{+\infty} u_T(t) \left[\int_{-\infty}^{+\infty} V_T(\omega) e^{j\omega t}\, d\omega \right] dt$$

$$= 2\pi \int_{-\infty}^{+\infty} u_T(t) v_T(t)\, dt. \tag{16-14}$$

This relation is known as Parsevals identity; it has occurred previously in a slightly different form [see (9–114)]. If (16–14) is divided by $4\pi T$, and the limit $T \to \infty$ is taken, we obtain

$$\overline{uv} = \lim_{T \to \infty} \frac{1}{4\pi T} \int_{-\infty}^{+\infty} U_T^*(\omega) V_T(\omega)\, d\omega$$

$$= \frac{1}{2\pi} \int_{-\infty}^{+\infty} \Phi_{uv}(\omega)\, d\omega, \tag{16-15}$$

where

$$\Phi_{uv}(\omega) = \lim_{T \to \infty} \frac{1}{2T} U_T^*(\omega) V_T(\omega) \tag{16-16}$$

is defined to be the *cross-power spectral density*. If $u = v$, it is defined as the *power spectral density*, and referred to simply as the *spectral density*. To understand the reason for this terminology consider $v(t)$ to be the voltage across a 1-ohm resistor. The left-hand side of (16–15) represents the average power dissipated. Let $\Phi(\omega) = \Phi[f]$, where $\omega = 2\pi f$ and consider the power dissipated by the spectral terms in a frequency range df to be $\Phi[f]\, df$. If this is integrated over the complete frequency range, the expression (16–15) will result. Thus $\Phi[f]$ can be considered to represent the dissipated power per unit frequency interval.

Care must be taken in the interpretation of (16–16), since it does not exist for all functions. The situation is the same as it was with the ergodic

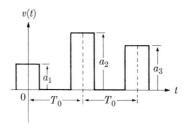

FIG. 16–2. A random function with periodic terms.

hypothesis (16–8). The mathematical complications that arise can be avoided if (16–16) is restricted to a class of functions having the necessary statistical properties. In effect this means that (16–16) must be averaged over all possible functions.

EXAMPLE 1. As an example of the use of (16–16) consider the waveform shown in Fig. 16–2. A pulse $g(t)$ occurs with a period T_0 and random amplitudes, $a_1, a_2, \ldots$. We have

$$v(t) = \sum_{k=-\infty}^{+\infty} a_k g(t - kT_0).$$

This can be truncated by choosing $T = NT_0$, where N can be taken to be arbitrarily large. Equation (16–11) yields

$$V_T(\omega) = \sum_{k=-N}^{N} a_k \int_{-T}^{+T} g(t - kT_0)e^{-j\omega t} \cdot dt \qquad (16\text{–}17a)$$

$$V_T(\omega) = G(\omega) \sum_{k=-N}^{N} a_k e^{-j\omega kT_0}, \qquad (16\text{–}17b)$$

where

$$G(\omega) = \int_{-\infty}^{+\infty} g(\tau)e^{-j\omega\tau}\, d\tau \qquad (16\text{–}18)$$

is the Fourier transform of $g(t)$. This result is obtained by substituting $\tau = t - kT_0$ into the integral in (16–17a) and noting that, since N is large, the limits in (16–18) can be taken to be $\pm\infty$. Substituting (16–17b) into (16–16) yields

$$\Phi_{vv}(\omega) = \frac{1}{T_0}|G|^2 \lim_{N\to\infty} \frac{1}{2N} \left\{ \sum_{k=-N}^{N} \sum_{l=-N}^{N} a_k a_l e^{-j\omega(k-l)T_0} \right\}. \qquad (16\text{–}19)$$

In order to evaluate this limit we can make use of the ergodic hypothesis and first take (with N fixed) an assembly average by considering a large number of waveforms of the type shown in Fig. 16–2. That this is reasonable can be seen by noting that segments of length $2T$ of the same waveform can be taken to be the member functions of the assembly. The reason that an assembly average is more convenient is that k and l are considered fixed so that the phase factor in (16–19) need not be considered in this average. For fixed values of k and l, the members of the assembly will have amplitudes $a_{k1}, a_{k2}, \ldots,$ and $a_{l1}, a_{l2}, \ldots.$ In order to retain a simple symbolism we denote the possible values of these sequences by a_k and a_l. We have the following assembly averages:

$$\overline{a_k a_l} = \begin{cases} \overline{a_k^2} = \overline{a^2}, & k = l, & (16\text{–}20a) \\ \overline{a_k}\,\overline{a_l} = (\overline{a})^2, & k \neq l, & (16\text{–}20b) \end{cases}$$

where the latter result ($k \neq l$) follows from the fact that the values of a_k are independent of a_l.

We consider now the terms with $k = l$ in the sum (16–19). The exponential phase factor is then unity. The assembly average of $a_k a_l$ yields $\overline{a^2}$ [see (16–20a)]. There are $2N + 1$ terms of this type and

$$\lim_{N \to \infty} \frac{2N + 1}{2N} \overline{a^2} = \overline{a^2}.$$

We consider now the terms in (16–19) where $k \neq l$. The assembly average of $a_k a_l$ yields $(\overline{a})^2$ [see (16–20b)]. The resulting sum for these terms can be evaluated by adding and subtracting the terms where $k = l$. The final result is

$$\Phi_{vv}(\omega) = \frac{|G|^2}{T_0}\{\overline{a^2} - (\overline{a})^2 + (\overline{a})^2 \lim_{N \to \infty} |S|^2\}, \qquad (16\text{–}21)$$

where

$$S = \frac{1}{\sqrt{2N}} \sum_{k=-N}^{N} e^{-j\omega k T_0} \qquad (16\text{–}22)$$

is a geometric series in $e^{-j\omega T_0}$. Evaluating the sum yields

$$|S|^2 = \frac{1}{2N} \frac{1 - \cos(2N + 1)\omega T_0}{1 - \cos \omega T_0}. \qquad (16\text{–}23)$$

From this expression it can be seen that

$$\lim_{N \to \infty} |S|^2 = \begin{cases} 0, & \omega \neq \dfrac{2\pi n}{T_0}, \quad (n = 0, \pm 1, \ldots), \\[4mm] \infty, & \omega = \dfrac{2\pi n}{T_0}. \end{cases} \qquad (16\text{–}24)$$

To determine the nature of the singularity at $\omega = 2\pi n/T_0$, we note that (16–23) is a periodic function in ω, so that it is sufficient to consider the interval $-\pi/T_0 \leq \omega \leq \pi/T_0$. The integral

$$\int_{-\pi/T_0}^{\pi/T_0} |S|^2 \, d\omega = \frac{2N+1}{2N} \frac{2\pi}{T_0} \tag{16–25}$$

can be evaluated by substituting (16–22), which yields a double sum. Due to their periodicity all terms of the form $e^{j\omega n T_0} (n \neq 0)$ yield zero when integrated. There are $2N + 1$ terms where $n = 0$, each of which yields $2\pi/T_0$. It follows from (16–24) and (16–25) that

$$\lim_{N \to \infty} |S|^2 = \frac{2\pi}{T_0} \sum_{n=-\infty}^{+\infty} \delta\left(\omega - \frac{2\pi n}{T_0}\right),$$

where $\delta(\omega)$ is the delta function. ▲

In order to interpret this result it should be noted that $v(t)$ has periodic terms of the form $e^{j 2\pi n t/T_0}$ which contain a finite average power. This results in an infinite power density at the frequencies $f = n/T_0$. The random components in $v(t)$ result in a continuous spectrum and yield the continuous part of $\Phi_{vv}(\omega)$.

It would appear that as $v(t)$ becomes more random $\Phi_{vv}(\omega)$ will become smoother. That this is essentially correct will be illustrated by a second example.

EXAMPLE 2. Consider the waveform shown in Fig. 16–3, where $v(t)$ switches between the values ± 1 at the instants $t_1, t_2, \ldots$. For convenience we choose $t_1 = -T$ and $t_{N+1} = T$. Equation (16–11) yields

$$V_T(\omega) = \frac{1}{j\omega} \sum_{k=1}^{N} (-1)^k (e^{-j\omega t_{k+1}} - e^{-j\omega t_k})$$

$$= \frac{1}{j\omega} \left\{ -2 \sum_{k=1}^{N} (-1)^k e^{-j\omega t_k} - e^{-j\omega t_1} + (-1)^N e^{-j\omega t_{N+1}} \right\}.$$

Substituting this into (16–16) yields

$$\Phi_{vv}(\omega) = \frac{1}{\bar{T}} \frac{4}{\omega^2} \lim_{N \to \infty} \frac{1}{N} \left\{ \sum_{k=1}^{N} \sum_{l=1}^{N} (-1)^{k+l} e^{-j\omega(t_k - t_l)} + f \right\}, \tag{16–26}$$

where

$$\bar{T} = \frac{T_1 + T_2 + \cdots T_N}{N} = \frac{2T}{N}$$

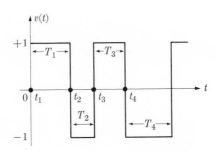

FIG. 16–3. A random switching function.

is the average time interval between switching instants, and f is of the form

$$f = \sum(-1)^k e^{-j\omega t_k}. \tag{16–27}$$

In order to evaluate (16–26), we first consider N fixed and take an assembly average as was done in Example 1. Let $p(x)$ be the probability density function for the time intervals between switching instants. Since $p(x) = 0$ if $x < 0$, it follows from (16–4) that

$$E(e^{-j\omega x}) = \overline{e^{-j\omega x}} = \int_0^\infty p(x)e^{-j\omega x}\, dx = P(\omega).$$

The assembly average of $e^{-j\omega x}$ is thus the Fourier transform of $p(x)$. If the assembly average of f is taken [see (16–27)], we obtain

$$\bar{f} = \sum(-1)^k P(\omega) = \pm P(\omega) \qquad \text{or} \qquad 0;$$

hence $\lim_{N\to\infty} \bar{f}/N = 0$, and this term need not be considered any further. We consider now the sum of those terms for which $k > l$ in the bracket of (16–26). We set $k = l + m$ and take the assembly average of the phase factor

$$e^{-j\omega(t_k - t_l)} = e^{-j\omega T_l} e^{-j\omega T_{l+1}} \cdots e^{-j\omega T_{k-1}},$$

which yields

$$\overline{e^{-j\omega(t_k - t_l)}} = P^m,$$

since the time intervals are all independent of each other. Furthermore $(-1)^{k+l} = (-1)^m$ and there are $N - m \cong N$ such terms in the sum. Dividing by N and taking the limit yields $(-1)^m P^m$. Summing over all possible values of m, we obtain

$$\sum_{m=1}^{\infty} (-1)^m P^m = -\frac{P}{1+P}, \qquad k > l. \tag{16–28}$$

Similarly, if we sum those terms for which $k < l$ in the bracket of (16–26), take the assembly average, and then the limit as $N \to \infty$, we obtain the conjugate complex of (16–28). The limit for the terms where $k = l$ is unity. Thus

$$\Phi_{vv}(\omega) = \frac{4}{\omega^2 \overline{T}} \left(1 - 2 \operatorname{Re}\left[\frac{P}{1 + P}\right]\right),$$

which is a continuous function of ω for all practical probability functions $p(x)$. ▲

An extreme case occurs when $\Phi(\omega) = $ constant. A signal which has a constant power spectral density is defined as *white noise*. It consists of a random sequence of uncorrelated impulses. White noise can only be approximated, since it implies [see (16–15)] an infinite average power.

With the aid of the transforms given by (16–11) and (16–13), an important relationship between the spectral density and correlation function can be obtained. Let us consider the integral

$$\phi_T(\tau) = \frac{1}{2T} \int_{-\infty}^{+\infty} u_T(t) v_T(t + \tau)\, dt. \qquad (16\text{–}29)$$

It follows from (16–7) that

$$\phi_{uv}(\tau) = \lim_{\tau \to \infty} \phi_T(\tau). \qquad (16\text{–}30)$$

If the Fourier transform of (16–29) is taken and the order of integrations interchanged, we obtain

$$\int_{-\infty}^{+\infty} \phi_T(\tau) e^{-j\omega\tau}\, d\tau = \frac{1}{2T} \int_{-\infty}^{+\infty} u_T(t) e^{j\omega t}\left[\int_{-\infty}^{+\infty} v_T(t + \tau) e^{-j\omega(t+\tau)}\, d\tau\right] dt$$

$$= \frac{1}{2T}\, U_T^*(\omega)\, V_T(\omega). \qquad (16\text{–}31)$$

If the limit $T \to \infty$ is now taken, we obtain [see (16–16)]

$$\Phi_{uv}(\omega) = \int_{-\infty}^{+\infty} \phi_{uv}(\tau) e^{-j\omega\tau}\, d\tau.$$

The Fourier transform of the correlation function is the spectral density. The inverse transform is

$$\phi_{uv}(\tau) = \frac{1}{2\pi} \int_{-\infty}^{+\infty} \Phi_{uv}(\omega) e^{j\omega\tau}\, d\omega.$$

16–5 The response of linear systems to random signals. Let us consider a linear system where the input signal $u_T(t)$ is random. By definition of the system transfer function $H(s)$, we have

$$V_T(\omega) = H(j\omega)U_T(\omega).$$

Suppose that the spectral density Φ_{uu} of the input is known and we wish to determine Φ_{vv}. We have, using the definition (16–16)

$$\Phi_{vv}(\omega) = \lim_{T\to\infty} \frac{1}{2T} |V_T|^2 = |H|^2 \lim_{T\to\infty} \frac{1}{2T} |U_T|^2 = |H|^2 \Phi_{uu}(\omega).$$
$$(16\text{–}32)$$

Another important relation is obtained by considering the convolution integral (we do not require the truncated signals here)

$$v(t) = \int_0^\infty u(t - x)h(x)\,dx.$$

Multiplying with $u(t - \tau)$ and taking a time average, we obtain

$$\phi_{uv}(\tau) = \int_0^\infty \phi_{uu}(\tau - x)h(x)\,dx. \qquad (16\text{–}33)$$

The Fourier transform of (16–33) yields [see (16–31)]

$$\Phi_{uv}(\omega) = H(j\omega)\Phi_{uu}(\omega). \qquad (16\text{–}34)$$

Equations (16–33) and (16–34) are useful in problems dealing with the estimation of system dynamics. In these problems the system impulse response $h(t)$ is not known, and the correlation functions are measured experimentally. The spectral densities can be determined from the Fourier transforms of the correlation functions and then $H(j\omega)$ is determined using (16–34).

EXAMPLE 3.   To illustrate the use of (16–32), consider the network shown in Fig. 16–4, where the current source is taken to have a random output. It can, for example, be a noise diode. We assume it to have a constant spectral density which can be normalized to unity, $\Phi_{ii} = 1$. The

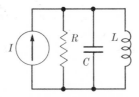

FIG. 16–4. A parallel RLC-network.

transfer function relating the voltage response to the current input is the impedance function

$$Z(s) = Z[p] = \frac{1}{\omega_0 C} \frac{p}{p^2 + 2\zeta p + 1},$$

where $s = \omega_0 p$, $\omega_0^2 L C = 1$, and $2\zeta = \omega_0 L / R$. It follows from (16–32) that

$$\Phi_{vv}(\omega) = |Z(j\omega)|^2 \cdot 1 \tag{16–35}$$

is the spectral density of the voltage response. Suppose that we wish to determine the mean-square value of the voltage. We can do this by substituting (16–35) into (16–15), where, for convenience, we also substitute $\omega = s/j$. This yields

$$\overline{v^2} = \frac{1}{2\pi j} \int_{-j\infty}^{+j\infty} \Phi_{vv}\left(\frac{s}{j}\right) ds$$

$$= \frac{1}{\omega_0 C^2} \frac{1}{2\pi j} \int_{-j\infty}^{+j\infty} \frac{-p^2}{(p^2 + 2\zeta p + 1)} \frac{dp}{(p^2 - 2\zeta p + 1)}. \tag{16–36}$$

This integral can be evaluated by completing the path of integration in either the left or right half of the p-plane with identical results. In the left half of the plane the poles are $p_1 = -\zeta + j\beta$, $p_2 = -\zeta - j\beta$, where $\beta = \sqrt{1 - \zeta^2}$. The residue at p_1 is

$$F(p_1) = \frac{-p_1^2}{(p_1 - p_2)(p_1^2 - 2\zeta p_1 + 1)} \frac{p_2}{p_2} = \frac{p_1}{j 8 \zeta \beta},$$

which can be easily evaluated by multiplying numerator and denominator with p_2 as shown and noting that $p_1 p_2 = 1$. Thus

$$\overline{v^2} = \frac{1}{\omega_0 C^2} \, 2 \operatorname{Re}[F(p_1)] = \frac{R}{2C} \cdot \blacktriangle$$

In general, mean-square values are determined from an integral of the type

$$I = \frac{1}{2\pi j} \int_{-j\infty}^{+j\infty} \frac{G(s)}{F(s)F(-s)} \, ds, \tag{16–37}$$

where

$$F(s) = a_0 s^n + a_1 s^{n-1} + \cdots + a_n$$

and

$$G(s) = b_0 s^{2n-2} + b_1 s^{2n-4} + \cdots + b_{n-1};$$

$G(s)$ is an even function of s. A direct method of evaluating this integral

FIG. 16–5. A servosystem.

is discussed in Appendix E where it is shown that

$$I = \frac{(-1)^n}{2a_0} \frac{\begin{vmatrix} b_0 & a_0 & 0 & 0 & & 0 & 0 & 0 & \cdots & 0 \\ b_1 & a_2 & -a_1 & a_0 & & 0 & 0 & 0 & \cdots & 0 \\ b_2 & a_4 & -a_3 & a_2 & -a_1 & a_0 & 0 & \cdots & 0 \\ & \vdots & & & & & & & \\ b_{n-1} & \cdots & & & & & & (-1)^n a_n \end{vmatrix}}{\begin{vmatrix} -a_1 & a_0 & 0 & 0 & & 0 & 0 & 0 & \cdots & 0 \\ -a_3 & a_2 & -a_1 & a_0 & & 0 & 0 & 0 & \cdots & 0 \\ -a_5 & a_4 & -a_3 & a_2 & -a_1 & a_0 & 0 & \cdots & 0 \\ & \vdots & & & & & & & \\ -a_{2n-1} & \cdots & & & & & & (-1)^n a_n \end{vmatrix}} \qquad (16\text{–}38)$$

It is left as an exercise to evaluate (16–36) using this formula.

EXAMPLE 4. As a final example consider the servosystem shown in Fig. 16–5. Suppose that the input spectral density is

$$\Phi_{uu}\left(\frac{s}{j}\right) = \frac{2Ac}{c^2 - s^2} \qquad (16\text{–}39)$$

(for convenience we express all equations in terms of $s = j\omega$) and that the mean-square error $\overline{\epsilon^2}$ is to be evaluated. The open-loop transfer function is

$$G(s) = \frac{K}{s(1 + \tau s)}. \qquad (16\text{–}40)$$

The transfer function $H_\epsilon(s)$ relating the error to the input, is

$$\frac{E(s)}{U(s)} = \frac{1}{1 + G(s)} = H_\epsilon(s).$$

The spectral density for the error can now be found using (16–32):

$$\Phi_{\epsilon\epsilon}\left(\frac{s}{j}\right) = H_\epsilon(s) H_\epsilon(-s) \Phi_{uu}\left(\frac{s}{j}\right). \qquad (16\text{–}41)$$

The mean-square value can be obtained by substituting (16–39) and

(16–40) into (16–41) and using (16–15) where $u = v = \epsilon$. This takes the form

$$\overline{\epsilon^2} = 2AcI,$$

where I is the integral (16–37) and

$$F(s) = (\tau s^2 + s + K)(s + c) \qquad G(s) = s(1 + \tau s)(-s)(1 - \tau s).$$

The coefficients to be used in (16–38) are (note that $n = 3$)

$$
\begin{array}{lll}
a_0 = \tau, & a_3 = cK, & b_0 = \tau^2, \\
a_1 = 1 + c\tau, & a_4 = a_5 = 0, & b_1 = -1, \\
a_2 = c + K, & & b_2 = 0.
\end{array}
$$

Substituting into (16–38) yields

$$\overline{\epsilon^2} = \frac{Ac[1 + \tau(c + K)]}{c + K + c^2\tau}. \ \blacktriangle$$

Problems

16–1. A first probability density function of the form

$$p_1(x) = \frac{1}{\sigma\sqrt{2\pi}} e^{-x^2/2\sigma^2}$$

is known as a Gaussian distribution function. Show that (a) Pr $(-x \leq v \leq x) = $ erf $(x/\sigma\sqrt{2})$ [see Appendix (C–1)] and (b) $E(v^2) = \sigma^2$ (σ is known as the standard deviation).

16–2. Determine the expected value of the function $f(v) = |v|$ if $p_1(x)$ is the Gaussian distribution given in Problem 16–1.

16–3. If $u(t)$ is a random signal and the ergodic hypothesis is assumed to be valid, show that

$$\frac{d\phi_{uu}(\tau)}{d\tau} = \phi_{uv}(\tau) = E[u(t)v(t + \tau)],$$

where $v(t) = du(t)/dt$.

16–4. A first probability density function of the form

$$p_1(x) = \begin{cases} axe^{-bx^2}, & x > 0, \\ 0, & x < 0, \end{cases}$$

is known as a Rayleigh distribution. (a) Show that we must have $a = 2b$. (b) Prove that the expected value of the function $f(v) = v^2$ is b^{-1}.

16–5. Determine the spectral density of the signal shown in Fig. 16–6, where a pulse $g(t)$ is repeated at the instants of time $kT_0 + a_k$ ($k = -1, 0, 1, 2, \ldots$);

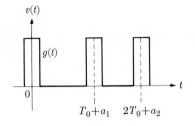

FIGURE 16–6   FIGURE 16–7

T_0 is a fixed period and the a_k's are random uncorrelated variables. Their distribution is given by the probability density function $p_1(a)$ and $\overline{a_k} = 0$.

16–6. A signal $u(t)$ has the correlation function

$$\phi_{uu}(\tau) = Ae^{-c|\tau|}.$$

Prove that the spectral density is given by (16–39).

16–7. The spectral density for the input to the simple RC-filter shown in Fig. 16–7 is

$$\Phi_{uu} = \frac{2Ac}{c^2 + \omega^2}.$$

Compute the value of $\overline{v^2}$.

16–8. If $v(t)$ is the output response of a linear system whose impulse response is $h(t)$, show that

$$\phi_{vv}(\tau) = \int_0^\infty \int_0^\infty \phi_{uu}(\tau + x_1 - x_2)h(x_1)h(x_2)\, dx_1\, dx_2$$

$$= \int_\tau^\infty h(t - \tau)\left[\int_0^\infty \phi_{uu}(t - x)h(x)\, dx\right] dt,$$

where $\phi_{uu}(\tau)$ is the correlation function of the input.

16–9. The input to the simple RC-filter shown in Fig. 16–7 is a stationary random signal whose correlation function is that given in Problem 16–6. (a) Use the integrals given in Problem 16–8 to compute $\phi_{vv}(\tau)$. (b) Compute the spectral density $\Phi_{vv}(\omega)$ from $\phi_{vv}(\tau)$. (c) Determine the output spectral density using (16–32).

16–10. The input to the servosystem shown in Fig. 16–5 is $u(t) + n(t)$, where $n(t)$ is white noise and is uncorrelated with the signal $u(t)$. Determine the increase due to noise in the mean-square error computed in Example 4.

GENERAL REFERENCES

DAVENPORT, W. B., and W. L. ROOT, *An introduction to the Theory of Random Signals and Noise*, McGraw-Hill, New York, 1958.

LANING, J. H., and R. H. BATTIN, *Random Processes in Automatic Control*, McGraw-Hill, New York, 1956.

APPENDIX A

HYPERBOLIC FUNCTIONS

1. $\sinh x = \dfrac{e^x - e^{-x}}{2}$

2. $\cosh x = \dfrac{e^x + e^{-x}}{2}$

3. $\cosh^2 x - \sinh^2 x = 1$

4. $\sinh jx = j \sin x$

5. $\cosh jx = \cos x$

6. $\sinh (x + y) = \sinh x \cosh y + \cosh x \sinh y$

7. $\cosh (x + y) = \cosh x \cosh y + \sinh x \sinh y$

8. $\sinh 2x = 2 \sinh x \cosh x$

9. $\cosh 2x = \cosh^2 x + \sinh^2 x$

10. $\dfrac{d}{dx} (\sinh u) = \cosh u \dfrac{du}{dx}$

11. $\dfrac{d}{dx} (\cosh u) = \sinh u \dfrac{du}{dx}$

12. $\tanh \dfrac{x}{2} = \dfrac{\cosh x - 1}{\sinh x}$

APPENDIX B

LAGUERRE POLYNOMIALS

Laguerre polynomials $L_n(z)$ are defined by

$$L_n(z) = \frac{e^z}{n!} \frac{d^n}{dz^n} (z^n e^{-z}). \tag{B-1}$$

Differentiating this expression leads to the recurrence formula

$$L_{n-1} = \frac{dL_{n-1}}{dz} - \frac{dL_n}{dz}. \tag{B-2}$$

The explicit forms of these polynomials are

$$L_0(z) = 1,$$
$$L_1(z) = -z + 1,$$
$$L_2(z) = \frac{z^2}{2} - 2z + 1,$$
$$L_3(z) = -\tfrac{1}{6}z^3 + \tfrac{3}{2}z^2 - 3z + 1,$$
$$L_4(z) = \tfrac{1}{24}z^4 - \tfrac{2}{3}z^3 + 3z^2 - 4z + 1, \tag{B-3}$$
$$\vdots$$

It follows from (B–3) that $L_n(0) = 1$.
We consider now the function

$$H(s) = \frac{s^n}{(s+a)^{n+1}}. \tag{B-4}$$

This has a pole of order $n + 1$ at $s = -a$. The pole coefficient is $F(s) = s^n e^{st}$. Thus

$$h(t) = \frac{1}{n!} \left[\frac{d^n (s^n e^{st})}{ds^n} \right]_{s=-a}$$

$$= \frac{1}{n!} \left[\frac{d^n (z^n e^{-z})}{dz^n} \right]_{z=+at}, \tag{B-5}$$

where the substitution $z = -st$ has been used. It follows from (B–1) and (B–5) that

$$\mathcal{L}[e^{-at} L_n(at)] = \frac{s^n}{(s+a)^{n+1}}. \tag{B-6}$$

334

If we replace a with $a - b$, we obtain

$$\mathscr{L}[e^{-(a-b)t}L_n\{(a - b)t\}] = \frac{s^n}{(s + a - b)^{n+1}}. \tag{B-7}$$

If s is now replaced by $s + b$, we find with the aid of the s-translation theorem that

$$\mathscr{L}[e^{-at}L_n\{(a - b)t\}] = \frac{(s + b)^n}{(s + a)^{n+1}}. \tag{B-8}$$

Let us consider now the integral

$$v_n(x) = \tfrac{1}{2}\int_0^x e^{-u/2}L_n(u)\,du. \tag{B-9}$$

Using the recurrence formula (B-2) with n replaced by $n + 1$ and integrating by parts yields

$$v_{n+1}(x) = -v_n(x) + e^{-x/2}[L_n(x) - L_{n+1}(x)]. \tag{B-10}$$

This formula can be used to determine the $v_n(x)$ recursively:

$$v_0(x) = 1 - e^{-x/2},$$
$$v_1(x) = -1 + (1 + x)e^{-x/2},$$
$$v_2(x) = 1 - \left(1 + \frac{x^2}{2}\right)e^{-x/2},$$
$$v_3(x) = -1 + \left(1 + x - \frac{x^2}{2} + \frac{x^3}{6}\right)e^{-x/2}, \tag{B-11}$$
$$\vdots$$

APPENDIX C

ERROR FUNCTIONS

The error function erf z is defined by

$$\operatorname{erf} z = \frac{2}{\sqrt{\pi}} \int_0^z e^{-u^2}\, du, \qquad (\text{C--1})$$

and the complementary error function erfc z is defined by

$$\operatorname{erfc} z = 1 - \operatorname{erf} z = \frac{2}{\sqrt{\pi}} \int_z^\infty e^{-u^2}\, du. \qquad (\text{C--2})$$

It can be shown that erf $\infty = 1$.

Substituting $v = u^2$ and integrating successively by parts, we find that

$$\operatorname{erfc} z = \frac{1}{\sqrt{\pi}} \int_{z^2}^\infty e^{-v} \frac{dv}{\sqrt{v}} = \frac{e^{-z^2}}{z\sqrt{\pi}} - \frac{1}{2\sqrt{\pi}} \int_{z^2}^\infty e^{-v} v^{-3/2}\, dv$$

$$= \frac{e^{-z^2}}{z\sqrt{\pi}} \left[1 - \frac{1}{2z^2} + \frac{1 \cdot 3}{(2z^2)^2} + \right.$$

$$\left. \cdots + (-1)^n \frac{1 \cdot 3 \cdots (2n-1)}{(2z^2)^n} \right] + R_n, \qquad (\text{C--3})$$

where the remainder R_n is

$$R_n = (-1)^{n+1} \frac{1 \cdot 3 \cdots (2n+1)}{2^{n+1}\sqrt{\pi}} \int_{z^2}^\infty e^{-v} v^{-(n+3/2)}\, dv. \qquad (\text{C--4})$$

It follows from (C–4) that $\lim_{z \to \infty} R_n = 0$. Thus, if we substitute $t = z^2$, we obtain the asymptotic series

$$e^t \operatorname{erfc} t \sim \frac{1}{\sqrt{\pi t}} \left[1 - \frac{1}{2t} + \frac{1 \cdot 3}{(2t)^2} + \cdots + (-1)^n \frac{1 \cdot 3 \cdots (2n-1)}{(2t)^n} + \cdots \right].$$

$$(\text{C--5})$$

With the aid of (C–2) and the substitution $z = \frac{1}{2}\sqrt{b/t}$, we obtain

$$\frac{d(\operatorname{erfc} z)}{dt} = \frac{1}{2t}\sqrt{\frac{b}{\pi t}}\, e^{-b/4t}. \qquad (\text{C--6})$$

The Laplace transform of (C–6) yields (note that erfc $z = 0$ for $t = 0$)

$$s\mathcal{L}[\operatorname{erfc} z] = \frac{1}{2}\sqrt{\frac{b}{\pi}} \int_0^\infty \frac{e^{-b/4t} e^{-st}}{t\sqrt{t}}\, dt. \qquad (\text{C--7})$$

336

This integral can be evaluated with the aid of (14–11). Using the substitution $\alpha^2 = a$, we find that

$$\frac{e^{-\alpha\sqrt{s}}}{\sqrt{s}} = \frac{1}{\sqrt{\pi}} \int_0^\infty \frac{e^{-\alpha^2/4t} e^{-st}}{\sqrt{t}} \, dt. \tag{C-8}$$

Differentiating this with respect to α, we obtain

$$e^{-\alpha\sqrt{s}} = \frac{\alpha}{2\sqrt{\pi}} \int_0^\infty \frac{e^{-\alpha^2/4t}}{t\sqrt{t}} e^{-st} \, dt. \tag{C-9}$$

Comparing (C–7) and (C–9) yields

$$\mathcal{L}\left[\operatorname{erfc} \frac{1}{2}\sqrt{\frac{b}{t}}\right] = \frac{e^{-\sqrt{bs}}}{s}. \tag{C-10}$$

Consider the substitution $z = \pm\sqrt{bt} + \frac{1}{2}\sqrt{a/t}$. We have

$$\frac{d(\operatorname{erfc} z)}{dt} = -\frac{2}{\sqrt{\pi}} \left[e^{-(bt\pm\sqrt{ab}+a/4t)}\right]\left[\pm\frac{1}{2}\sqrt{\frac{b}{t}} - \frac{1}{4t}\sqrt{\frac{a}{t}}\right]. \tag{C-11}$$

Thus (note that $\operatorname{erfc} z = 0$ for $t = 0$)

$$s\mathcal{L}[\operatorname{erfc} z] = \mp \sqrt{\frac{b}{\pi}} e^{\mp\sqrt{ab}} \int_0^\infty e^{-(st+bt+a/4t)} \frac{dt}{\sqrt{t}}$$

$$+ \frac{1}{2}\sqrt{\frac{a}{\pi}} e^{\mp\sqrt{ab}} \int_0^\infty e^{-(st+bt+a/4t)} \frac{dt}{t\sqrt{t}}. \tag{C-12}$$

Equations (C–8) and (C–9) can be used to evaluate the integrals in (C–12). Thus

$$s\mathcal{L}[\operatorname{erfc} z] = \mp\sqrt{b}\, e^{\mp\sqrt{ab}} \frac{e^{-\sqrt{a(s+b)}}}{\sqrt{s+b}} + e^{\mp\sqrt{ab}} e^{-\sqrt{a(s+b)}}$$

$$= e^{\mp\sqrt{ab}-\sqrt{a(s+b)}}\left[1 \mp \sqrt{\frac{b}{s+b}}\right]. \tag{C-13}$$

If we let

$$z_1 = \sqrt{bt} + \frac{1}{2}\sqrt{\frac{a}{t}}$$

and

$$z_2 = -\sqrt{bt} + \frac{1}{2}\sqrt{\frac{a}{t}}, \tag{C-14}$$

we obtain, with the aid of (C–13),

$$e^{\sqrt{ab}}\mathcal{L}[\operatorname{erfc} z_1] + e^{-\sqrt{ab}}\mathcal{L}[\operatorname{erfc} z_2] = \frac{2}{s} e^{-\sqrt{a(s+b)}}. \tag{C-15}$$

Choosing $z = z_1$ in (C–13) gives

$$\mathcal{L}[\text{erfc } z_1] = \frac{e^{-\sqrt{ab}-\sqrt{a(s+b)}}}{s}\left[1 - \sqrt{\frac{b}{s+b}}\right]. \qquad \text{(C–16)}$$

Replacing $s + b$ by s and applying the s-translation theorem, we find that

$$\mathcal{L}[e^{bt}\text{ erfc } z_1] = \frac{e^{-\sqrt{ab}-\sqrt{as}}}{s-b}\left[\frac{\sqrt{s}-\sqrt{b}}{\sqrt{s}}\right] = \frac{e^{-(\sqrt{ab}+\sqrt{as})}}{\sqrt{s}(\sqrt{s}+\sqrt{b})}. \qquad \text{(C–17)}$$

We consider now the substitution $z = \sqrt{at}$. We have

$$\frac{d(\text{erf } z)}{dt} = \sqrt{\frac{a}{\pi t}}\, e^{-at}. \qquad \text{(C–18)}$$

Thus (note that erf $z = 0$ for $t = 0$)

$$s\mathcal{L}[\text{erf } z] = \sqrt{\frac{a}{\pi}}\int_0^\infty \frac{e^{-at}e^{-st}}{\sqrt{t}}\, dt = \sqrt{\frac{a}{s+a}}, \qquad \text{(C–19)}$$

where we have used

$$\mathcal{L}\left[\frac{1}{\sqrt{\pi t}}\right] = \frac{1}{\sqrt{s}}$$

[see (14–11), taking $a = 0$]. Thus

$$\mathcal{L}[\text{erf }\sqrt{at}] = \frac{1}{s}\sqrt{\frac{a}{s+a}}. \qquad \text{(C–20)}$$

Using the same substitution $z = \sqrt{at}$, we find that

$$\frac{d(\text{erfc } z)}{dt} = -\sqrt{\frac{a}{\pi t}}\, e^{-at}. \qquad \text{(C–21)}$$

Thus (note that erfc $z = 1$ for $t = 0$)

$$s\mathcal{L}[\text{erfc } z] = 1 - \sqrt{\frac{a}{\pi}}\int_0^\infty \frac{e^{-at}e^{-st}}{\sqrt{t}}\, dt = 1 - \sqrt{\frac{a}{s+a}}. \qquad \text{(C–22)}$$

From (C–22) we obtain

$$\mathcal{L}[\text{erfc }\sqrt{at}] = \frac{1}{s}\frac{\sqrt{s+a}-\sqrt{a}}{\sqrt{s+a}}. \qquad \text{(C–23)}$$

Replacing s by $s + a$ and applying the s-translation theorem gives

$$\mathcal{L}[e^{at}\text{ erfc }\sqrt{at}] = \left(\frac{1}{s-a}\right)\left(\frac{\sqrt{s}-\sqrt{a}}{\sqrt{s}}\right) = \frac{1}{\sqrt{s}\,(\sqrt{s}+\sqrt{a})}. \qquad \text{(C–24)}$$

If we replace s by $s + b$ in (14–11) and apply the s-translation theorem, we find that

$$\mathcal{L}^{-1}\left[\frac{e^{-\sqrt{a(s+b)}}}{\sqrt{s+b}}\right] = \frac{e^{-(bt+a/4t)}}{\sqrt{\pi t}}, \qquad t > 0. \qquad \text{(C–25)}$$

Equation (C–25) (with $a = 0$) and the convolution theorem can be used to obtain

$$\mathcal{L}^{-1}\left[\frac{1}{s}\frac{1}{\sqrt{s+b}}\right] = \int_0^t \frac{e^{-b\tau}}{\sqrt{\pi\tau}} \, d\tau = \frac{1}{\sqrt{b}} \operatorname{erf}\sqrt{bt}, \qquad t > 0, \qquad \text{(C–26)}$$

and

$$\mathcal{L}^{-1}\left[\frac{\sqrt{s+b}}{s+a}\right] = \mathcal{L}^{-1}\left[\left(1 + \frac{b-a}{s+a}\right)\frac{1}{\sqrt{s+b}}\right]$$

$$= \frac{e^{-bt}}{\sqrt{\pi t}} + \sqrt{(b-a)}\, e^{-at} \operatorname{erf}\sqrt{(b-a)t}, \qquad t > 0. \qquad \text{(C–27)}$$

We consider now the identity

$$\frac{1}{\sqrt{a(s+b)} + \sqrt{c(s+d)}} = \frac{1}{a-c}\frac{1}{s+\alpha}[\sqrt{a(s+b)} - \sqrt{c(s+d)}],$$

where

$$\alpha = \frac{ab-cd}{a-c}.$$

With the aid of (C–27) we obtain

$$\mathcal{L}^{-1}\left[\frac{1}{\sqrt{a(s+b)} + \sqrt{c(s+d)}}\right] = \frac{1}{a-c}\left[\sqrt{\frac{a}{\pi t}}\, e^{-bt} - \sqrt{\frac{c}{\pi t}}\, e^{-dt}\right]$$

$$+ \frac{\sqrt{ack}}{a-c}\, e^{-\alpha t}[\operatorname{erfc}\sqrt{akt} - \operatorname{erfc}\sqrt{ckt}], \qquad t > 0, \qquad \text{(C–28)}$$

where

$$k = \frac{d-b}{a-c}.$$

APPENDIX D

BESSEL FUNCTIONS

The solutions of the second-order differential equation

$$\frac{d^2 J_n}{dz^2} + \frac{1}{z}\frac{dJ_n}{dz} + \left(1 - \frac{n^2}{z^2}\right) J_n = 0 \tag{D-1}$$

are known as Bessel functions. It can be shown by direct substitution that the series

$$J_n = J_n(z) = \sum_{k=0}^{\infty} \frac{(-1)^k z^{n+2k}}{2^{n+2k} k! \Gamma(n + k + 1)} \tag{D-2}$$

satisfies (D-1). Here J_n is known as the Bessel function of the first kind of order n. The *gamma function* $\Gamma(n)$ satisfies the relations

$$\Gamma(n + 1) = n\Gamma(n),$$

$$\Gamma(1) = 1, \qquad \Gamma(\tfrac{1}{2}) = \sqrt{\pi}. \tag{D-3}$$

By means of (D-2) and (D-3), the recurrence formulas

$$\frac{d(z^{-n} J_n)}{dz} = -z^{-n} J_{n+1} \tag{D-4a}$$

and

$$J_{n-1} + J_{n+1} = \frac{2n}{z} J_n \tag{D-4b}$$

can be obtained. Equation (D-4a) yields

$$\frac{dJ_n}{dz} = \frac{n}{z} J_n - J_{n+1}. \tag{D-4c}$$

With the aid of (D-4b) and (D-4c) it is easy to derive

$$\frac{dJ_n}{dz} = \tfrac{1}{2}(J_{n-1} - J_{n+1}) \tag{D-4d}$$

and

$$\frac{dJ_n}{dz} = J_{n-1} - \frac{n}{z} J_n. \tag{D-4e}$$

For the subsequent discussion the following theorem is required. If

$$F(s) = \mathcal{L}[f(t)] = \int_0^\infty f(t)e^{-st}\, dt,$$

then

$$-\frac{dF}{ds} = \int_0^t tf(t)e^{-st}\, dt = \mathcal{L}[tf(t)]. \tag{D-5}$$

Thus multiplication by t in the time domain represents the operation $-d/ds$ in the s-domain.

Consider now Bessel's equation (D-1) which, with $n = 0$, can be put into the form

$$\frac{d}{dt}\left(t\frac{dJ_0}{dt}\right) + tJ_0 = 0. \tag{D-6}$$

Let $F_0 = \mathcal{L}[J_0(t)]$ denote the Laplace transform of $J_0(t)$. It follows from (D-2) that $J_0(0) = 1$. Thus

$$\mathcal{L}\left[\frac{dJ_0}{dt}\right] = sF_0 - 1.$$

Applying theorem (D-5) to (D-6) yields the transformed equation

$$s\left[-\frac{d}{ds}(sF_0 - 1)\right] - \frac{dF_0}{ds} = 0.$$

The solution of this equation is $F_0 = CR^{-1}$, where $R^2 = s^2 + 1$. To determine the constant C we use the initial-value theorem, which yields

$$J_0(0) = 1 = \lim_{s\to\infty} sF_0 = C.$$

Thus

$$F_0 = \mathcal{L}[J_0(t)] = \frac{1}{\sqrt{s^2 + 1}}. \tag{D-7}$$

Consider now the recurrence formula (D-4d). Since $J_n(0) = 0$ for $n \geq 1$, it follows that

$$F_{n+1} = F_{n-1} - 2sF_n, \tag{D-8}$$

where

$$F_n = \mathcal{L}[J_n(t)].$$

Equation (D-8) is satisfied by

$$F_n = \frac{(R - s)^n}{R} = \frac{(\sqrt{s^2 + 1} - s)^n}{\sqrt{s^2 + 1}} = \frac{(\sqrt{s^2 + 1} + s)^{-n}}{\sqrt{s^2 + 1}}. \tag{D-9}$$

From the recurrence formula (D–4c) we obtain

$$\mathcal{L}\left[n\frac{J_n(t)}{t}\right] = sF_n + F_{n+1} = (R - s)^n$$
$$= (\sqrt{s^2 + 1} - s)^n = (\sqrt{s^2 + 1} + s)^{-n}. \quad \text{(D–10)}$$

The scaling theorem can then be applied to (D–9) and (D–10) to obtain

$$\mathcal{L}\left[\frac{1}{a^n}J_n(at)\right] = \frac{(\sqrt{s^2 + a^2} + s)^{-n}}{\sqrt{s^2 + a^2}}, \quad \text{(D–11a)}$$

$$\mathcal{L}\left[\frac{nJ_n(at)}{a^nt}\right] = (\sqrt{s^2 + a^2} + s)^{-n}. \quad \text{(D–11b)}$$

If $n = \frac{1}{2}$, it can be shown by direct substitution that

$$J_{1/2}(z) = \sqrt{\frac{2}{\pi z}}\sin z. \quad \text{(D–12)}$$

It follows from the recurrence formula (D–4a) that

$$z^{-n-2}J_{n+2} = \frac{d}{z\,dz}(-z^{-n-1}J_{n+1}) = \left(\frac{d}{z\,dz}\right)\left(\frac{d}{z\,dz}\right)(z^{-n}J_n).$$

Thus, if k is any positive integer,

$$z^{-n-k}J_{n+k} = (-1)^k\left(\frac{d}{z\,dz}\right)^k(z^{-n}J_n).$$

Applying this result to (D–12) yields

$$J_{k+1/2}(z) = (-1)^k\sqrt{\frac{2}{\pi}}z^{k+1/2}\left(\frac{d}{z\,dz}\right)^k\left(\frac{\sin z}{z}\right). \quad \text{(D–13)}$$

From (D–11a) we obtain, for $n = 0$,

$$\mathcal{L}[J_0(at)] = \frac{1}{R}, \quad \text{(D–14)}$$

where we have set $R = \sqrt{s^2 + a^2}$. We let $z = at$ and consider the operation

$$\frac{1}{a}\frac{df(z)}{da} = t^2z^{-1}\frac{df(z)}{dz}.$$

Thus, if this operation is performed on (D–14), we obtain

$$\mathcal{L}\left[-t^2z^{-1}\frac{dJ_0}{dz}\right] = \mathcal{L}[t^2z^{-1}J_1] = R^{-3},$$

where the recurrence formula (D–4a) has been used. Performing this operation n times yields

$$\mathcal{L}[t^n J_n(at)] = 1 \cdot 3 \cdots (2n - 1) a^n R^{-(2n+1)}$$

$$= \frac{(2a)^n \Gamma(n + \frac{1}{2})}{\sqrt{\pi}} R^{-(2n+1)}. \tag{D–15}$$

This has been proved for the case where n is an integer. It follows from (D–2) that J_n is an analytic function of n. Considering (D–15) in this manner, we see that the left-hand side, and thus the right-hand side, can be extended to nonintegral values of n. If, in particular, n is replaced by $n + \frac{1}{2}$, we obtain

$$\mathcal{L}[t^{n+1/2} J_{n+1/2}(at)] = \frac{(2a)^{n+1/2}}{\sqrt{\pi}} n! \frac{1}{(s^2 + a^2)^{n+1}}. \tag{D–16}$$

Substituting $s = ja$ into (D–9) yields

$$\frac{(ja + \sqrt{1 - a^2})^{-n}}{\sqrt{1 - a^2}} = \int_0^\infty e^{-jat} J_n(t) \, dt. \tag{D–17}$$

Thus

$$\mathrm{Re}\left[\frac{(ja + \sqrt{1 - a^2})^{-n}}{\sqrt{1 - a^2}}\right] = \int_0^\infty \cos at \, J_n(at) \, dt,$$

$$\mathrm{Im}\left[\frac{(ja + \sqrt{1 - a^2})^{-n}}{\sqrt{1 - a^2}}\right] = -\int_0^\infty \sin at \, J_n(at) \, dt.$$

If $a < 1$, we can set $e^{j\theta} = \sqrt{1 - a^2} + ja$ where $\sin \theta = a$. Thus

$$\int_0^\infty \cos at \, J_n(t) \, dt = \frac{\cos n\theta}{\sqrt{1 - a^2}}, \tag{D–18a}$$

$$\int_0^\infty \sin at \, J_n(t) \, dt = \frac{\sin n\theta}{\sqrt{1 - a^2}}. \tag{D–18b}$$

If $a > 1$, we use $j^{n+1} = e^{(\pi/2)(n+1)j}$ to obtain

$$\int_0^\infty \cos at \, J_n(t) \, dt = - \frac{\sin(\pi n/2)}{(a + \sqrt{a^2 - 1})^n \sqrt{a^2 - 1}}, \tag{D–19a}$$

$$\int_0^\infty \sin at \, J_n(t) \, dt = \frac{\cos(\pi n/2)}{(a + \sqrt{a^2 - 1})^n \sqrt{a^2 - 1}}. \tag{D–19b}$$

If $a = 0$, (D–17) yields

$$\int_0^\infty J_n(t)\, dt = 1. \tag{D–20}$$

We consider the function $f(t)$ defined by

$$(-1)^m f(t) = -J_0 + 2J_2 + \cdots + (-1)^{m+1} 2J_{2m}. \tag{D–21}$$

Differentiating and using the recurrence formula (D–4d) yields

$$(-1)^m \frac{df}{dt} = 2J_1 - 2J_3 + \cdots + (-1)^{m+1} 2J_{2m-1} - (-1)^{m+1} J_{2m+1}.$$

A second differentiation yields

$$(-1) \frac{d^2 f}{dt^2} = J_0 - 2J_2 + \cdots - (-1)^{m+1} 2J_{2m}$$
$$+ (-1)^{m+1} \left(J_{2m} - \frac{dJ_{2m+1}}{dt} \right). \tag{D–22}$$

Thus, adding (D–21) and (D–22),

$$\frac{d^2 f}{dt^2} + f = -J_{2m} + \frac{dJ_{2m+1}}{dt}. \tag{D–23}$$

Let us consider now the function $g(t)$ defined by

$$g(t) = tJ_{2m+1}. \tag{D–24}$$

Differentiating and using the recurrence formula (D–4e) yields

$$\frac{dg}{dt} = tJ_{2m} - 2mJ_{2m+1}.$$

A second differentiation and use of the recurrence formula (D–4c) yields

$$\frac{d^2 g}{dt^2} = J_{2m} + 2mJ_{2m} - tJ_{2m+1} - 2m \frac{dJ_{2m+1}}{dt}. \tag{D–25}$$

Adding (D–24) and (D–25) yields

$$\frac{d^2 g}{dt^2} + g = J_{2m} + 2m \left(J_{2m} - \frac{dJ_{2m+1}}{dt} \right). \tag{D–26}$$

It follows from (D–23) and (D–26) that the function $f_p = g + 2mf$ is a particular integral of the differential equation

$$\frac{d^2 f_p}{dt^2} + f_p = J_{2m}, \tag{D–27}$$

which satisfies the initial conditions $f_p(0) = -(-1)^m 2m$ and $f_p'(0) = 0$.

Let $S(t)$ be the solution of (D–27) which satisfies the initial conditions $S(0) = S'(0) = 0$. This can be obtained either by means of the convolution theorem

$$S(t) = \int_0^t \sin(t - u) J_{2m}(u) \, du$$

or by the fact that the general solution of (D–27) consists of the sum of a particular integral and the characteristic function $c_1 \cos t + s_1 \sin t$. The solution meeting the specified initial conditions is

$$S(t) = (-1)^m 2m \cos t + f_p(t).$$

Thus

$$\int_0^t \sin(t - u) J_{2m}(u) \, du = t J_{2m+1}(t) + (-1)^m 2m$$

$$\times [\cos t - J_0(t) + 2J_2(t) + \cdots + (-1)^{m+1} 2J_{2m}(t)]. \qquad \text{(D–28)}$$

Let us consider (D–9) in the form

$$F_n = \frac{(R + s)^{-n}}{R}.$$

Differentiating with respect to s yields

$$\frac{F_{n-1}}{R^2} = -\frac{dF_n}{ds} - (n - 1)\frac{1}{R} F_n. \qquad \text{(D–29)}$$

The inverse transform of (D–29) is

$$\mathcal{L}^{-1}\left[\frac{1}{s^2 + 1} \frac{(\sqrt{s^2 + 1} + s)^{-n-1}}{\sqrt{s^2 + 1}}\right]$$

$$= t J_n(t) - (n - 1)\int_0^t J_0(t - u) J_n(u) \, du, \qquad \text{(D–30)}$$

where the convolution theorem and (D–5) and (D–9) have been used.

We consider now the function $f(t) = J_0(z)$, where $z = 2\sqrt{t}$. It can be shown by differentiating twice with respect to t and using (D–6) that $f(t)$ satisfies the differential equation

$$\frac{d}{dt}\left(t \frac{df}{dt}\right) + f = 0, \qquad \text{(D–31)}$$

where $f(0) = J_0(0) = 1$. Transforming (D–31) into the s-domain and using theorem (D–5) yields

$$s\left[-\frac{d}{ds}(sF-1)\right]+F=0,\qquad \frac{dF}{ds}+\frac{s-1}{s^2}F=0.$$

The solution is $F=(C/s)e^{-1/s}$. The initial-value theorem can be used to show that $C=1$. Thus

$$J_0(2\sqrt{t})=\frac{1}{2\pi j}\int_{c-j\infty}^{c+j\infty}e^{st-1/s}\frac{ds}{s}.$$

The scaling theorem can be used to show that

$$\mathcal{L}[J_0(2\sqrt{ut})]=\frac{1}{s}e^{-u/s}. \tag{D–32}$$

We consider now the function

$$h(t)=\int_0^\infty J_0(2\sqrt{ut})\frac{dg(u)}{du}\,du. \tag{D–33}$$

Taking the Laplace transform and using (D–32) yields

$$H(s)=\int_0^\infty \frac{1}{s}e^{-u/s}\frac{dg(u)}{du}\,du.$$

Thus

$$H\left(\frac{1}{s}\right)=s\int_0^\infty e^{-su}\frac{dg(u)}{du}\,du=s[sG(s)-g(0)].$$

If $g(0)=0$, we obtain

$$H\left(\frac{1}{s}\right)=s^2 G(s). \tag{D–34}$$

If the argument, z, in (D–2) is pure imaginary, it is more convenient to deal with the modified Bessel function defined by

$$I_n(z)=j^{-n}J_n(jz), \tag{D–35a}$$

which is real for z real. The differential equation (D–1) and the recurrence formulas (D–4a), (D–4b), and (D–4e) are now

$$\frac{d^2 I_n}{dz^2}+\frac{1}{z}\frac{dI_n}{dz}-\left(1+\frac{n^2}{z^2}\right)I_n=0, \tag{D–35b}$$

$$\frac{d}{dz}(z^{-n}I_n)=z^{-n}I_{n+1}, \tag{D–35c}$$

$$I_{n-1}-I_{n+1}=\frac{2n}{z}I_n, \tag{D–35d}$$

$$\frac{d}{dz}(z^n I_n)=z^n I_{n-1}. \tag{D–35e}$$

If $n = 0$, we have $I_0(z) = J_0(jz)$. Thus, if we replace u by $-a^2u/4$ in (D–32), we obtain

$$\mathcal{L}[I_0(a\sqrt{ut})] = \frac{e^{a^2u/4s}}{s}. \tag{D–36}$$

Taking the inverse transform of (D–36) and substituting $t = 1$ yields

$$I_0(a\sqrt{u}) = \frac{1}{2\pi j} \int_{c-j\infty}^{c+j\infty} e^{p+a^2u/4p} \frac{dp}{p}, \tag{D–37}$$

where, for convenience, we have used p for the complex variable.

Let us consider now the problem of evaluating the integral

$$f(t, b) = \frac{1}{2\pi j} \int_{c-j\infty}^{c+j\infty} \frac{e^{st-b\sqrt{s^2-a^2}}}{\sqrt{s^2 - a^2}} ds. \tag{D–38}$$

The similarity of (D–37) and (D–38) suggests a change of variables. Let

$$\frac{dp}{p} = \frac{ds}{\sqrt{s^2 - a^2}},$$

which has the solution

$$p = k(s + \sqrt{s^2 - a^2}). \tag{D–39}$$

Equating coefficients of the exponentials in (D–37) and (D–38) yields

$$p + \frac{a^2u}{4p} = st - b\sqrt{s^2 - a^2}. \tag{D–40}$$

Substituting (D–39) into (D–40) and comparing terms yields the two equations

$$\frac{u}{4k} - k = b, \qquad \frac{u}{4k} + k = t,$$

which can be solved for u and k. This yields $k = (t - b)/2$ and $u = 2k(b + t) = t^2 - b^2$. Since $\sqrt{u}$ is to be real, we must have $t > b$. Thus, by means of the substitution (D–39) the integral (D–37) is transformed into (D–38) so that $f(t, b) = I_0(a\sqrt{t^2 - b^2})$ for $t > b$.

For large s the integrand behaves like $e^{s(t-b)}/s$. Thus, if $t < b$, the path of integration can be completed in the right half of the s-plane. Since no singularities are enclosed, it follows from Cauchy's theorem that $f(t, b) = 0$. Thus

$$\mathcal{L}[u(t - b)I_0(a\sqrt{t^2 - b^2})] = \frac{e^{-b\sqrt{s^2-a^2}}}{\sqrt{s^2 - a^2}} = \mathcal{L}[f(t, b)], \tag{D–41}$$

where $u(t)$ is the unit-step function.

We now set $b = u$ in (D–38) and consider the function

$$h(t) = \int_0^t f(t, u) \frac{dg(u)}{du} \, du = \int_0^\infty f(t, u) \frac{dg(u)}{du} \, du,$$

where the latter result follows from the fact that $f(t, u) = 0$ for $t < u$. The Laplace transform of $h(t)$ is, using (D–41),

$$H(s) = \int_0^\infty \frac{e^{-u\sqrt{s^2 - a^2}}}{\sqrt{s^2 - a^2}} \frac{dg(u)}{du} \, du. \tag{D–42}$$

Thus

$$H(\sqrt{s^2 + a^2}) = \frac{1}{s} \int_0^\infty e^{-su} \frac{dg(u)}{du} \, du = \frac{1}{s} [sG(s) - g(0)].$$

If $g(0) = 0$, we obtain

$$H(\sqrt{s^2 + a^2}) = G(s),$$

where

$$h(t) = \int_0^t I_0(a\sqrt{t^2 - u^2}) \frac{dg(u)}{du} \, du. \tag{D–43}$$

If we replace t by $t + b$, the t-translation theorem requires that the factor e^{bs} be introduced in the Laplace transform. Thus (D–41) will then have the form

$$\mathcal{L}[I_0(z)] = \frac{e^{b(s - \sqrt{s^2 - a^2})}}{\sqrt{s^2 - a^2}}, \tag{D–44}$$

where

$$z = a\sqrt{(t + b)^2 - b^2}. \tag{D–45}$$

It follows from (D–45) that

$$\frac{\partial z}{\partial b} = a^2 t z^{-1}.$$

Differentiating (D–44) with respect to b gives

$$\mathcal{L}\left[\frac{dI_0}{dz} a^2 t z^{-1}\right] = a^2 \mathcal{L}\left[\left(\frac{t}{z}\right) I_1\right] = \frac{(s - \sqrt{s^2 - a^2})}{\sqrt{s^2 - a^2}} e^{b(s - \sqrt{s^2 - a^2})},$$

where the recurrence formula (D–35c) has been used. After n successive differentiations we obtain

$$a^{2n} \mathcal{L}\left[\left(\frac{t}{z}\right)^n I_n(z)\right] = \frac{(s - \sqrt{s^2 - a^2})^n e^{b(s - \sqrt{s^2 - a^2})}}{\sqrt{s^2 - a^2}}. \tag{D–46}$$

If we now replace t with $t - b$ and apply the t-translation theorem, we see that a factor e^{-bs} is introduced on the right-hand side of (D–46). Thus

$$a^n \mathcal{L}\left[u(t-b)\left(\frac{t-b}{t+b}\right)^{n/2} I_n(a\sqrt{t^2-b^2})\right] = \frac{(s-\sqrt{s^2-a^2})^n e^{-b\sqrt{s^2-a^2}}}{\sqrt{s^2-a^2}}.$$

(D–47)

The inverse transform of (D–41) can be written in the form

$$\frac{e^{-b\sqrt{s^2-a^2}}}{\sqrt{s^2-a^2}} = \int_b^\infty I_0(a\sqrt{t^2-b^2})e^{-st}\,dt.$$

Differentiating with respect to b gives

$$-e^{-b\sqrt{s^2-a^2}} = -e^{-bs} + \int_b^\infty \frac{dI_0(z)}{dz}\frac{dz}{db}e^{-st}\,dt,$$

where $z = a\sqrt{t^2-b^2}$. Since

$$\frac{dI_0(z)}{dz} = I_1(z),$$

we obtain

$$a^2 b \mathcal{L}\left[u(t-b)\frac{1}{z}I_1(a\sqrt{t^2-b^2})\right] = e^{-b\sqrt{s^2-a^2}} - e^{-bs}. \qquad \text{(D–48)}$$

Consider now (14–11) which, taking $a = 0$, gives

$$\frac{1}{\sqrt{t}} = \Gamma\left(\frac{1}{2}\right)\frac{1}{2\pi j}\int_{c-j\infty}^{c+j\infty} e^{st}s^{-1/2}\,ds,$$

where we have set [see (D–3)] $\sqrt{\pi} = \Gamma(\frac{1}{2})$. Integration by parts yields

$$\frac{1}{\sqrt{t}} = \frac{1}{t}\Gamma\left(\frac{3}{2}\right)\frac{1}{2\pi j}\int_{c-j\infty}^{c+j\infty} e^{st}s^{-3/2}\,ds,$$

where we have set $\Gamma(\frac{3}{2}) = \frac{1}{2}\Gamma(\frac{1}{2})$. Integrating by parts n times, we find that

$$\frac{t^{n-1/2}}{\Gamma(n+\frac{1}{2})} = \frac{1}{2\pi j}\int_{c-j\infty}^{c+j\infty}\frac{e^{st}}{s^{n+1/2}}\,ds. \qquad \text{(D–49)}$$

This formula has been proven for integral values of n. However, it can be shown to be valid for all n where $\text{Re}[n] > -\frac{1}{2}$.

Consider now the problem of determining the asymptotic expansion for $J_n(t)$. The inverse transform of (D–15) is, taking $a = 1$,

$$t^n J_n(t) = \frac{2^n \Gamma(n+\frac{1}{2})}{\sqrt{\pi}}\frac{1}{2\pi j}\int_{c-j\infty}^{c+j\infty}\frac{e^{st}}{(s^2+1)^{n+1/2}}\,ds.$$

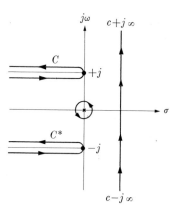

FIGURE D–1

The branch points of the integrand are the roots of $s^2 + 1 = 0$. To make the integrand into a single-valued function of s, branch cuts of the type shown in Fig. D–1 are required. The integral can then be transformed into two integrals taken around the branch cuts along the paths C and C^*. We consider the integral along the path C and let $s = j + p$. It follows that

$$(s^2 + 1) = (s + j)(s - j) = j2p\left(1 - j\,\frac{p}{2}\right)$$

$$(s^2 + 1)^{n+1/2} = p^{n+1/2}2^{n+1/2}e^{j(2n+1)\pi/4}\left(1 - j\,\frac{p}{2}\right)^{n+1/2},$$

where we have used $j = e^{\pi j/2}$. Thus, if we let $t^n I_n$ denote this integral,

$$t^n I_n = \frac{\Gamma(n + \frac{1}{2})}{\sqrt{2\pi}}\,e^{j[t-(2n+1)\pi/4]}\,\frac{1}{2\pi j}\int_C \frac{e^{pt}}{p^{n+1/2}}\left(1 - j\,\frac{p}{2}\right)^{-n-1/2}dp.$$

$$(D\text{–}50)$$

On the path C, $\mathrm{Re}[p] < 0$; thus, for large t, the contribution to the integral comes mainly from a small region near $p = 0$. In this region we can use the Taylor expansion

$$\left(1 - j\,\frac{p}{2}\right)^{-n-1/2} = 1 + a_2p^2 + a_4p^4 + \cdots + j(b_1p + b_3p^3 + \cdots),$$

where

$$b_1 = \frac{2n + 1}{2^2}, \qquad a_2 = -\frac{(2n + 1)(2n + 3)}{2!2^4},$$

$$b_3 = -\frac{(2n + 1)(2n + 3)(2n + 5)}{3!2^6},$$

$$a_4 = \frac{(2n + 1)(2n + 3)(2n + 5)(2n + 7)}{4!2^8}.$$

The integral in (D–50) can then be written as

$$\frac{1}{2\pi j}\int_C \frac{e^{pt}}{p^{n+1/2}}\,[1 + a_2 p^2 + a_4 p^4 + \cdots + j(b_1 p + b_3 p^3 + \cdots)]\,dp$$

$$\sim \left[1 + a_2 \frac{d^2}{dt^2} + a_4 \frac{d^4}{dt^4} + \cdots + j\left(b_1 \frac{d}{dt} + b_3 \frac{d^3}{dt^3} + \cdots\right)\right]$$

$$\times \frac{1}{2\pi j}\int_C \frac{e^{pt}}{p^{n+1/2}}\,dp. \qquad (D–51)$$

The formal equivalence of the last two expressions can be seen by differentiating under the integral sign. By transforming the path C, it can be seen that the two integrals on the right-hand sides of (D–49) and (D–51) are identical. Thus

$$I_n = \frac{e^{j[t-(2n+1)\pi/4]}}{\sqrt{2\pi}}\,(U_n + jV_n), \qquad (D–52)$$

where

$$U_n \sim t^{-n}\left(1 + a_2 \frac{d^2}{dt^2} + a_4 \frac{d^4}{dt^4} + \cdots\right)t^{n-1/2}$$

$$= \frac{1}{\sqrt{t}}\left(1 - \frac{(4n^2 - 1)(4n^2 - 9)}{2!\,2^6}\frac{1}{t^2} + \cdots\right),$$

$$V_n \sim t^{-n}\left(b_1 \frac{d}{dt} + b_3 \frac{d^3}{dt^3} + \cdots\right)t^{n-1/2}$$

$$= \frac{1}{\sqrt{t}}\left(\frac{4n^2 - 1}{2^3}\frac{1}{t} - \frac{(4n^2 - 1)(4n^2 - 9)(4n^2 - 25)}{3!\,2^9}\frac{1}{t^3} + \cdots\right).$$

The integral along the path C^* is similarly evaluated by means of the substitution $s = -j + p$. The result can be obtained by replacing j with $-j$ in (D–52). Thus

$$J_n(t) \sim I_n + I_n^* = 2\,\mathrm{Re}[I_n]$$

$$\sim \sqrt{\frac{2}{\pi}}\left[U_n \cos\left(t - \frac{2n+1}{4}\pi\right) - V_n \sin\left(t - \frac{2n+1}{4}\pi\right)\right]. \qquad (D–53)$$

Let us consider now the function

$$G_n(s) = \frac{1}{s}\frac{(s + \sqrt{1 + s^2})^{-2n}}{\sqrt{1 + s^2}} = \frac{F_{2n}(s)}{s},$$

which has a simple pole at $s = 0$ and branch points at $s = \pm j$ (see Fig. D–1) and where (D–9) has been used. The inverse transform of $G_n(s)$ can be evaluated by transforming the path of integration given by $c + j\omega$,

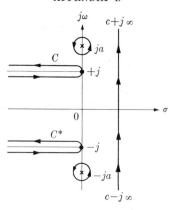

FIGURE D-2

into a contour enclosing the pole at the origin and paths C and C^* along the branch cuts. Thus

$$g_n(t) = 1 + \frac{1}{2\pi j} \int_{C+C^*} \frac{F_{2n}(s)}{s} e^{st} \, ds. \tag{D-54}$$

To evaluate this integral we first consider the inverse transform of (D-9)

$$J_n(t) = \frac{1}{2\pi j} \int_{C+C^*} F_n(s) e^{st} \, ds = 2 \, \mathrm{Re} \left[\frac{1}{2\pi j} \int_C F_n(s) e^{st} \, ds \right]. \tag{D-55}$$

It follows from (D-53) that

$$I_{2n} \sim \frac{1}{2\pi j} \int_C F_{2n}(s) e^{st} \, ds. \tag{D-56}$$

We consider now the integral in (D-54) along the path C and designate this by I. For large t, the main contribution to this integral comes from a small region near $s = +j$. In this region we can substitute $s = j + p$ and use the Taylor expansion $1/s = -j + p + \cdots = D(p)$. It follows that

$$I = \frac{1}{2\pi j} \int_C D(p) F_{2n}(j+p) e^{jt} e^{pt} \, dp \tag{D-57a}$$

$$\sim e^{jt} D\left(\frac{d}{dt}\right) \frac{1}{2\pi j} \int_C F_{2n}(j+p) e^{pt} \, dp \tag{D-57b}$$

$$\sim e^{jt} D\left(\frac{d}{dt}\right) e^{-jt} \frac{1}{2\pi j} \int_C F_{2n}(s) e^{st} \, ds \tag{D-57c}$$

$$\sim e^{jt} D\left(\frac{d}{dt}\right) e^{-jt} I_{2n}. \tag{D-57d}$$

The formal equivalence of (D–57a) and (D–57b) can be seen by differentiating under the integral sign. Equation (D–57c) follows from (D–57b) by substituting $p = -j + s$, and (D–57d) follows from (D–57c) by substituting (D–56). The asymptotic expansion of (D–54) is thus (see D–52)

$$g_n(t) \sim 1 + 2\,\mathrm{Re}\left[e^{jt} D\left(\frac{d}{dt}\right) e^{-jt} I_{2n}\right]$$

$$\sim 1 + (-1)^n \sqrt{\frac{2}{\pi t}}\left[\frac{2n^2}{t}\cos\left(t - \frac{\pi}{4}\right) + \left(1 - \frac{2n^4}{t^2}\right)\sin\left(t - \frac{\pi}{4}\right)\right]. \tag{D–58}$$

We consider now the problem of determining an asymptotic expansion for $h(t) = \mathcal{L}^{-1}[H(s)]$, where

$$H(s) = \frac{a}{s^2 + a^2}\,F_n(s) = \frac{a}{s^2 + a^2}\,\frac{(\sqrt{1 + s^2} - s)^n}{\sqrt{1 + s^2}}. \tag{D–59}$$

This function has simple poles at $s = \pm ja$ and branch points at $s = \pm j$ (see Fig. D–2). The pole coefficient at $s = ja$ is

$$F(s) = \frac{ae^{st}}{s + ja}\,\frac{(\sqrt{1 + s^2} - s)^n}{\sqrt{1 + s^2}}.$$

The integrals along the branch cuts can be approximated by noting that for large t, the main contribution comes from the regions near the branch points. Thus, if $a \neq 1$,

$$\frac{a}{s^2 + a^2} \cong \frac{a}{a^2 - 1}$$

$$\frac{1}{2\pi j}\int_{C+C^*}\frac{a}{s^2 + a^2}\,F_n e^{st}\,ds \cong \frac{a}{a^2 - 1}\,\frac{1}{2\pi j}\int_{C+C^*}F_n e^{st}\,ds$$

$$= \frac{a}{a^2 - 1}\,\mathcal{L}^{-1}[F_n]$$

$$= \frac{a}{a^2 - 1}\,J_n(t). \tag{D–60}$$

Thus, combining (D–59) and (D–60)

$$h(t) \cong \mathrm{Re}\left[\frac{e^{jt}}{j}\,\frac{(\sqrt{1 - a^2} - ja)^n}{\sqrt{1 - a^2}}\right] + \frac{a}{a^2 - 1}\,J_n(t).$$

To obtain the complete asymptotic expansion we must consider the term

$$\frac{a}{s^2 + a^2} = \frac{a}{a^2 - 1}\,\frac{1}{1 + x} = \frac{a}{a^2 - 1}\,(1 - x + x^2 - \cdots), \tag{D–61}$$

where

$$x = \frac{s^2 + 1}{a^2 - 1}.$$

The expansion (D–61) is valid for $a \neq 1$ and for s in the regions near $s = \pm j$. Let I denote the integral

$$I = \frac{1}{2\pi j} \int_C H(s)e^{st}\, ds.$$

We use the substitution $s = j + p$ so that

$$x = \frac{p(2j + p)}{a^2 - 1}.$$

Let

$$D(p) = 1 - x + x^2 - \cdots. \tag{D–62}$$

We obtain

$$I = \frac{ae^{jt}}{a^2 - 1} \frac{1}{2\pi j} \int_C D(p)F_n(j + p)e^{pt}\, dp$$

$$\sim \frac{ae^{jt}}{a^2 - 1} D\left(\frac{d}{dt}\right) \frac{1}{2\pi j} \int_C F_n(j + p)e^{pt}\, dp$$

$$= \frac{ae^{jt}}{a^2 - 1} D\left(\frac{d}{dt}\right) \frac{e^{-jt}}{2\pi j} \int_C F_n(s)e^{st}\, ds.$$

The formal equivalence of the first two integrals can be seen by differentiating under the integral sign. The last integral results from the substitution $p = -j + s$. Thus, if we use (D–52) and (D–56),

$$I \sim \frac{ae^{jt}}{a^2 - 1} D\left(\frac{d}{dt}\right) e^{-jt} I_n$$

$$\sim \frac{a}{a^2 - 1} \frac{e^{j[t - (2n+1)\pi/4]}}{\sqrt{2\pi}} D\left(\frac{d}{dt}\right)(U_n + jV_n). \tag{D–63}$$

Ordering the series (D–62) according to powers of p yields

$$D(p) = 1 - \frac{2j}{a^2 - 1}\, p + \cdots.$$

Equation (D–63) yields

$$I \sim \frac{a}{a^2 - 1} \frac{e^{j[t - (2n+1)\pi/4]}}{\sqrt{2\pi}} \left[1 + j\left(\frac{4n^2 - 1}{8} + \frac{1}{a^2 - 1}\right)\frac{1}{t} + \cdots\right].$$

The asymptotic expansion for the integrals around the branch cuts is

$$I + I^* = 2 \operatorname{Re}[I] \sim \frac{a}{a^2 - 1} \sqrt{\frac{2}{\pi t}}$$

$$\times \left[\cos\left(t - \frac{2n + 1}{4} \pi \right) \right.$$

$$\left. - \left(\frac{4n^2 - 1}{8} + \frac{1}{a^2 - 1} \right) \frac{1}{t} \sin\left(t - \frac{2n + 1}{4} \pi \right) + \cdots \right].$$

$$\text{(D–64)}$$

A rigorous proof that the expansions are actually asymptotic must consider the remainder term $R_m(t)$ in the series and show that

$$\lim_{t \to +\infty} R_m(t) = 0.$$

It can be shown that this is the case for the expansions given here.

APPENDIX E

EVALUATION OF THE MEAN-SQUARE INTEGRAL

Let us consider the integral

$$I = \frac{1}{2\pi j} \int_{-j\infty}^{+j\infty} \frac{G(s)}{F(s)F(-s)} \, ds, \qquad (E\text{--}1)$$

where

$$F(s) = a_0 s^n + a_1 s^{n-1} + \cdots + a_n,$$

and

$$G(s) = b_0 s^{2n-2} + b_1 s^{2n-4} + \cdots + b_{n-1};$$

$G(s)$ is an even function in s. Let s_k ($k = 1, 2, \ldots n$) be the n zeros of $F(s)$ which are assumed to be distinct and to be in the left half of the s-plane. A partial-fraction expansion of the integrand of (E–1) has the form

$$\frac{G(s)}{F(s)F(-s)} = \sum_{k=1}^{n} C_k \left(\frac{1}{s - s_k} + \frac{1}{-s - s_k} \right). \qquad (E\text{--}2)$$

The integral (E–1) can be evaluated by completing the path of integration in the left or right half of the s-plane. We obtain

$$I = \sum_{k=1}^{n} C_k.$$

The disadvantage of this approach is that it requires the determination of the values of s_k. An alternative and more direct method will now be discussed. Multiplying (E–2) with $F(s)F(-s)$ yields

$$G(s) = \sum_{k=1}^{n} C_k [H_k(s)F(-s) + H_k(-s)F(s)], \qquad (E\text{--}3)$$

where

$$H_k(s) = \frac{F(s)}{s - s_k} = c_{1k} s^{n-1} + \cdots + c_{nk}$$

and $c_{1k} = a_0$. Let

$$X_1 = \sum_{k=1}^{n} C_k c_{1k} = a_0 \sum_{k=1}^{n} C_k = a_0 I$$

$$X_m = \sum_{k=1}^{n} C_k c_{mk}, \qquad m = 2, 3, \ldots, n.$$

356

If $G(s)$ and $F(s)$ are substituted into (E–3) and the coefficients of like powers of s equated, we obtain, after dividing by $2(-1)^n$,

$$\frac{(-1)^n b_0}{2} = -a_1 X_1 + a_0 X_2$$

$$\frac{(-1)^n b_1}{2} = -a_3 X_1 + a_2 X_2 - a_1 X_3 + a_0 X_4$$

$$\frac{(-1)^n b_2}{2} = -a_5 X_1 + a_4 X_2 - a_3 X_3 + a_2 X_4 - a_1 X_5 + a_0 X_6 \qquad \text{(E–4)}$$

$$\vdots$$

$$\frac{(-1)^n b_{n-1}}{2} = -a_{2n-1} X_1 + \cdots + (-1)^n a_n X_n.$$

where $a_k = 0$ if $k > n$. It should be noted that only the even powers of s need be considered, since $G(s)$ is an even function of s. These linear equations can be solved for X_1 using determinants. Since $I = X_1/a_0$ the formula (16–38) is obtained.

The case where there are multiple zeros can be considered by a limiting procedure starting with distinct zeros. Since the zeros are continuous functions of the coefficients a_k, the formula (16–38) remains valid.

APPENDIX F

TABLE OF LAPLACE TRANSFORMS

For more extensive tables see A. Erdelyi, *"Tables of Integral Transforms,"* Vol. 1, McGraw-Hill, New York, 1954.

$F(s)$	$f(t)$
$\dfrac{1}{s}$	$u(t) =$ unit-step function at $t = 0$
$\dfrac{1}{s^{n+1}}$	$\dfrac{t^n}{n!}, \qquad n = 0, 1, 2, \ldots$
$\dfrac{1}{s^{n+1}}$	$\dfrac{t^n}{\Gamma(n+1)}, \qquad \text{Re}[n] > -\tfrac{1}{2},$
	where $\Gamma(z)$ is the gamma function
$\dfrac{s}{s^2 + a^2}$	$\cos at$
$\dfrac{a}{s^2 + a^2}$	$\sin at$
$\dfrac{1}{(s+a)^{n+1}}$	$\dfrac{t^n e^{-at}}{n!}, \qquad n = 0, 1, 2, \ldots$
$\dfrac{(s+b)^n}{(s+a)^{n+1}}$	$e^{-at} L_n[(a-b)t], \qquad n = 0, 1, 2, \ldots,$
	where $L_n(z)$ is the Laguerre polynomial of order n.
$\dfrac{1}{s^2 + 2\zeta s + 1}$	$\dfrac{1}{\beta} e^{-\zeta t} \sin \beta t, \qquad \text{where} \qquad \beta = \sqrt{1 - \zeta^2}$
$\dfrac{1}{s(s^2 + 2\zeta s + 1)}$	$1 - \dfrac{e^{-\zeta \tau}}{\beta} \sin(\beta t + \phi), \qquad \text{where} \qquad \cos \phi = \zeta$

$$1 - \frac{e^{-\zeta_1 t}\sin(\beta_1 t + 2\phi_1)}{2\beta_1(\zeta_1-\zeta_2)} - \frac{e^{-\zeta_2 t}\sin(\beta_2 t+2\phi_2)}{2\beta_2(\zeta_2-\zeta_1)}$$

where $\beta_k = \sqrt{1-\zeta_k^2}$ and $\cos\phi_k = \zeta_k$

$$\frac{1}{s(s^2 + 2\zeta_1 s + 1)(s^2 + 2\zeta_2 s + 1)}$$

$$1 - \frac{e^{-\zeta_1 t}\sin(\beta_1 t+3\phi_1)}{4\beta_1(\zeta_2-\zeta_1)(\zeta_3-\zeta_1)} - \frac{e^{-\zeta_3 t}\sin(\beta_3 t+3\phi_3)}{4\beta_3(\zeta_1-\zeta_3)(\zeta_2-\zeta_3)} - \frac{e^{-\zeta_2 t}\sin(\beta_2 t+3\phi_2)}{4\beta_2(\zeta_1-\zeta_2)(\zeta_3-\zeta_2)}$$

$$\frac{1}{s(s^2 + 2\zeta_1 s + 1)(s^2 + 2\zeta_2 s + 1)(s^2 + 2\zeta_3 s + 1)}$$

$$1 - \frac{e^{-t}}{4(1-\zeta_1)(1-\zeta_2)} + \frac{e^{-\zeta_1 t}[\sin(\beta_1 t+2\phi_1)-\sin(\beta_1 t+3\phi_1)]}{4\beta_1(1-\zeta_1)(\zeta_2-\zeta_1)} + \frac{e^{-\zeta_2 t}[\sin(\beta_2 t+2\phi_2)-\sin(\beta_2 t+3\phi_2)]}{4\beta_2(1-\zeta_2)(\zeta_1-\zeta_2)}$$

$$\frac{1}{s(s+1)(s^2+2\zeta_1 s+1)(s^2+2\zeta_2 s+1)}$$

$$\frac{\sqrt{\pi}}{n!}\left(\frac{t}{2a}\right)^{n+1/2} J_{n+1/2}(at), \qquad n = 0, 1, 2, \ldots,$$

where $J_n(z)$ is the Bessel function of the first kind of order n.

$$\frac{1}{(s^2 + a^2)^{n+1}}$$

$$\frac{\sqrt{\pi}}{n!}\left(\frac{t}{2\beta}\right)^{n+1/2} e^{-\zeta t} J_{n+1/2}(\beta t)$$

$$\frac{1}{(s^2 + 2\zeta s + 1)^{n+1}}$$

$$1 - \frac{e^{-\zeta t}}{2\zeta\beta}\sin(\beta t + 2\phi)$$

$$\frac{1}{(2\zeta s)} \frac{s + 2\zeta}{(s^2 + 2\zeta s + 1)}$$

$$1 + \frac{e^{-\zeta_1 t}}{4\beta_1\zeta_1\zeta_2}\left[\sin(\beta_1 t+3\phi_1) + \frac{1}{2(\zeta_2-\zeta_1)}\sin(\beta_1 t+4\phi_1)\right] + \frac{e^{-\zeta_2 t}}{4\beta_2\zeta_2\zeta_1}\left[\sin(\beta_2 t+3\phi_2) + \frac{1}{2(\zeta_1-\zeta_2)}\sin(\beta_2 t+4\phi_2)\right]$$

$$\frac{1}{4\zeta_1\zeta_2 s} \frac{(s + 2\zeta_1)}{(s^2 + 2\zeta_1 s + 1)} \frac{(s + 2\zeta_2)}{(s^2 + 2\zeta_2 s + 1)}$$

(Continued)

TABLE OF LAPLACE TRANSFORMS (*Continued*)

$F(s)$	$f(t)$
$\dfrac{(s+2\zeta)^n}{(s^2+2\zeta s+1)^{n+1}}$	$\dfrac{\sqrt{\pi}}{n!}\, e^{-2\zeta t}\dfrac{d^n}{dt^n}\left[e^{\zeta t}\left(\dfrac{t}{2\beta}\right)^{n+1/2} J_{n+1/2}(\beta t)\right]$, $\quad n = 0, 1, 2, \ldots$
$a^n\dfrac{[s+\sqrt{a^2+s^2}]^{-n}}{\sqrt{a^2+s^2}}$	$J_n(at)$, $\quad \text{Re}[n] > -1$
$a^n[s+\sqrt{a^2+s^2}]^{-n}$	$\dfrac{n}{t} J_n(at)$, $\quad \text{Re}[n] > 0$
$\dfrac{1}{s}\, e^{-a/s}$	$J_0(2\sqrt{at})$
$\dfrac{1}{1+s^2}\dfrac{(s+\sqrt{1+s^2})^{-n-1}}{\sqrt{1+s^2}}$	$t J_n(t) - (n-1)\displaystyle\int_0^t J_0(t-u)J_n(u)\,du$, $\quad \text{Re}[n] > -1$
$\dfrac{1}{s}\dfrac{1}{\sqrt{1+1/s^2}}\left[\dfrac{1}{s}+\sqrt{1+\dfrac{1}{s^2}}\right]^{-n}$	$\displaystyle\int_0^\infty J_0(2\sqrt{tu})J_n(u)\,du$, $\quad \text{Re}[n] > -1$
$\dfrac{(\sqrt{s^2-a^2}+\sqrt{1+s^2-a^2})^{-n}}{\sqrt{(s^2-a^2)(1+s^2-a^2)}}$	$\displaystyle\int_0^t I_0(a\sqrt{t^2-u^2})J_n(u)\,du$, $\quad \text{Re}[n] > -1,$ where $I_n(z)$ is the modified Bessel function of the first kind of order n.
$\dfrac{e^{u/4s}}{s}$	$I_0(\sqrt{ut})$

$\dfrac{e^{-b\sqrt{s^2-a^2}}}{\sqrt{s^2-a^2}}$	$u(t-b)I_0(z)$, where $u(t)$ is the unit-step function and $z = a\sqrt{t^2 - b^2}$
$e^{-b\sqrt{s^2-a^2}} - e^{-bs}$	$a^2 bu(t-b)\,\dfrac{I_1(z)}{z}$
$\dfrac{(s - \sqrt{s^2 - a^2})^n}{\sqrt{s^2 - a^2}}\, e^{-b\sqrt{s^2-a^2}}$	$a^n u(t-b)\left(\dfrac{t-b}{t+b}\right)^{n/2} I_n(z)$, $\quad n = 0, 1, 2, \ldots$
$\dfrac{e^{-\sqrt{as}}}{\sqrt{s}}$	$\dfrac{e^{-a/4t}}{\sqrt{\pi t}}$
$\dfrac{e^{-\sqrt{as}}}{s}$	$\dfrac{1}{2t}\sqrt{\dfrac{a}{\pi t}}\, e^{-a/4t}$
$\dfrac{e^{-\sqrt{bs}}}{s}$	$\text{erfc}\,\dfrac{1}{2}\sqrt{\dfrac{b}{t}}$
	where erfc z is the complementary error function
$\dfrac{2}{s}\, e^{-\sqrt{a(s+b)}}$	$e^{\sqrt{ab}}\,\text{erfc}\left(\sqrt{bt}+\tfrac{1}{2}\sqrt{a/t}\right) + e^{-\sqrt{ab}}\,\text{erfc}\left(-\sqrt{bt}+\tfrac{1}{2}\sqrt{a/t}\right)$
$\dfrac{e^{-(\sqrt{ab}+\sqrt{as})}}{\sqrt{s}(\sqrt{s}+\sqrt{b})}$	$e^{bt}\,\text{erfc}\left(\sqrt{bt}+\tfrac{1}{2}\sqrt{a/t}\right)$
$\dfrac{1}{s}\sqrt{\dfrac{a}{s+a}}$	$\text{erf}\sqrt{at}$
	where erf z is the error function

(Continued)

TABLE OF LAPLACE TRANSFORMS (*Continued*)

$F(s)$	$f(t)$
$\dfrac{1}{s}\dfrac{\sqrt{s+a}-\sqrt{a}}{\sqrt{s+a}}$	$\operatorname{erfc}\sqrt{at}$
$\dfrac{1}{\sqrt{s}(\sqrt{s}+\sqrt{a})}$	$e^{at}\operatorname{erfc}\sqrt{at}$
$\dfrac{e^{-\sqrt{a(s+b)}}}{\sqrt{s+b}}$	$\dfrac{e^{-(bt+a/4t)}}{\sqrt{\pi t}}$
$\dfrac{1}{s\sqrt{s+b}}$	$\dfrac{1}{\sqrt{b}}\operatorname{erf}\sqrt{bt}$
$\dfrac{\sqrt{s+b}}{s+a}$	$\dfrac{e^{-bt}}{\sqrt{\pi t}}+\sqrt{b-a}\,e^{-at}\operatorname{erf}\sqrt{(b-a)t}$
$\dfrac{1}{\sqrt{a(s+b)}+\sqrt{c(s+d)}}$	$\dfrac{1}{a-c}\left[\sqrt{\dfrac{a}{\pi t}}\,e^{-bt}-\sqrt{\dfrac{c}{\pi t}}\,e^{-dt}\right]$ $+\dfrac{\sqrt{ack}}{a-c}\,e^{-at}[\operatorname{erfc}\sqrt{akt}-\operatorname{erfc}\sqrt{ckt}],$

$$\text{where }\ \alpha=\frac{ab-cd}{a-c}\quad\text{and}\quad k=\frac{d-b}{a-c}$$

ANSWERS TO ODD–NUMBERED PROBLEMS

CHAPTER 1

1-1. (a) $H = a \dfrac{1 + Ts}{1 + aTs}$, where $a = \dfrac{R_2}{R_1 + R_2}$, $T = R_1 C_1$

(b) $H = \dfrac{BAN}{Js^2 + Ds + K}$

(c) $H = \dfrac{K}{Js(s + D/J)}$

CHAPTER 2

2-1. $u = \sigma^3 - 3\sigma\omega^2$, $v = 3\sigma^2\omega - \omega^3$

2-3. $V(s) = \dfrac{1}{s + a}$, $V(s) = \dfrac{b}{(s + a)^2 + b^2}$

CHAPTER 3

3-1. $v_o(t) = a - (a - 1)e^{-t/T}$ $a = \dfrac{R_2}{R_1 + R_2}$, $T = \dfrac{R_1 R_2}{R_1 + R_2} C$

3-3. (a) $i_1(t) = \frac{1}{4}(3 - 2e^{-t} - e^{-2t})$
$i_2(t) = \frac{1}{4}(1 - 2e^{-t} + e^{-2t})$

(b) $i_1(t) = \frac{1}{20}(5e^{-t} + 2e^{-2t} - 7\cos t + 9\sin t)$
$i_2(t) = \frac{1}{20}(5e^{-t} - 2e^{-2t} - 3\cos t + \sin t)$

3-5. (a) $v_o(t) = \frac{1}{9}(9 - 4e^{-t} + 4e^{-10t})$

(b) $v_o(t) = \frac{1}{65}\{\frac{10}{9}(e^{-10t} - e^{-t}) + 22e^{-10t} + 43\cos 5t - 12\sin 5t\}$

3-7. (a) $R_1 i_1(t) = \frac{1}{2} + \dfrac{e^{-\tau}}{2}(\cos\tau - \sin\tau)$

$R_1 i_2(t) = \frac{1}{2} - \dfrac{e^{-\tau}}{2}(\cos\tau + \sin\tau)$, where $\tau = \omega_n t$

(b) $R_1 i_2(t) = \frac{2}{5}(e^{-\tau} - 1)\cos\tau + \frac{1}{5}(e^{-\tau} + 1)\sin\tau$
$R_1 i_1(t) = \frac{1}{5}(1 - e^{-\tau})\cos\tau + \frac{2}{5}(1 + e^{-\tau})\sin\tau$

CHAPTER 4

4-1. $v_o(t) = -K\left(1 - \dfrac{T_1}{T_1 - T_2} e^{-t/T_1} - \dfrac{T_2}{T_2 - T_1} e^{-t/T_2}\right)$

$\cong -t\left(1 - \dfrac{t}{2T_1}\right)$, $t \ll K$

4-3. $\dfrac{1}{G_0} v_o(t) = 1 - \dfrac{e^{-\tau}}{4(1 - \zeta_1)(1 - \zeta_2)} + \dfrac{e^{-\zeta_1\tau}}{4\beta_1(1 - \zeta_1)(\zeta_2 - \zeta_1)}$

$$\times \left[\sin\left(\beta_1\tau + 2\phi_1\right) - \sin\left(\beta_1\tau + 3\phi_1\right)\right]$$

$$+ \dfrac{e^{-\zeta_2\tau}}{4\beta_2(1 - \zeta_2)(\zeta_1 - \zeta_2)}$$

$$\times \left[\sin\left(\beta_2\tau + 2\phi_2\right) - \sin\left(\beta_2\tau + 3\phi_2\right)\right],$$

where $G_0 = V_3(0)/V_0(0)$ is the zero-frequency gain, $\tau = \omega_n t$, $\cos \phi_k = \zeta_k, \beta_k = \sqrt{1 - \zeta_k^2}$

4-5. $v_o(t) = 1 + 3.892 e^{-3t} \cos t - 36.65 e^{-3t} \sin t - 3.892 e^{-2t} \cos 3.46t + 5.93 e^{-2t} \sin 3.46t$

4-9. $T = 2.4$, $a = 1.3$, $b = 3.7$

4-11. $\dfrac{1}{\alpha^2} = 0.72$, $\zeta_1 = 0.91$, $T = 2.95$, $\zeta_2 = 0.785$

4-15. The normalized response is

$$\omega_n g(\tau) = 1 - \dfrac{e^{-\zeta_1\tau} \sin\left(\beta_1\tau + 3\phi_1\right)}{4\beta_1(\zeta_2 - \zeta_1)(\zeta_3 - \zeta_1)} - \dfrac{e^{-\zeta_2\tau} \sin\left(\beta_2\tau + 3\phi_2\right)}{4\beta_2(\zeta_1 - \zeta_2)(\zeta_3 - \zeta_2)}$$

$$- \dfrac{e^{-\zeta_3\tau} \sin\left(\beta_3\tau + 3\phi_3\right)}{4\beta_3(\zeta_1 - \zeta_3)(\zeta_2 - \zeta_3)}.$$

4-21. $v_o'(t) = \dfrac{\zeta_1}{\zeta_2} + \dfrac{\zeta_2 - \zeta_1}{\zeta_2} e^{-\omega_c \zeta_2 t}$, $2\zeta_1 = \dfrac{\omega_c L}{R_1} \ll 1$, $2\zeta_2 = 2\zeta_1 + \dfrac{\omega_c L}{R_2} \ll 1$

CHAPTER 5

5-3. (a) $v_c(t) = e^{-t} - \frac{1}{5} e^{-2t} + \frac{1}{5} \cos t - \frac{2}{5} \sin t$

(b) $v(t) = v_c(t) + v_p(t)$, where
$$v_p(t) = \tfrac{1}{4} e^{-t} - \tfrac{1}{5} e^{-2t} + \tfrac{1}{20} e^{-3t} - \tfrac{1}{10} \cos t$$

5-5. $R_1 i_2(t) = -\frac{2}{5} e^{-\tau/2} \cos \dfrac{\sqrt{3}}{2} \tau$, where $\tau = \omega_n t$

CHAPTER 6

6-1. (b) $\omega_c^2(T_1 T_2 + T_1 T_3 + T_2 T_3) = 1$, $d = K(T_1 + T_2 + T_3)$
$0 < K < \omega_c^2(T_1 + T_2 + T_3 - \omega_c^2 T_1 T_2 T_3)$

6-3. (a) and (b) are not Hurwitz; (c) has zeros on the $j\omega$-axis; (d) is Hurwitz and the sequence of residues is $\frac{4}{15}$, 2, 1, 4, 1.

6-5. $I = (T_1 + T_2 + \cdots T_n) - (\tau_1 + \tau_2 + \cdots + \tau_m)$

6-7. For (a) and (b) the closed-loop system is unstable. (c) Stability is possible provided a is sufficiently small and that $T_1 > T$.

6-9. $G_c = \dfrac{1 + \frac{1}{3}s}{1 + s}$, $\theta = 30°$, $M_p = 2$, $\epsilon(\infty) = \frac{1}{46}$

6-11. (a) $K = 14$ (b) $G_c = \dfrac{1}{2} \dfrac{1 + 2s}{1 + s}$, $\theta = 30°$

6-13. Inner loop-phase margin 30°, gain margin 13 db, maximum phase lead 100°

Closed loop-phase margin 60°, gain margin 15 db, $M_p \cong 1$, bandwidth = 3 cps, $\epsilon(\infty) = 0.97°$

CHAPTER 7

7-1. See Chapter 8, Example 1

7-3. See Chapter 8, Problem 8-1

7-5. See Chapter 8, Example 2

CHAPTER 8

8-1. $v_o(t) = 1 - 0.11956e^{-13.64\tau} + 0.83091e^{-4.492\tau} + 0.04623e^{-0.2611\tau}$
$- 1.75906e^{-1.32\tau} \cos 2.128\tau - 0.09085e^{-1.32\tau} \sin 2.128\tau,$

where $\tau = 50t$

8-3. $v_o(t) = 1 + 0.01674e^{-29.99t} + 0.24735e^{-1.721t} \cos 9.24t$
$- 0.5099e^{-1.721t} \sin 9.24t - 1.26362e^{-2.287t} \cos 2.563t$
$+ 1.07284e^{-2.287t} \sin 2.563t$

CHAPTER 9

9-1. $v_m(t) = \dfrac{1}{n} \displaystyle\sum_{k=1}^{n} \sin 2m\phi_k \cot \phi_k \cos \omega_k t,$

where $\phi_k = \dfrac{(2k - 1)\pi}{4n}$, $\omega_k = \dfrac{1}{2\sqrt{LC}} \dfrac{1}{\sin \phi_k}$

9-3. $i_m(t) = \dfrac{1}{nR} + \dfrac{2}{nR} \displaystyle\sum_{k=1}^{n-1} \cos^2 \phi_k \cos 2m\phi_k e^{s_k t},$

where $\phi_k = \dfrac{\pi k}{2n}$, $s_k = -\dfrac{4}{RC} \sin^2 \phi_k$

9-5. $i_m(t) = \dfrac{1}{n} \sqrt{\dfrac{C_1}{L_1}} \displaystyle\sum_{k=1}^{n} F_k \dfrac{\cos m\beta_k}{\sqrt{1 + [(\omega_2/2\omega_1) \sin \phi_k]^2}} (\sin \omega_{k1} t + \sin \omega_{k2} t),$

where $\beta_k = \dfrac{\pi k}{n}$.

For the definition of ω_1, ω_2, ω_{k1}, ω_{k2}, and F_k see Example 3 and (9–59).

9-7. $i'_n(t) = \sqrt{\dfrac{C_2}{L_2}} \displaystyle\int_0^{t/\sqrt{L_1 C_2}} J_{2n}(u) \, du$

9-11. See Fig. 9–23, where $L = M$, $C = a/T$

CHAPTER 10

10-1. $y_n(x) = \sin \dfrac{\pi n x}{l}, \quad \omega_n = \dfrac{\pi a n}{l}, \quad n = 1, 2, \ldots$

$$u_n(t) = \frac{2F}{Apl} \frac{\sin \pi n/2}{\omega_n^2} (1 - \cos \omega_n t)$$

10-3. $x_n = \dfrac{\alpha}{[\pi(n-1) + x_n]} \dfrac{\tan x_n}{x_n}, \quad n = 2, 3, \ldots$

$\beta_1 = \sqrt{\dfrac{\alpha \beta_1}{\tan \beta_1}}, \quad n = 1$

$\beta_1 = 0.861, \quad \beta_2 = 3.44, \quad \beta_3 = 6.44$

10-5. $\beta_1 \cong \sqrt{\dfrac{1}{\alpha_1} + \dfrac{1}{\alpha_2} - \dfrac{1}{3}\left(\dfrac{1}{\alpha_1^2} + \dfrac{1}{\alpha_2^2} - \dfrac{1}{\alpha_1 \alpha_2}\right)}$

10-7. (a) $y_n(x) = (\sin \beta_n + \cosh \beta_n)\left(\sin \dfrac{\beta_n x}{l} - \sinh \dfrac{\beta_n x}{l}\right)$

$$+ (\cos \beta_n - \cosh \beta_n)\left(\cos \dfrac{\beta_n x}{l} - \cosh \dfrac{\beta_n x}{l}\right)$$

$\cos \beta_n \cosh \beta_n = 1, \quad (y_n, y_m) = 0 \quad (n \neq m)$

To evaluate (y_n, y_n) consider (10–31) and (10–34) for an arbitrary value of ω_n and let $\omega_n \to \omega_m$ = angular frequency of the mth mode. Determine the limit of (10–34) by differentiation with respect to β_n/l. Substituting $z = \beta_n x/l$ yields

$$(y_m, y_m) = \frac{l}{4}[y_m^2 - 2y_m' y_m''' + (y_m'')^2]_{x=l},$$

where $y_m' = (dy_m/dz)$. For the boundary conditions of this problem $(y_n, y_n) = (l/4)(y_n'')_{x=l}^2$.

(b) $u(x, t) = \displaystyle\sum_{n=1}^{\infty} u_n(t) y_n(x)$

$$u_n(t) = \frac{y_n(l/2)}{A\rho \omega_n(y_n, y_n)} \int_0^t F(\tau) \sin \omega_n(t - \tau) \, d\tau$$

CHAPTER 11

11-1. $v(0, t) = \dfrac{Z_0}{Z_0 + R}\left[u(t) + \Gamma_i(1 + \Gamma_0)u\left(t - \dfrac{2l}{c}\right)\right.$

$$\left. + \Gamma_0 \Gamma_i^2(1 + \Gamma_0)u\left(t - \dfrac{4l}{c}\right) + \cdots\right],$$

where $u(t)$ is the unit-step function and $\Gamma_0 = (R - Z_0)/(R + Z_0)$
(a) $\Gamma_i = -1$ (b) $\Gamma_i = +1$

11-3. $v(x, t) = \dfrac{1}{2}\left[e^{-\alpha x}v_g\left(t - \dfrac{x}{c}\right) + \Gamma_l e^{-\alpha(2l-x)}v_g\left(t - \dfrac{2l - x}{c}\right)\right],$

where $\Gamma_l = \dfrac{R_l - Z_0}{R_l + Z_0}$

11-5. $i(l, t) = \dfrac{2}{Z_0}\displaystyle\sum_{n=0}^{\infty}v_n\left[t - (2n + 1)\dfrac{l}{c}\right],$

where $v_n(t) = \begin{cases} 0, & t < 0, \\ e^{-\zeta t}\left[L_{2n}(2\zeta t) - \alpha\displaystyle\int_0^t L_{2n}(2\zeta\tau)\,d\tau\right], & t > 0, \end{cases}$

and $\zeta = \dfrac{1}{C_1 Z_0}$

11-7. $v_1(l, t) = \begin{cases} 0, & 0 \le t < \dfrac{l}{c_1}, \\ \dfrac{2e^{-\alpha_1 l/c_1}}{1 + Z_{01}/Z_{02}}\,(1 - e^{-\zeta(t - l/c_1)}), & \dfrac{l}{c_1} < t < \dfrac{3l}{c_1}, \end{cases}$

where $\zeta = (1 + Z_{01}/Z_{02})\dfrac{1}{Z_0 C_1}$

CHAPTER 12

12-1. $N = WEb, C_g = \dfrac{Wl(\epsilon - Eb^2)}{d}$

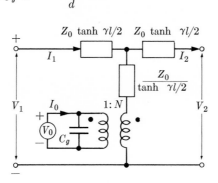

FIGURE 1

12-3. (c) $T = \sqrt{b_1^2 + b_2^2 + \left(\dfrac{Z_1}{Z_2} + \dfrac{Z_2}{Z_1}\right)b_1 b_2},$

where $b_1 = \dfrac{2l_1}{a_1}, b_2 = \dfrac{l_2}{a_2}$ (low-pass case)

(d) (1) $K \cong \dfrac{4}{\pi}\dfrac{Z_1}{Z_2}\left(1 - \dfrac{Z_1}{Z_2}\right)$ (2) $K \cong \dfrac{2}{\pi}\dfrac{Z_2}{Z_1}\left(1 - \dfrac{Z_1}{2Z_2}\right)$

12–5. $l_1 = 0.725$ cm, $d_1 = 0.24$ cm, $\tau_D = 16.8 \times 10^{-5}$ sec   (low-pass case),
$\tau_D = 18/K\omega_0 = 5.73 \times 10^{-4}$ sec   (bandpass case)

CHAPTER 13

13–1. $v_L(t) = \delta(t) - \dfrac{\omega_n}{2} \dfrac{\cos \omega_n(t - T/2)}{\sin (\omega_n T/2)}$

$v_C(t) = \dfrac{\omega_n}{2} \dfrac{\cos \omega_n(t - T/2)}{\sin (\omega_n T/2)}, \quad 0 \le t < \dfrac{T}{2}$

13–3. $v_o(t) = \dfrac{2\omega_0 b}{a^2 + \omega_0^2} \dfrac{e^{-at}}{1 - e^{-aT}} + b \dfrac{\sin (\omega_0 t - \alpha)}{\sqrt{a^2 + \omega_0^2}},$

where $\omega_0 = \dfrac{\pi}{T}, \quad a = \dfrac{R_1 + R_2}{R_1 R_2} \dfrac{1}{C}, \quad b = \dfrac{1}{R_1 C}, \quad \tan \alpha = \dfrac{\pi}{aT}$

13–5. $v(x, t) = \dfrac{8}{T} \displaystyle\sum_{n=1}^{\infty} \dfrac{\cos (\omega_n/c)(l - x)}{\cos (\omega_n l/c)} \dfrac{\sin \omega_n t}{\omega_n}$

provided that $\alpha \ll 1$ and where $\omega_n = (2\pi/T)(2n - 1)$

CHAPTER 14

14–5. $\sqrt{\dfrac{R}{c}}\, i(x, t) = \sqrt{\omega}\, e^{-\sqrt{a\omega/2}} \cos\left[\omega t - \sqrt{\dfrac{a\omega}{2}} - \dfrac{\pi}{4}\right]$

$- \dfrac{\omega}{\pi} \displaystyle\int_0^{\infty} \dfrac{\sqrt{r} \cos \sqrt{ar}}{r^2 + \omega^2} e^{-rt}\, dr, \quad \text{where} \quad - \dfrac{\omega}{\pi} \displaystyle\int_0^{\infty} \dfrac{\sqrt{r} \cos \sqrt{ar}}{r^2 + \omega^2} e^{-rt}\, dr$

$\sim \left[\dfrac{1}{\omega} \dfrac{d}{dt} - \dfrac{1}{\omega^3} \dfrac{d^3}{dt^3} + \dfrac{1}{\omega^5} \dfrac{d^5}{dt^5} - \cdots\right] \dfrac{1}{\sqrt{\pi t}} e^{-a/4t}$

14–7. $R_g i(0, t) = e^{\tau} \operatorname{erfc} \sqrt{\tau}, \quad v(0, t) = 1 - e^{\tau} \operatorname{erfc} \sqrt{\tau}, \quad$ where

$$\tau = \dfrac{R}{R_g} \dfrac{t}{R_g C}$$

[For the asymptotic expansion see Appendix (C–5).]

14–9. $i(x, t) = \dfrac{1}{Rl}\left[e^{-at} h(t) + a \displaystyle\int_0^t e^{-a\tau} h(\tau)\, d\tau\right],$

where

$h(t) = 1 + 2 \displaystyle\sum_{n=1}^{\infty} \cos \dfrac{\pi n x}{l} e^{-(\pi n/l)^2 (t/RC)} \qquad \text{and} \qquad a = \dfrac{G}{C}.$

14–11. (a) $i_{pc}(t) = \dfrac{e^{-bt}}{t\sqrt{\pi}} \displaystyle\sum_{n=1}^{\infty} (-1)^n \sqrt{\dfrac{a_n}{t}}\, e^{-a_n/4t}$,

where

$$b = \frac{1}{\tau_p} \quad \text{and} \quad \sqrt{a_n b} = (2n-1)\frac{W}{L_p}.$$

(b) $i_{pc}(t) = \left(\dfrac{\pi D_p}{W^2}\right) e^{-t/\tau_p} \displaystyle\sum_{n=0}^{\infty} (-1)^n (2n+1) e^{-\sigma_n(t/\tau_p)}$,

where $\sqrt{\sigma_n} = \dfrac{\pi}{2}(2n+1)\dfrac{L_p}{W}$

CHAPTER 15

15–1. $i(x, t) = \sqrt{\dfrac{C}{L}}\, e^{-bt} I_0\left(a\sqrt{t^2 - \left(\dfrac{x}{c}\right)^2}\right) + GC\displaystyle\int_{x/c}^{t} e^{-b\tau} I_0(z)\, d\tau$

$$v(x, t) = e^{-xb/c} + \frac{a^2 x}{c}\int_{x/c}^{t} e^{-b\tau}\frac{I_1(z)}{z}\, d\tau, \qquad t > \frac{x}{c}$$

where

$$2a = \frac{R}{L} - \frac{G}{C}, \quad 2b = \frac{G}{C} + \frac{R}{L}, \quad z = a\sqrt{\tau^2 - \left(\frac{x}{c}\right)^2}$$

15–3. $i(x, t) = \dfrac{e^{-bt}}{R_0(1 - A^2)}\left[I_0\left(b\sqrt{t^2 - \left(\dfrac{x}{c}\right)^2}\right) - A e^{-\alpha b(t - x/c)}\right.$

$$\left. + \int_{x/c}^{t} e^{-\alpha b(t-\tau)}\left[b(1-\alpha)I_0(z) - \frac{Ab^2 x}{c}\frac{I_1(z)}{z}\right] d\tau, \right.$$

where

$$A = \frac{R_g}{R_0}, \quad \alpha = \frac{1 + A^2}{1 - A^2}, \quad b = \frac{R}{2L}$$

15–7. $c_{10} = 1,\ c_{11} = -2k,\ c_{12} = 2k^2,\ c_{13} = -(2k^3 + 2k)$

$c_{20} = 1,\ c_{21} = -4k,\ c_{22} = 8k^2,\ c_{23} = -(12k^3 + 4k)$,

$c_{24} = 16k^4 + 16k^3$,

$c_{25} = -(20k^5 + 36k^3 + 4k), \ldots,$ where $k = \dfrac{2}{bC_l}\sqrt{\dfrac{C}{L}}$

CHAPTER 16

16-5. $\Phi(\omega) = \dfrac{|G(\omega)|^2}{T_0}\left\{1 - |P_1(\omega)|^2 + |P_1(\omega)|^2\,\dfrac{2\pi}{T_0}\sum_{n=-\infty}^{+\infty}\delta\left(\omega - \dfrac{2\pi n}{T_0}\right)\right\}$

16-7. $\overline{v^2} = \dfrac{A}{1 + cT}$

16-9. (a) $\phi_{vv}(\tau) = \dfrac{A}{T}\,\dfrac{1}{(cT)^2 - 1}\,[cT^2 e^{-\tau/T} - Te^{-c\tau}], \qquad \tau > 0$

(b) $\Phi_{vv}(\omega) = \dfrac{2Ac}{(cT)^2 - 1}\left[\dfrac{T^2}{1 + (\omega T)^2} - \dfrac{1}{c^2 + \omega^2}\right]$

INDEX

ABCDE69876543